Kuhlenbeck: The Central Nervous System of Vertebrates

Hartwig Kuhlenbeck

The Central Nervous System of Vertebrates

A General Survey of its Comparative Anatomy with an Introduction to the Pertinent Fundamental Biologic and Logical Concepts

ACADEMIC PRESS INC., NEW YORK AND LONDON

Volume 2

Invertebrates
and Origin of Vertebrates

With 238 figures

ACADEMIC PRESS INC., NEW YORK AND LONDON

Sole distributors for the United States and Canada
Academic Press Inc., 111 Fifth Avenue, New York, N. Y. 10003

Library of Congress Catalog Card Number 66–28671

Published with the aid of a generous contribution by the
Werner-Reimers-Stiftung, Frankfurt/Main, Germany

Originally published in Switzerland by
S. Karger AG, Arnold-Böcklin-Strasse 25, 4000 Basel 11 (Switzerland)

«Die vergleichende Anatomie, Histologie, Architektonik und Embryologie des Zentralnervensystems bildet ferner einen umfangreichen Zweig und zugleich eine unentbehrliche Methode der neurobiologischen Forschung. Sie verrät die zahlreichen Wege, durch welche die Evolution der Nervensysteme der verschiedenen Tiersorten im phylogenetischen Zusammenhang ihre heutige Verschiedenartigkeit zustande gebracht hat. Vertieft man sich dabei genügend in den Zusammenhang von Form und Funktion, so gelangt man in eine wunderbare Welt der Harmonie zwischen Geist und lebendem Nervensystem...

Wer vergleichende Anatomie des Nervensystems sagt, sagt also auch vergleichende Physiologie – Psychologie und – Biologie, und das ist ein Gebiet, aus welchem die künftige Forschung mit vollen Zügen schöpfen kann...

Dass der Mensch für den Menschen sich zunächst interessiert, ist verzeihlich und naheliegend. Hat er aber einmal erkannt, dass er nur ein Glied in der Tierreihe bildet und dass sein Hirn, das Organ seiner Seele, aus dem Tiergehirn und somit aus der Tierseele stammt, so muss er doch zur Erkenntnis gelangen, dass das Studium der Neurobiologie dieser seiner Verwandten das grösste Licht auf sein eigenes Nerven- und Seelenleben werfen muss.»

August Forel
(«*Die Aufgaben der Neurobiologie*»)

Preface

The lectures on the central nervous system of vertebrates, given by the author during his first sojourn in Japan, 1924–1927 (Taishô 13 to Shôwa 2), intended to foster the interest in comparative neurologic studies based upon the morphologic principles established by the *Gegenbaur* or *Jena-Heidelberg School of Comparative Anatomy*. Notwithstanding their introductory and elementary nature, these lectures, published by Gustav Fischer, Jena, in 1927, included a number of advanced as well as independent concepts, and represented, as it were, the outline of a further program.

Despite various vicissitudes, and although I found the prevailing intellectual climate in the realm of biologic sciences rather unfavorable to the pursuit of investigations related to the domain of classical morphology, I have, *tant bien que mal*, carried on with my studies as originally planned, and propose to summarize my viewpoints in the present series, designed to represent a general survey, and projected to comprise five separate volumes, of which the first two are now completed. It can easily be seen that the present series follows closely the outline of my old 'Vorlesungen', meant to stress 'die grossen Hauptlinien der Hirnarchitektur und die allgemeinen Gesetzmässigkeiten, welche in Bau und Funktion des Nervensystems erkannt werden können'.

Comparative anatomy of the vertebrate central nervous system requires a very broad and comprehensive background of biological data, evaluated by means of a rational, consistent, and appropriate logical procedure. Without the relevant unifying concepts, comparative neurology becomes no more than a trivial description of apparently unrelated miscellaneous and bewildering configurational varieties, loosely held together by a string of hazy 'functional' notions. A perusal of the multitudinous literature dealing with matters involving the morphologic aspects of neurobiology reveals, to the critical observer, considerable confusion as regards many fundamental questions.

For this reason, the present attempt at an integrated overall presentation includes a somewhat detailed scrutiny of problems concerning the significance of configuration and configurational variety with respect to evolution and to correlated reasonably 'natural' taxonomic classifications. Because comparative anatomy of the central nervous system embodies the morphological clues required to infer the presumable phylogenetic evolution of the brain, a number of general questions referring to ontogenetic evolution are critically considered: it is evident that both the inferred phylogenetic sequences and the observable ontogenetic sequences represent evolutionary processes suitable for a comparison outlining the obtaining invariants.

Moreover, the comparison of organic forms involves procedures closely related to *analysis situs*. Thus, a simplified and elementary discussion of the here relevant principles of *topology* was deemed necessary.

Finally, since vertebrate comparative anatomy and vertebrate evolution, including the origin of vertebrates, cannot be properly assessed in default of an at least moderately adequate familiarity with the vast array of invertebrate organic forms, a general and elementary survey of invertebrate comparative neurology from the vertebrate neurobiologist's viewpoint, that is as seen by an 'outsider' with a modicum of first-hand acquaintance, has been included as volume two of this series. The approximately 20 pages and 12 figures dealing with this matter in my 1927 'Vorlesungen' have thus, of necessity, become rather expanded.

U.S. N.I.H. Grant NB 4999–01, which is acknowledged with due appreciation, made possible the completion of Volumes 1 and 2 of this series, and, for the time being, the continuation of these studies, by supporting a 'Research Professorship' established to that effect, following my superannuation, at the Woman's Medical College of Pennsylvania.

Concluding this preamble to the present series, I may state with CICERO (*De oratore*, III, 61, 228): '*Edidi quae potui, non ut volui sed ut me temporis angustiae coegerunt; scitum est enim causam conferre in tempus, cum afferre plura si cupias non queas.*'

H.K.

Table of Contents of the Present Volume

Volume 2 Invertebrates and Origin of Vertebrates

This work was supported in part by U.S. N.I.H. Grant NB 04999-01-02 for the Analysis of the Morphologic Pattern of the Vertebrate Neuraxis in Terms of a Topologic Homology Concept.

Table of Contents of the Complete Work

Volume 1 Propaedeutics to Comparative Neurology

IV. Remarks on the Nervous System of Invertebrates, the Theories Concerning Origin of Nervous System, and the Theories on the Origin of Vertebrates

1. General Comments

Invertebrates, in contradistinction to vertebrates, represent not only a much larger and more numerous set of classes, but also comprise a much greater variety of morphologically very different forms. With respect to the number of species (cf. chapter II, section 2), we may very roughly estimate the ratio of invertebrates to vertebrates as approximately 900 000 to 70 000 or about 13 to 1. This, of course, is merely a 'formal' ratio, and not an 'actual' ratio of 'biomass'.

Thus, although a brief synopsis of the various types of invertebrate nervous systems seems desirable if not outright indispensable as an introduction to a general survey of the vertebrate central nervous system, such synopsis must, of necessity, remain uncomfortably sketchy. It can here only stress a few points which may be considered significant for such comparative approach[1].

---

[1] Because of the considerable difficulties involved, only two authors (as far as I could ascertain up to the time of this writing) have undertaken the formidable task of presenting a detailed comprehensive survey of morphologically oriented invertebrate comparative neurology (DROOGLEVER FORTUYN, 1920, and B. HANSTRÖM, 1928). In his outstanding contribution, based upon numerous original investigations, HANSTRÖM (1928) refers, with considerable detail, to approximately 1800 pertinent publications on this subject. Since that time, the interest of biologists studying the invertebrate nervous system has significantly shifted from classical morphologic problems to well-nigh exclusively functional or at most structural questions. Although very numerous investigations of the nervous system in various invertebrate groups have been undertaken within the last 35 years, rather little has been added to the major morphologic data emphasized in HANSTRÖM's work or in the still very useful shorter survey by PLATE (1922). Recent progress in physiologic studies on the nervous system of some large invertebrate groups (coelenterates, crustaceans, insects, cephalopods) has been concisely summarized by HUBER (1963).

L. PLATE (1862–1937), whose discreditable personal conduct toward his great predecessor ERNST HAECKEL must be deplored as well as censured, was, nevertheless, a very brilliant teacher and an excellent all-around zoologist. His thorough laboratory course (Zoologisches Praktikum), in which I had the good fortune to participate, imparted a most serviceable first-hand acquaintance with representative invertebrates. My teacher FRIEDRICH MAURER (1859–1936), one of the major disciples of CARL GEGENBAUR, and

Two invertebrate phyla, namely Protozoa and Porifera, do not possess a nervous system. Yet, some Protozoa display fibrillar structures, e.g. related to the basal bodies of cilia and flagella. Such fibrils are regarded as conductile for 'impulses' and as forming part of a 'neuro-motor system' (CHEN, 1944; LUND, 1935; and others).

The multitudinous protozoan forms vary among each other with respect to the differentiation of 'organelles' and related intracellular structures, or, in other words, with regard to 'intracellular specialization'. In certain instances, 'organ-like' structures are very conspicuously developed within the protoplasmic substratum ('complexly differentiated unicellular forms'). Organisms displaying such features provide, as it were, further answers to the long ago debated questions of an almost, by now, forgotten old controversy.

In the first half of the 19th century, CHR. G. EHRENBERG (1795–1876) claimed that all 'Infusoria' represented 'complete organisms' possessing a full set of organs (including gastrointestinal system, musculature, nervous system, etc.), essentially identical with those of higher forms. F. DUJARDIN (1801–1862), on the other hand, contested this view, asserting that such animals consisted only of a homogeneous substratum, which he named 'sarcode', capable of sustaining all vital activities. DUJARDIN's sarcode was, in fact, one of the earliest formulations of the concept protoplasm. C. TH. VON SIEBOLD (1804–1885), who discerned unicellular animals and restricted the term Protozoa to such forms, supported DUJARDIN's view, which became generally accepted in the years after 1850. Although the subsequently improved technical

---

successor to the chair held in turn by GEGENBAUR, O. HERTWIG, and FÜRBRINGER in Jena, was wont to stress the significance of invertebrates with remarks of the following sort: 'Anatomie des Menschen kann man nur auf Grund der vergleichenden Anatomie der Wirbeltiere verstehen. Wer aber keine ausreichende Kenntnis der Wirbellosen hat, versteht auch die vergleichende Anatomie der Wirbeltiere nicht.'

Additional comment of May 1965: After the printing of the present second volume of this series was already completed, an elaborate account, in two volumes, of 'Structure and Function in the Nervous System of Invertebrates' (Freeman and Co., San Francisco and London, 1965) was published by BULLOCK and HORRIDGE, with chapters by three additional collaborators (BERN, HAGADORN, SMITH). This extensive compilation and survey covers more than 9000 references and thus provides a much needed recent systematic reference file for invertebrate neurobiology. It is hardly necessary to add that the purport of my (if somewhat extensive) chapter of 'remarks' on invertebrate neurobiology, and the purport of BULLOCK's and HORRIDGE's treatise are, in many respects, significantly divergent, quite apart from substantial differences concerning numerous aspects of our respective fundamental 'scientific', biologic, and neurologic viewpoints.

methods disclosed a variety of protoplasmatic structural differentiations such as the diverse cytoplasmic and nuclear components, including the details at present investigated by means of electron microscopy, essential features of DUJARDIN's and v. SIEBOLD's early interpretation have become firmly incorporated into contemporary biologic science.

However, prior to the proper definition of the group Protozoa, the more loosely circumscribed term Infusoria subsumed both protozoan and small metazoan organisms. The size of some of these latter, such as Rotifera, Gastrotricha, and Tardigrada (discussed further below in sections 5 and 7) remains within an order of magnitude corresponding to that of many Protozoa. Clearly, with respect to this sort of metazoan 'Infusoria', EHRENBERG's view was entirely correct. In Figure A, the unicellular, protoplasmic organization of a well differentiated protozoan (Paramecium) is compared, by PORTMANN (1964), with the

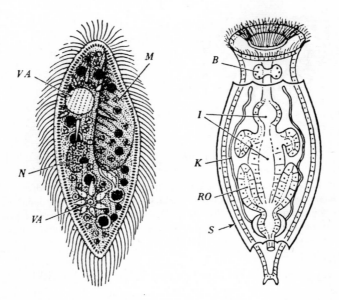

Figure A. Paramecium (left) and Rotifer (right). Although of roughly identical size, one organism has a 'unicellular', and the other a 'multicellular' structure (from PORTMANN, 1964). B: brain; I: gastrointestinal tract; K: protonephridial apparatus; M: 'mouth'; N: nucleus; RO: gonads; S: shell; VA: pulsating vacuole (cf. also Figs. 29, 30, 31). Generally speaking, the total length of a paramecium (pertaining to an order of 'small ciliates'), as measured in my own sample slides, falls within an order of magnitude of about 0.15 to 0.3 mm.

multicellular organization in a metazoan form (Rotifer) of essentially identical body size.

If forms of dubious taxonomic status, such, for example, as Volvox globator, and so-called Mesozoa, are discounted, *Porifera (sponges)* might be regarded as the only phylum of Metazoa without a nervous system. Porifera are sessile marine, but in some instances also fresh water organisms. In simple forms the body is shaped like a flask with thick, porous wall, and with a single main opening, designated as osculum (Fig. 1 A). Water enters the central cavity by means of the

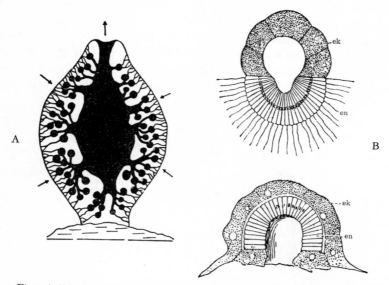

Figure 1. Diagrams illustrating the configurational aspects of Porifera. *A* Simple calcareous sponge (channels and cavities black). Osculum at top, arrows indicate direction of water flow. (After PARKER, 1919, from HERRICK, 1924.) *B* Embryonic blastula and gastrula stages of Sycandra. (After F. H. SCHULTZE from R. HERTWIG, 1912.) ek: ectoderm (macromeres); en: entoderm (micromeres).

numerous pores, which provide systems of canals within the body wall, and leaves through the osculum; the water is propelled by flagellated cells. In the more complex forms, numerous oscula are present.

Upon stimulation of the surface, localized responses are obtained, whereby the neighboring pores or oscula slowly contract. This type of 'excitation conduction' and responses can be roughly compared to similar phenomena in some plants (cf. chapt. I, p. 37). Porifera, however, in contradistinction to plants, possess spindle-shaped contractile elements, of a primitive muscular type, considered by PARKER (1919) as 'independent effectors', reacting to a diffusely propagated disturbance.

Because of the cited contractile, that is, motor responses in sponges, some older as well as some recent authors have attempted to interpret certain histologic elements in Porifera as nervous and sensory cells, thus claiming that, in these organisms, a nervous system exists. This claim does not seem justified, and JONES (1962) has recently presented a detailed review of the relevant problems. Likewise, BARNES (1963) assumes that 'there is probably no nervous system in the sponge'. On the basis of my own acquaintance with the histology of Porifera, in PLATE's laboratory, dating back, however, to 1919–1920, I am inclined to agree with JONES and BARNES. Evidently, the contractile elements of sponges, including the choanocytes, pinacocytes, porocytes, and collencytes, may not only contract, but transmit states of excitation, and such conduction could manifest a variety of complex patterns. Nevertheless, such structural and functional relationships do not seem to constitute a 'nervous system' in the generally accepted conventional sense.

This question, moreover, has significant bearings on an important overall problem which, in general, is ignored or slurred over, but which, since my early studies, I have always kept in mind and occasionally pointed out, namely, how can one establish 'identity' of a particular cell type with reasonable certainty, or, here somewhat more naively expressed, by what criteria is one justified to recognize a *nerve cell?* Particularly with regard to neoplastic growth and tissue cultures (H. K. and M. WIENER KIRBER, 1959), we have discussed some of this problem's aspects and implications. In the present chapter, this question may be conveniently ignored in accordance with 'established' neurobiologic procedure, since it shall be dealt with in one of the sections of chapter V (volume 3) of this series.

The ontogenetic development of Porifera differs in some important aspects from that of other Metazoa. The blastula-like stage depicted in Figure 1 B is designated as amphiblastula; it consists of a hemisphere formed by flagellated micromeres, and of another one formed by a lesser number of macromeres. This arrangement is, at least in some calcareous sponges, the result of a process called inversion, whereby the flagella-bearing surface, originally facing the blastocoel, is turned inside-out, so that the flagella become directed toward the exterior.

Subsequently, gastrulation occurs as shown in the figure. But in contradistinction to other metazoans, the ectoderm is formed by the macromeres, and the entoderm by the micromeres. This reversal in the arrangement of layers and a number of additional peculiarities have posed difficult and undecidable problems as regards the phylogenetic relationship of Porifera which many zoologists regard as a so-called dead-end phylum.

The sponge gastrula attaches itself to the bottom by the side of the blastopore, which closes and disappears (cf. also Fig. 210 in section 14 of this chapter). Although giving the appearance of a blastopore, the osculum of simple asconoid sponges does thus not derive from that opening, but originates, like the various pores, and the additional oscula of more differentiated forms, by secondary canalization. Also, it should be noted that, in asconoid sponges, the osculum represents, as it were, the anal opening.

2. Coelenterates and Echinoderms

The nervous system of *Coelenterates* is of particular interest since this phylum may be considered to comprise the 'lowest' or the most 'primitive' Metazoa displaying nervous tissue. In Hydrozoa (including Hydra[2] as well as other hydroid polyps), and Anthozoa (Actinia) a diffuse net of nerve cells with two or more processes is located at the base of the ectoderm (Figs. 2 to 4). At the base of the entoderm, there

---

[2] The nerve net of the fresh-water polyp hydra (which has no medusa stage) is not very conspicuous, and its structural elements are difficult to display in histologic preparations. KLEINENBERG (1872) denied the presence of a nervous system in hydra, but WOLFF (1904) and particularly HADZI (1909) rather convincingly demonstrated the nervous system of that polyp. It is amusing that electron microscopists have recently disputed the existence of nerve cells in hydra (LENHOFF, 1961). Reporting on a symposium on ultra-structures of hydra, this author states: 'the light microscopists claimed that hydra has a nerve net, demonstrable by staining techniques, whereas electron microscopists were unable to find any structures resembling neural elements'. Now, if careful histologic techniques demonstrate nerve cells by means of the light microscope, I believe that this evidence stands. To deny such structures on the basis of electron-photomicrographs would, e. g., correspond to the denial of a well substantiated histologic structure because it could no longer be found in a spodogram, that is, in the histologic picture displayed by micro-incineration. Some further comments on the evaluation of electron-photomicrographs with respect to nerve tissue will be included in chapter V (The Structural Elements of the Vertebrate Nervous System), volume 3 of this series.

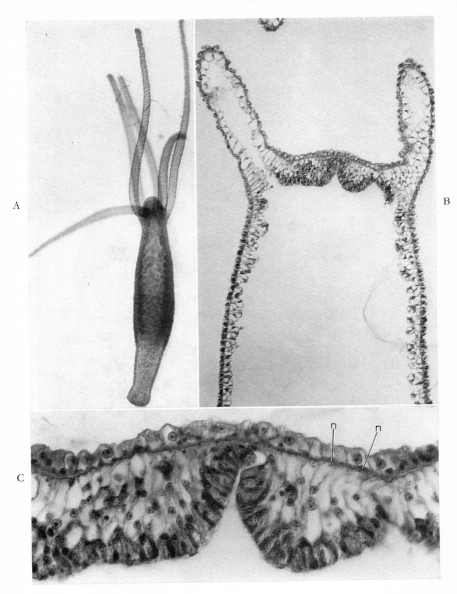

Figure 2. General aspects of Hydra. (Original.) *A* Whole mount ($\times$ 40, red. $^2/_3$). *B* longitudinal section (low power, $\times$ 220, red. $^2/_3$). *C* longitudinal section (higher power, $\times$ 660, red. $^2/_3$). A few nerve cells (*n*) shown at the base of the ectoderm. (Hematoxylin-eosin.)

may be a somewhat similar nervous network, although consisting of a far lesser number of elements (HANSTRÖM, 1928); the available observations and data are here much less definite or certain. As regards the ectoderm, there are scattered 'receptive' or 'sensory cells' provided with branching basal processes, similar to the processes of nerve cells, and connecting with the nerve net, which latter, in turn, is connected with contractile cells, likewise pertaining to the ectoderm.

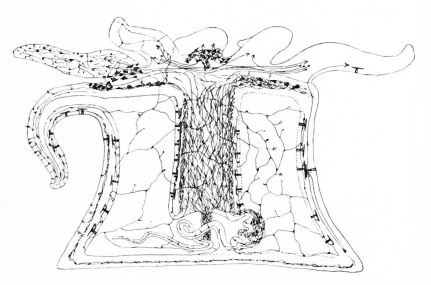

Figure 3. General arrangement of the nerve net in an Actinia. (After WOLFF, 1904.)

In medusae (Hydromedusae) pertaining to the class Hydrozoa, there is also a subepithelial nerve net which, however, displays at the margin of the umbrella a concentration into one or two so-called nerve rings. The sensitive and motile tentacles are connected by nervous strands with such ring (Fig. 5). An entodermal plexus has been described.

The nervous system of medusae pertaining to the class Scyphozoa is rather similar to that of Hydrozoa and Anthozoa, although Scyphomedusae appear to display some peculiarities as regards the patterns of condensation (Fig. 6). The nervous system of Ctenophora, again,

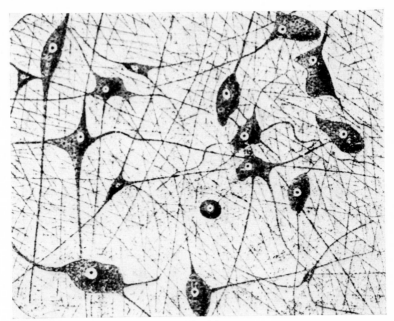

Fig. 4 A

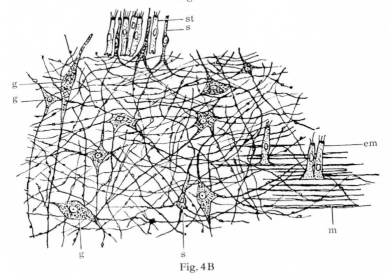

Fig. 4 B

Figure 4. Details of coelenterate nerve nets. *A* Nerve cells and nerve fibers of an Actinia. (After R. Hertwig, 1912.) *B* Coelenterate nerve net showing connections with sensory and muscle cells. (After O. HERTWIG from HERRICK, 1924.) em: epitheloid muscle cell; g: nerve cell; m: muscle cell; s: sensory cell; st: supporting cell.

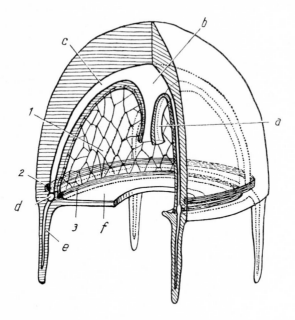

Figure 5. Nerve net of a Hydromedusa. (After Bütschli, 1921, from Beccari, 1947.)
1: subumbrellar nerve net; 2: external nerve ring; 3: internal nerve ring; a: manubrium;
b: 'stomach'; c: radial canal; d: circular canal; e: tentacle; f: velum.

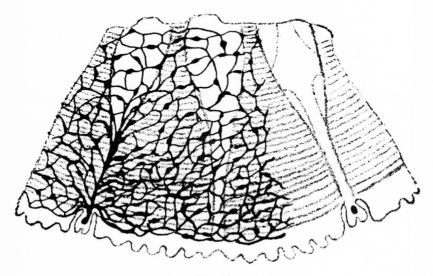

Fig. 6 A

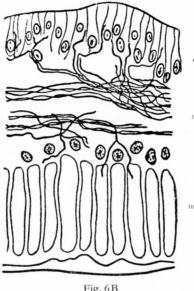

Fig. 6 B

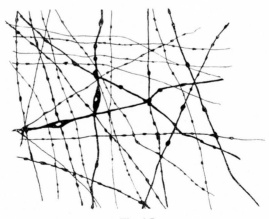

Fig. 6 C

Figure 6. Nervous structures of Scyphozoa. *A* Nerve net and musculature (parallel stripes) from the subumbrellar surface of Rhizostoma. (After BETHE from HERRICK, 1924.) *B* Cross-section through bell-musculature of Rhizostoma. (After PARKER, 1919.) e: subumbrellar surface epithelium; n: nerve fibers; m: musculature. *C* Entodermal nerve plexus of Rhizostoma. (After BOZLER, 1927, from HANSTRÖM, 1928.)

conforms in general to that of Hydrozoa, Anthozoa and Scyphozoa. The presence of an entodermal nerve net, however, is here denied by several authors. A few additional remarks on ctenophores will be found below, after the following short comments on medusae and coelenterates in general.

The bell margin of some medusae is supplied with two types of specialized sense organs, namely eyes (ocelli) and statocysts. The two organs may be in close proximity within so-called marginal bodies. In a few species the eyes show a fair degree of differentiation in so far as a spherical, lens-like body, and a 'retinal layer' is present. While some medusae are negatively phototactic and descend to greater depth during the day, others display positive phototaxis, and still others seem to be rather indifferent to light. Again, it has been assumed that the ocelli might provide a generalized stimulus for muscular activity.

The statocysts are pits or vesicles containing sensory cells with hair-like processes stimulated by statoliths (calcareous concretions). When the bell-shaped animal tilts, the changes in the gravitational pressure exerted by the statoliths initiate a series of neuromuscular activities which return the bell to a horizontal position.

Coelenterates, which can also be classified as *Cnidaria* according to R. HERTWIG (1931) and others, are furthermore characterized by the development of 'nettle cells' or cnidoblasts throughout the epidermis. These highly specialized cells contain a nematocyst, namely a capsule including a coiled tube. On the surface, the cnidoblast is provided with a hair-like cnidocil, presumably representing a triggering mechanism. Upon stimulation, the nematocyst explodes and becomes discharged with its expanding tube. This latter injects a paralyzing protein toxin into either prey or aggressor. Some coelenterates can cause not only painful but even serious damage to the human skin. After their discharge, the cnidoblasts degenerate and are replaced by the differentiation of interstitial cells into new nettle cells.

Although many present-day zoologists classify *Ctenophora*, or *Comb Jellies*, as a separate small phylum with approximately 80 species, it appears quite permissible, in a simpler classification adapted to the purpose of comparative neurology, to regard the comb jellies as an aberrant group of coelenterates. The body plan of these animals displays a radial symmetry and is quite similar to that of medusae. Eight ciliated bands, designated as comb rows, distinguish and characterize the ctenophores.

The nervous system, as studied by HEIDER (1927) in Beroë, consists of a rather diffuse ectodermal nerve net encircling the edge of the cap beneath the comb rows (Fig. 7) and extending toward the tip of the cap in form of longitudinal strips between the ciliated bands. It is claimed that both syncytial connections and connections by close apposition (contact) obtain within that nerve net.

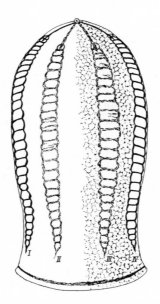

Figure 7. Diagram of nerve net and comb rows in Beroë. (After HEIDER, 1927, from HANSTRÖM, 1928.) The fibrous frame of four comb rows (I–IV) is shown, and the nerve net is indicated in the right half of the figure. The narrow ring encircling the mouth (bottom) is a fibrous supporting structure.

As a rule, ctenophores do not possess cnidoblasts, but, instead, adhesive cells called colloblasts, connected to the end of a stalk consisting of a straight filament surrounded by a coiled, contractile one. The surface of the colloblast secretes sticky spherules by means of which a prey is secured. However, one ctenophore, Euchlora rubra, is reported to be provided with nematocysts (BARNES, 1963). This rare species, on the other hand, lacks colloblasts. BARNES (1963) cites this finding as evidence 'of the coelenterate origin of the Ctenophora', while I am inclined to interpret it as additional justification for the inclusion of comb jellies into the coelenterate phylum.

Since, as a whole, this phylum subsumes several classes with different orders, and with a large number of species, it must be stressed that the net-like nervous system of this group of organisms displays a wide variety of patterns. Generally speaking, this system is not necessarily a uniform network, but may represent, in some forms, a more complex combination of different net-systems. As regards the types of nervous elements forming said networks, there are larger bipolar as well as tripolar nerve cells, and smaller multipolar ones.

Some net systems transmit excitation in a diffuse manner and without polarisation, that is, without a specific, invariable direction of the impulse conduction. In other instances, evidence of polarisation has been recorded. This question, which involves the problem of synaptic or non-synaptic connections between nerve cells, will be taken up further below in section 3 (Phylogenetic Theories Concerning Origin of Nervous System).

Echinodermata, although displaying a parameric radial symmetry characterized by five rays in the adult form, develop from bilaterally symmetric larvae, such as the Pluteus-larvae of Echinoids and Ophiuroids, or similar larvae of Asteroids and Holothuroids. These larvae have ciliated locomotor bands and resemble the Tornaria-larva of Balanoglossus. There are also certain similarities with the Trochophoralarva of annelids and other forms (cf. p. 72, footnote 12).

However, in Echinodermata, the archenteron connects with a secondary anterior stomodeum, which becomes the mouth, while the primary blastopore represents the larval anus. Echinodermata are thus, together with Chordata, designated as deuterostome animals, in which the anus derives from the blastopore or originates secondarily near the closed blastopore. Annelids, arthropods, and molluscs, on the other hand, are protostome animals, in which the blastopore becomes the mouth. The significance of a distinction between protostomes *(Proterostomia)* and deuterostomes *(Deuterostomia)* will be discussed at the end of this chapter, in an appraisal of theories concerning the origin of vertebrates.

A peculiar feature of echinoderm organization is the presence of canals and surface appendages constituting the water-vascular or ambulacral system, used for locomotion, or, in sessile forms, for the motion of tentacles. This canal system is derived from the celomic cavity, and connects with the outside through the madreporite, a perforated calcareous plate, located on the aboral side. The water enters the ambulacral system through the madreporite.

Echinoderms possess a concrete skeleton consisting of articulating or fused calcareous plates. This skeleton is provided with projecting tubercles or spines, which give the spiny appearance of the body surface indicated by the designation 'Echinodermata'.

Many forms of the class Holothuroidea or 'sea cucumbers' display the phenomenon of evisceration. Upon being strongly irritated, these animals expel a major part of their viscera, particularly of the rupturing intestinal tract, either through mouth or anus. Evisceration is then followed by regeneration. In some Holothuria, a less drastic type of reaction takes place, whereby a mass of tubules (*Cuvier's* tubules), connected with the cloaca, are ruptured and discharged through the anus. This is a defense mechanism by means of which attacking predators are entangled in a mass of stickly threads. New tubules of *Cuvier* are then formed by a regenerative process.

As regards the class Asteroidea, the so-called cardiac portion of the stomach is normally everted through the oral opening in feeding, and folds around the prey. Digestion already goes on before the stomach is retracted.

The *nervous system* of *Echinodermata* can be evaluated as *structurally* rather similar to that of Coelenterata (Fig. 8), although *morphologically* quite different, in accordance with the peculiar parameric organization obtaining in asteroids, crinoids, echinoids, ophiuroids, and holothurians. The echinoderm nervous system, like that of coelenterates, is non-ganglionated, that is, consists merely of nerve strands containing the nerve cells, and may display a somewhat pentagonal circumoral nerve ring, from the 'angles' of which radial nerve strands extend into the parameres, such as, e. g. 'arms' (Figs. 9, 10). In general, three different condensations can be distinguished, designated as ectoneural, hyponeural, and apical nervous system (Figs. 11–15). The ectoneural system includes the oral ring with radial strands. It is well developed in all echinoderms, but is said to lack a true ring in crinoids. Additional radial strands, with or without a true ring formation, are provided by fairly complex hyponeural and apical systems. In asteroids, the hyponeural and apical nerve strands are not as well developed as the ectoneural system which is here the most conspicuous one. The apical (entoneural) system is best developed in crinoids, and, according to KAPPERS (1929) occurs only in this group, where it may surpass the other systems in size. While the apical system seems indeed to be missing in holothurians, it has been rather convincingly demonstrated, by reliable authors, in asteroids, echinoids, and ophiuroids (cf. the

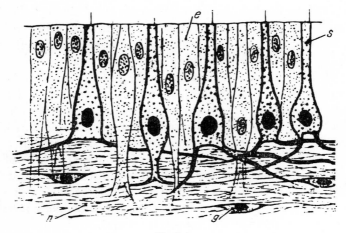

Fig. 8 A

Figure 8. Structural aspect of echinoderm nervous system compared with that in a coelenterate. *A* External nerve ring of the coelenterate hydromedusa Carmarina. (After O. and R. HERTWIG from PLATE, 1922.) e: surface epithelium; g: nerve cell; n: nerve ring; s: sensory cell. *B* and *C* Longitudinal sections through radial nerve of echinoderm Asterias rubens. *B* Longitudinal section through radial nerve of echinoderm Asterias rubens. (After MEYER, 1906, from PLATE, 1922.) nf: nerve fibers; nz: nerve cell; siz: sensory cell; stf: supporting fiber; stz: supporting cell. *C* Similar section with slightly different pattern. (After MEYER, 1906, from HANSTRÖM, 1928.) bf: basal process of sensory cell; c: cuticula; gs: so-called ground substance; gf: supporting fiber; glz: nerve cell; kz: so-called nuclear zone; nf: nerve fibers; nsch: so-called nerve layer; pf: peripheral ending of sensory cell; stz: supporting cells; sz: sensory cell.

evaluation by HANSTRÖM, 1928). An apical strand appeared identifiable in my own sample material of asteroids (Fig. 15). The apical nerve cord is also designated as 'aboral nervous system'.

It is of interest that the nerve cells of the hyponeural system (related to the mesodermal epithelium of the hyponeural canal), and the nerve cells of the apical system (related to the peritoneal epithelium) have been regarded as of mesodermal origin (CUÉNOT, 1891). Some parts of the ectoneural system, namely those which innervate pharynx and gut, are considered to be of entodermal origin (HANSTRÖM, 1928)[3].

---

[3] HANSTRÖM (1928) stresses the direct and close connections between the ectodermal and entodermal nervous systems of echinoderms and assumes likewise direct connections between the ectodermal and entodermal nervous systems of coelenterates by means of nerve fibers passing through the mesoglaea. The probability of such connections has been suggested by some observations.

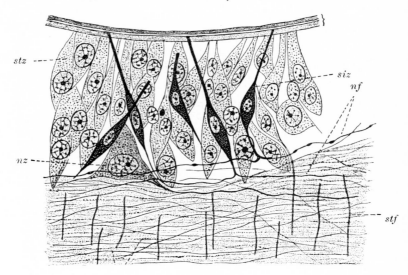

Fig. 8 B

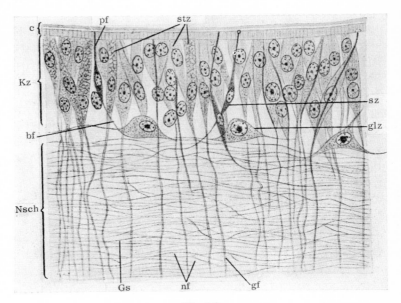

Fig. 8 C

Yet, according to the last-named author (1928), ectoneural and hyponeural nervous system should be evaluated as constituting an ecto-hyponeural morphologic unit, presumably also with close functional interrelations. In Crinoids and Ophiuroids, definite structural connections between apical and ecto-hyponeural systems seem evident, and HANSTRÖM emphasizes their probable functional con-

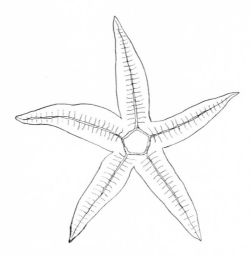

Figure 9. Simplified diagram showing general arrangement of ectoneural nerve strands in a starfish (Asterias). An eye spot (not shown), consisting of numerous pigment-cup ocelli, is located at the tip of each arm. Circumoral nerve ring and radial nerves are shown.

nections. Thus, although three different nervous systems (or subsystems) do indeed occur in echinoderms, HANSTRÖM is inclined to stress their combination into an overall anatomical and functional unity. At least in some forms, a subepithelial skin plexus is connected with the 'central' ectoneural system.

Polarized impulse conduction has been demonstrated in echinoderms, although some 'diffusely conducting' or unpolarized subsystems may also be present. The 'ground substance' or 'fiber layer' of 'nerve cords' (cf. Figs. 8 B, C and 13) can be regarded, at least in part, as representing a 'neuropil', including 'synapses' (SMITH, 1950). Generally speaking, the echinoderm nervous system, which clearly manifests some sort of centralization, can be evaluated as combining 'primitive' with more 'advanced' features. Although 'coelenterate-

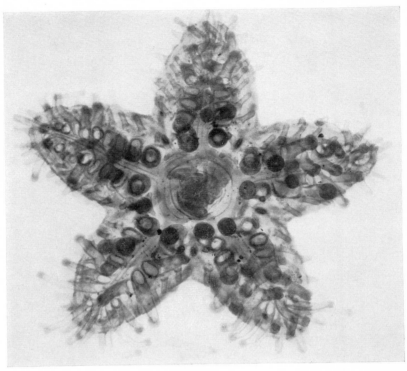

Figure 10. Whole mount of young Asterias, displaying circumoral nerve ring and course of radial nerves as indicated in the preceding diagram, but somewhat overspread by the additional structures ($\times$ 32, red. $^9/_{10}$). On both sides of the radial nerves, a row of ambulacral podia is shown. In addition, spines can be recognized. (Original.)

like' in some respects, it displays a set of quite distinct additional features. Because of considerable technical difficulties in obtaining suitable preparations of the echinoderm nervous system, numerous problems concerning histologic structure as well as details of fiber connections still remain poorly elucidated.

In a recent treatise on invertebrate zoology (BARNES, 1963), the functional rôle of the echinoderm nervous system has been summarized with the following generalized conclusions based on the available experimental studies and data.

As regards the motility of Asteroids, the integrity of both the radial nerves and the circumoral nerve ring seems to be essential in the coordination of the podia. Although the podia do not all move (or 'step') in unison, they are said to be coordinated to the extent of their

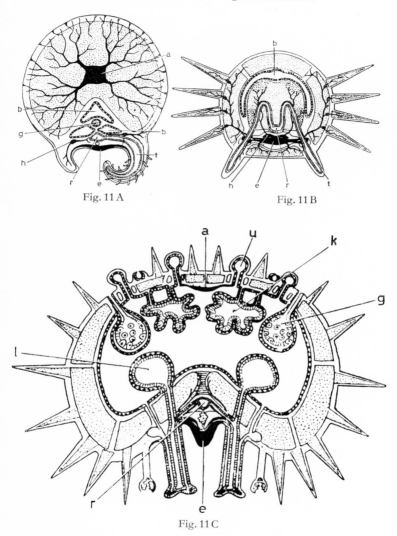

Fig. 11 A   Fig. 11 B

Fig. 11 C

Figure 11. Diagrammatic cross sections through the arms of representative echinoderms. (After LANG from SELENKA-GOLDSCHMIDT, 1919.) *A* Crinoid. *B* Ophiurid.
C Asteroid. Diagram *C* should be compared with an actual cross section shown in the
next Figure (12). a: radial strand of apical nervous system; b: celomic cavity of arm;
e: ectoneural radial nerve; g: gonad; h: hyponeural nerve strand (closely above ectoneural
nerve in *B* and *C*, as two well separated strands in *A*); k: stomach diverticulum (pyloric
cecum, so-called liver), with mesenteries; l: ampulla; r: radial canal; t: ambulacral
tentacle; u: papula ('branchial vesicle'). Lateral to each Asteroid podium so-called pedi-
cellaria can be seen.

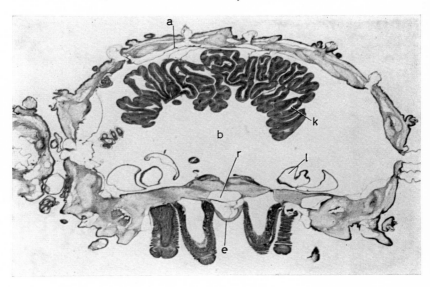

Figure 12. Cross section through arm of Asterias (Hematoxylin-eosin, × 20, red. ³/₄). This section corresponds to Fig. 11 C. Abbreviations as in Fig. 11. Further close-up details shown in Figs. 13 and 14. (Original.)

stepping (that is, 'to step or not to step'), and they appear to be coordinated insofar as they step in the proper direction, depending upon which arm is the leading one.

If the radial nerve of a given arm is severed, the podia, although capable of movement, are no longer coordinated with the podia of the other arms. If the circumoral ring is cut between two radial nerves, all movement is said to be inhibited, because coordination of the podia in *all* the arms is lost. It is believed that at the junction of each radial nerve with the circumoral nerve ring there exists a 'center'. This center, in a leading arm, is supposed to exert a temporary dominance over the 'centers' of the other arms. It is reported that in the majority of sea stars, including Asterias, any arm can act as a dominant arm. Such dominance seems to be determined by external stimuli. However, in a few species, one arm is said to be permanently dominant.

In many Echinoids, the ambulacral areas are provided with hard ovoid or spherical bodies (spheridia) regarded as organs of equilibrium. Experiments in at least one species have demonstrated that, if the spheridia are removed, the righting reaction is greatly delayed.

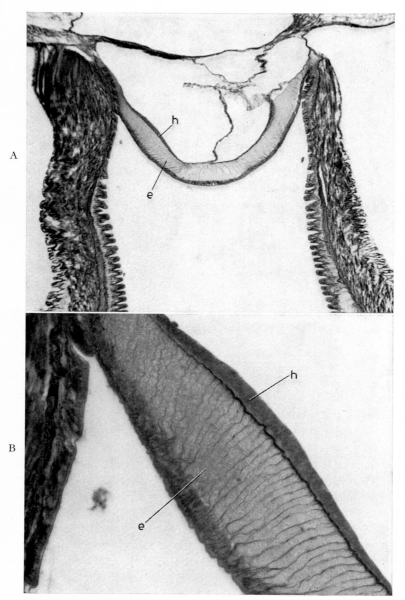

Figure 13. Ectoneural and hyponeural nerve strand of Asterias in cross section. (Original.) *A* Overall view ($\times$ 100, red. $^3/_4$). *B* Details at higher magnification (Hematoxylin-eosin, $\times$ 450, red. $^3/_4$). With still higher magnification and special techniques, pictures such as demonstrated by R. MEYER (1906) and shown above in Figs. 8 B and C can be obtained.

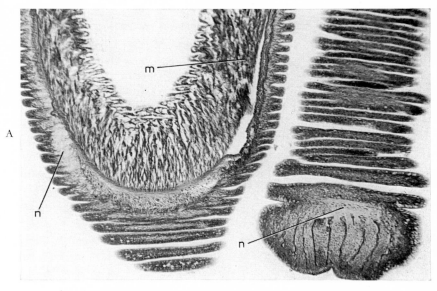

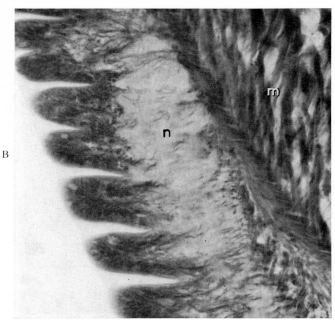

Figure 14. Details of nerve ring in podium of the starfish Asterias. (Original.) *A* General view ($\times$ 180, red. $^3/_4$). *B* Nerve ring at greater magnification ($\times$ 630, red. $^9/_{10}$). n: nerve ring; m: musculature. (Hematoxylin-eosin.)

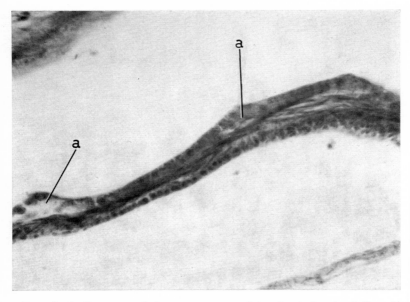

Figure 15. Rudimentary apical nervous system of Asterias, in location indicated on Figs. 11 C and 12 (Original; hematoxylin-eosin; × 520, red. $^1/_1$).

As regards Ophiuroids, experimental studies seem to indicate that the circumoral nerve ring plays a coordinating rôle in arm motility comparable to that of the nerve ring in Asteroids.

In Crinoids, the principal part of the nervous system is the apical or entoneural one (cf. Fig. 11 A). This apical system gives off five brachial nerves passing through an outer pentagonal nerve ring. In the stalked crinoids, the apical nervous system extends into the stalk and supplies small nerves to the cirri. If the apical system, including the outer pentagonal ring, is destroyed, the animal is reported to become totally immobilized. The brachial nerves contain the components for primary nervous conduction in the arms. On the other hand, destruction of both the hyponeural and ectoneural components is said to have a negligible effect on swimming, attaching, and righting behavior.

In Holothuroids, the circumoral nerve ring does not seem to play a dominant rôle in nervous integration. Thus, normal behavioral reactions, including movement, righting, and responses to light, have been reported as occurring in Thyone after removal of the anterior body portion containing the nerve ring. Likewise, control of respiratory pumping activities is said to be located in the cloaca.

Concerning another 'functional' aspect of the nervous system, namely *'neurosecretion'*, to which references will be found in various subsequent sections of this chapter, it does not seem unlikely that neurosecretory activities may occur in at least some Echinodermata (UNGER, 1960; FONTAINE, 1962; cf. also further below, footnote 7).

3. Phylogenetic Theories
Concerning Origin of Nervous System

The available data on structural differentiation of nervous tissue in Coelenterates as well as in Echinoderms, which may or may not be phylogenetically related to the former, have suggested a number of theories concerning the evolution of the nervous system.

Taking, for instance, structural differentiations in sponges, as well as some histologic elements of diverse sorts of coelenterates into consideration, 'epitheliomuscular cells' in ectoderm or in entoderm could be assumed to contract upon a stimulus directly affecting these cells which might then be regarded as 'neuromuscular' cells (that is, as combined receptors, conductors and effectors). In addition, subsequent evolutionary events could then have led to the realization of the four further possibilities:

(a) A sensory cell may transmit an impulse directly to a contractile element and thus represent a receptor and conductor.

(b) A sensory cell may transmit an impulse to a nerve cell, which, in turn, conducts the impulse to the muscular element.

(c) Between the sensory cell and the muscular element, two or more nerve cells are intercalated. This general arrangement obtains likewise in the central nervous system of more highly differentiated animals, whereby the complexity of the central nervous system is related to the patterns provided by the intercalated or internuncial conductors.

(d) It is possible that processes of nerve cells, ending by means of minute knob-like structures in connection with other cellular elements, e.g. epithelial cells, function as receptors, whereby the nerve cell in question then becomes, in some respects, a receptor as well as conductor.

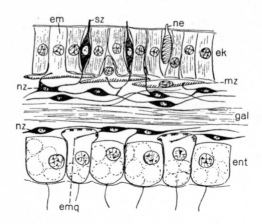

Figure 16. Diagram of primitive nerve system as displayed in coelenterates. (Combined after PLATE and other authors from K., 1927.) ek: ectoderm; em: epitheloid muscle cell; emq: cross section through epitheloid muscle cell; ent: entoderm; gal: mesenchyme; mz: muscle cell; ne: nettle-cell; nz: nerve cell; sz: sensory cell.

The various possibilities (a) to (d) are illustrated in the diagrammatic Fig. 16. It is evident that the evaluation of an element as 'receptor' or 'conductor' or both is, to some extent, arbitrary.

On the basis of the available data, nerve cells (as well as 'primitive' muscle cells) could perhaps be interpreted as modified and displaced epithelial cells. The manner in which the connected systems sensory cell, nerve cell and muscle cell (effector cell) have evolved in the course of phylogeny is open to diverse speculations. According to KLEINEN-BERG (1872) and PARKER (1919) the 'neuromuscular' cell should be considered the point of departure, from which the interconnected chain sensory cell, nerve cell and true muscle cell derived. O. and R. HERTWIG (1878, 1880) assumed that these three elements might have independently arisen from indifferent epithelial cells, and became secondarily connected. However, these authors also considered an origin of nerve cells from sensory cells (neurosensory elements). PLATE (1922) particularly favors the hypothesis that nerve cells were phylogenetically derived from sensory cells, while muscular elements had an 'independent' origin. According to PARKER (1919) 'muscle once developed as an effector gave occasion for the addition of receptors or sensory elements after which the adjustor or central nervous mechanism was differentiated'.

CHILD (1921, 1924) and HERRICK (1924) emphasize the gradients related to the assumed polarity arising in early metazoa, e. g. as an apico-basal polarity. Within such gradients, sensory cell, nerve cell, and muscle cell may have arisen from a single neuromotor cell, as KLEINENBERG supposed, or from separate cells, as the HERTWIGS believed, but in any case their polarities, according to HERRICK (1924), 'were predetermined by the general gradients within which they were developed'.

Actual observations, however, seem to indicate that, except in some instances, a strict polarity does not generally obtain in the diffuse nerve nets and in the nerve strands of coelenterates, including perhaps ctenophores. Locally applied stimuli result in diffuse impulse conduction which appears perfectly reversible, depending on the location of the stimulus. Stronger stimuli cause a more extensive reaction than weaker ones. This has been interpreted to mean that an impulse triggered by a weak stimulus does not spread as far as an impulse initiated by a stronger stimulus; or again, that, in such type of nervous system, some sort of 'decrement' obtains (HANSTRÖM, 1928).

It is not possible to detect structural differences in the various processes of nerve cells, and it seems permissible to assume that the nexus between nerve cells is not, as a general rule, synaptic (cf. chapt. I, p. 7), in the sense implying irreversibility of conduction. Thus, the 'primitive' nerve net of coelenterates has been regarded as an *asynaptic network* of '*protoneurons*', that is of undifferentiated, or 'non-polarized' nerve cells[4], with reversible conduction.

Many of the earlier authors had interpreted the histologic findings as indicating 'continuity' or 'anastomoses' between the processes of different nerve cells, or, in other words 'syncytial' or 'plasmodial' connections[5], without discernible boundaries between cells. Although

---

[4] Further comments on 'polarization', 'protosynapses', and synapses are made further below at the end of this section on page 31 as well as in section 6, page 85, section 8, page 121, and section 12, page 247, of this chapter. The concept of nerve cell 'polarization' and various interpretations concerning a structural or functional differentiation of nerve cell processes, such, e. g. as dendrites and neurites, will be discussed with additional details in the next chapter (V), which also includes an evaluation of the neuron theory (volume 3 of this series).

[5] The terms syncytium and plasmodium are here taken as synonyms, referring to cellular territories not separated by a microscopically discernible boundary structure. Some authors use these two terms with different denotations, indicating diverse types of cytoplasmic territories as regards genetic or configurational relation to the corresponding nuclei.

some of the pictures and descriptions concerning such connections appear rather convincing, other authors, particularly BOZLER (1927), have denied such protoplasmic anastomoses, and maintain mere contiguity, that is, close apposition of nerve cell processes, whereby boundaries remain, and the nerve cells completely retain their individuality (Fig. 17). This question, despite BOZLER's impressive findings, does not seem completely settled. Yet, it may be regarded as irrelevant with respect to the concept of an asynaptic network, which could obtain with as well as without actual 'anastomoses'.

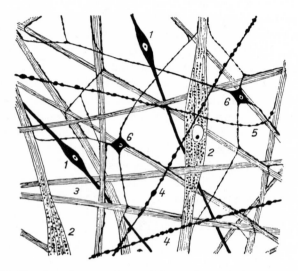

Figure 17. Ectodermal nerve plexus of the coelenterate scyphozoan Rhizostoma. ('Rongalitweiss'-technique; after a colored figure of BOZLER, 1927, from BECCARI, 1947.) 1: small bipolar cell; 2: large bipolar cell; 3, 4: various nerve fibers; 5: nerve fiber ending by apposition; 6: multipolar cell.

PARKER (1924) refers to experiments apparently demonstrating that strychnine has no effect on the nervous network of coelenterates. but a slight effect on the neuromuscular responses of echinoderms, In crustaceans and mollusks, however, the response to strychnine is said to be much more marked. It is believed that the effects of strychnine are dependent upon the presence and the degree of differentiation of synapses. Such interpretation would tend to corroborate the assumed asynaptic type of connection in the nerve net of coelenterates. Again, it has been pointed out (PARKER, 1919) that said nerve net, in which conduction appears to manifest a decrement, does not seem to transmit according to the 'all or none' principle. More than 40 years after these comments by PARKER, the relevant problems can be regarded as still not sufficiently or satisfactorily clarified.

Nevertheless, experiments by PORTMANN (1926) seem to indicate that in some portions of the body in certain Actinia a definite polarization becomes manifested, and an interesting experiment briefly reported by HARVEY (1922) appears to evince direction as well as lack of decrement in the propagation of a nervous impulse through the disk of a medusa (Cassiopea). HARVEY cut rings of tissue shaped like a doughnut from that disk and succeeded in starting a nerve impulse in one direction. This impulse was then entrapped and passed 'round and round the disc with a velocity of about 0.5 mps'. The course of the 'entrapped' impulse could be seen because the muscular elements were stimulated to contract with each revolution. In one of these experiments the nervous impulse continued to move for eleven days uninterruptedly without change in rate, travelling 537 miles (about 865 km), that is, approximately 77 to 78 km per day. 'It stopped after eleven days only because regenerating tissue gave rise to impulses which counteracted the entrapped impulse.' In commenting upon this and similar experiments, HERRICK (1924) states that such results can only be secured if the ring of tissue is large enough to allow a short interval of rest between successive passages of the nervous impulse. The muscle is said to show fatigue earlier than the nerve net.

An earlier series of experiments in Cassiopea undertaken by MAYER (1906, 1908) demonstrated that a stimulus applied at one point of the disk's periphery may start a 'rhythmic pulsation'. The stimulus is transmitted by the diffuse nervous network of the sub-umbrella in two directions, away from the stimulated locus. The contraction wave travels clockwise and anticlockwise from that locus to the opposite region of the disk. When the contraction waves meet, the initiated motion may end, so that the whole ring gives only a single contraction, and then ceases to pulsate. Quite often, however, a single contraction wave will continue in only one direction (either clockwise or counterclockwise, but not both) around the ring. The contraction wave becomes, as it were, 'trapped' in the circuit, and must continually proceed onward through the tissue. MAYER (1908) believes that this happens when the two 'waves' arising from the original stimulated point, and meeting on the opposite side of the ring, are unequal.

He assumes that annulling of the pulsation occurs, when two waves of equal magnitude, coming from opposite directions, meet each other. If, on the other hand, a weak and a strong 'wave' meet, then the weak one is said to become suppressed, and only the stronger one remains to travel continuously around the ring in one direction. MAYER (1906, 1908) cut different sorts of rings from the sub-umbrella tissue and studied the types of pulsation rhythms that could be experimentally obtained. 'The simplest circuit is, of course, a single ring (annulus) of sub-umbrella tissue; and such ring can readily be set into sustained pulsation.' MAYER (1908) showed that the conduction of the stimulus requires the presence of nerve tissue, since a pulsation wave could not pass through muscle tissue from which the nervous network had been peeled away.

If disks without marginal sense organs be set into rhythmical pulsations, they move with machine-like regularity, without pauses, and without any of the irregularities shown by normal medusae with sense organs. The pulsation rates in these latter medusae are slower, from about 15 to 50 pulses per min., depending on the diameter of the umbrella, while disks deprived of sense organs are said to pulsate at a rhythm of about 60 to 180 contractions per min.

Experiments of this type, however, require further clarification as regards the rôle of the muscular contraction in providing a possible proprioceptive, or positive feedback effect helping to maintain the circular process, which represents an example of 'closed circuit', 'reverberating circuit', or 'self-reexciting circuit' in the wider sense; the concept of a true self-reexciting circuit in the narrower sense, that is, of a purely nervous (not neuromuscular) closed cycle was briefly discussed in the introductory chapter I (p. 11) of volume 1.

The numerous more recent experiments undertaken by various authors, and concisely summarized by HUBER (1963) have, on the whole, likewise remained inconclusive. There is, however, little doubt that so-called 'spontaneity', or rather 'intrinsic neural activity' (cf. chapt. I, sect. 3, p. 17), occurs in the nerve nets of organic forms such as coelenterates. Moreover, evidence for some instances of 'coordination', 'facilitation', and 'inhibition' has been reported.

The velocity of neural impulse conduction in coelenterates appears very low, when compared with that obtaining in the vertebrate nervous system, where velocities up to slightly more than 100 mps (meters per second), that is, approaching one third of the 'standard velocity' of sound propagation may be reached. Generally speaking, very low neural conduction velocities seem to be characteristic for all invertebrates.

In coelenterates, the recorded lower range of conduction velocity lies perhaps between 0.01 and about 0.04 mps, while the higher range may lie between 0.07 and about 0.5 mps (as e.g. approximated in HARVEY's experiment mentioned above), although velocities unusually high in the aspect under consideration, namely of 1 to 2 mps, have been inferred in some cases.

It is possible that, in some coelenterates, rapidly conducting, transmitting ('durchleitende') net-systems with perhaps synaptic connections may be combined with slowly conducting non-polarized, asynaptic ones. At least for 'distance transmitting systems' in coelenterates, all-or-none characteristics, 'decrementless conduction', refractory periods, and probably synaptic delay have been assumed. However, refractory periods and synaptic delay seem to be here of unusually short duration.

As regards the problem of synaptic connection, histologic interpretations by PANTIN (1952), BATHAM et al. (1960), and other authors seem to substantiate the occurrence of 'true' synapses. On the other hand, McCONNEL (1932), SPANGENBERG and HAM (1960), and many of the older authors have maintained the occurrence, not merely of asynaptic, but of actually syncytial connections between some coelenterate nerve cells. In Velella, MACKIE (1960) distinguished a closed syncytial system, and an 'open' one with synaptic connections. HORRIDGE (1956 and other publications) believes that although plasmodial anastomoses probably do occur in the coelenterate nerve net, discontinuity between neurons seems to represent the rule.

Nevertheless, many doubts seem still to remain concerning the proper interpretations, particularly in attributing a specific type of organization to a slowly conducting, and another to a more rapidly conducting system. Yet, although the available histologic data may not be considered altogether convincing, it does not appear impossible that, within 'originally' essentially asynaptic networks of coelenterates, some sort of true synapses have 'already' become differentiated in various regions. On the other hand, it is, of course, not entirely impossible that all neural connections in coelenterates and echinoderms are still of an unpolarized, protosynaptic type which may, under certain fluctuating conditions, manifest apparent polarization, in accordance with the views of BULLOCK (1945, 1953) discussed further below with respect to observations in annelids (p. 85).

4. Platyhelminthes and Nemathelminthes

The condensations of the nerve net in coelenterates, and the arrangements into rings and strands seen in these forms as well as in echinoderms, might be evaluated as a 'tendency' toward 'centralization'.

Platyhelminthes, and, within that phylum, particularly *Turbellaria*, are generally regarded as the 'lowest' or most 'primitive' type of Metazoa with a true *central nervous system*. Bilateral symmetry, related to a polarized, cephalo-caudal axis, is here manifested. The Turbellarians are ciliated animals. The head is directed forward in locomotion, and

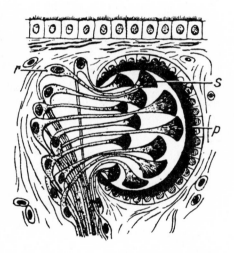

Figure 18. Eye of Turbellarian. (After HESSE, 1908, from SELENKA-GOLDSCHMIDT, 1919.) p: pigmented cup; r: 'retinal cell'; s: sensory ending of retinal cell.

may be provided with a pair of primitive eyes (Fig. 18). Such eyes have the shape of a pigmented epithelial bowl containing the receptor endings of sensory cells connected with the cerebral ganglion. The pigment screens the light from all directions but one, so that the variety transduced by the sensory cells encodes a more or less specific direction[6]. As a rule, negative phototaxis seems to obtain The paired eyes of Turbellaria, in many respects, manifest a striking analogy with the paired lateral eyes of Vertebrata. This analogy (paired stalk arising from brain, eye cup, inverted neurosensory elements) is of a much higher degree than the analogy between the 'spinal eyes' of Amphioxus and the vertebrate eyes. Again, the number of eyes in the various groups of Turbellaria differs; while one pair is quite commonly present, eyes may be entirely lacking, or two or three pairs are found. In polyclads and land planarians, an even larger number of eyes has been recorded, e.g. six pairs in Notoplana (HADENFELDT, 1929). Other sense organs of Turbellaria are represented by statocysts and various sorts of sensory cells innervating the epidermis. The statocyst may be represented by a vesicle within the 'brain'. A so-called 'auricle' or 'tentacle' (faintly visible in Fig. 22 at the level of the eye-spots), is sometimes also designated as the 'tactile lobe'.

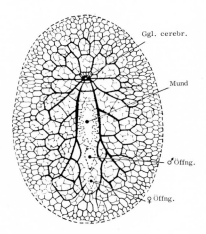

Figure 19. Nervous system of polycladid turbellarian Planocera. (After LANG from BÜTSCHLI, 1921, and HANSTRÖM, 1928.)

Generally speaking, a complex diffuse subepithelial (subectodermal) nervous net is found in Turbellaria. It extends to various depths, displaying concentrations into longitudinal strands and a 'cerebral ganglion' (Fig. 19). Thus, this type of nervous system might be considered as derived from a network such as obtains in coelenterates. It appears uncertain whether the acoel turbellarians in which the diffuse type of nerve network predominates, barely manifesting an indistinct concentration into strands and 'cerebral ganglion', should be

---

[6] Experimental findings indicate that the general body surface of planarians is also sensitive to light, but in a much lesser degree than the two differentiated eye-structures.

evaluated as 'primitive' or as 'regressive'. At any rate, with respect to nervous systems of this and similar sort, it could be said that central and peripheral nervous system are less distinctly differentiated from each other and that such systems therefore manifest a 'low' degree of development in the aspect under consideration.

HANSTRÖM (1928) expresses the opinion that in ancestral forms of turbellarians a concentration of nerve tissue into the orthogon pattern

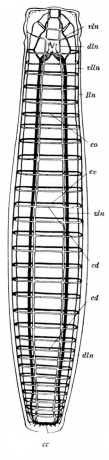

Figure 20. Nervous system of allocoel turbellarian Bothrioplana, displaying orthogon pattern. (After REISINGER, 1925, from HANSTRÖM, 1928.) cc: caudal commissure; cd: dorsal commissures; cv: ventral commissures; dln: dorsal connective; vlln: ventrolateral connective; lln: lateral connective; vln: ventral connective.

(REISINGER, 1925; HANSTRÖM, 1928) took place (cf. Fig. 20). Various reductions of the orthogon may have led to patterns such as shown in Figures 21 and 22. Several longitudinal strands run caudalward from the cerebral ganglion. A dorsal pair, a usually major ventral pair, often a lateral pair, and occasionally other parallel pairs can be regarded as derivatives of the orthogon. In contradistinction to coelenterates and echinoderms, an entodermal (or a mesodermal) nervous system in the

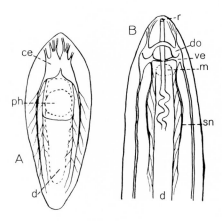

Figure 21. Diagram of nervous system in Platyhelminthes. (After various authors from K., 1927.) *A* Mesostomum (turbellarian) after B. HALLER, 1904, and others. *B* Carinella annulata. (Nemertean, after BÜTSCHLI, 1921, and others.) ce: cerebral ganglion; d: enteron; do: dorsal cerebral ganglion; m: oral opening; ph: pharynx; r: proboscis; sn: pharyngeal nerve; ve: ventral cerebral ganglion.

strict sense of the word seems to be lacking. Nerve cells are present in the strands, which latter may be interconnected by transverse commissures. Figure 23 compares the rostral end of the triclad Bdelloura, from a total mount in my sample collection, with a composite picture of the same region of Bdelloura traced by HANSTRÖM (1926, 1928) on the basis of *Golgi* preparations.

Structurally, the turbellarian central nervous system displays 'already' the 'unipolar' type of nerve cell characteristic for 'higher' invertebrates, although many bipolar and multipolar nerve cells are present, and remain in the majority. According to HADENFELDT (1929) at least seven different sorts of nerve cells, designated as types

A to G, can be found in polyclads. TURNER (1946) confirms these findings, and describes a few additional types of nerve cells in Leptoplana.

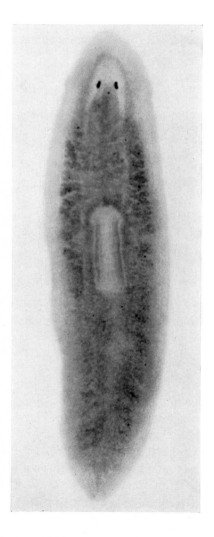

Figure 22. General aspect of Planaria in ventral view (total mount; × 28, red. $^9/_{10}$; original). The cerebral ganglia and ventral nerve strands appear as light outlines, and the pigment spots of the eye cups are visible. Diverticula of enteron dark, archistoma light and elongated (cf. Fig. 21 A).

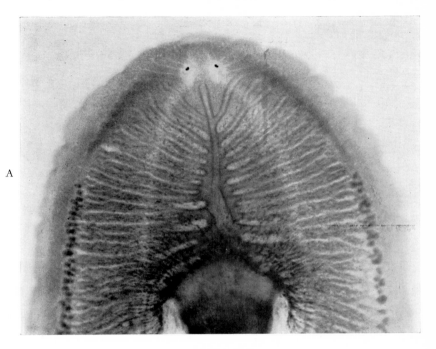

A

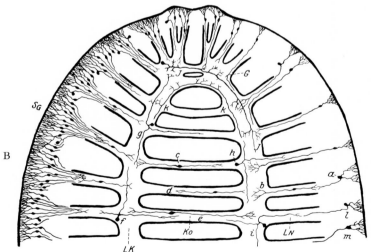

B

Figure 23. Anterior end of triclad turbellarian Bdelloura. *A* Total mount (× 19, red. ⁹/₁₀; cf. Fig. 22; original). *B* Composite *Golgi*-picture of cerebral ganglion and ventral nervous system. (From HANSTRÖM, 1926 and 1928.) G: cerebral ganglion; Lk: longitudinal connective; Ln: lateral nerves; Sg: lateral sensory ridge; a-m: various neuronal elements.

The brain (Fig. 24) of various polyclads manifests some features resembling those of more differentiated invertebrates, such as (peripheral) layers of nerve cells and central masses of fiber terminations, designated as neuropil (neuropilemes), and containing presumably synaptic connections. Within the nervous system, a differentiation of the tissue elements into conducting elements and supporting as well as covering 'glial' elements ('neuroglia') can be recognized.

It is perhaps possible to consider, with some reservations, the groups of granule cells protruding on both sides of the dorsal aspect of the brain, and capping a stalk of fibres, as primordia homologous to the pedunculated bodies (mushroom bodies, corpora pedunculata) of annelids and arthropods, discussed further below. The bilateral symmetric groups of larger cells located medially to these clusters

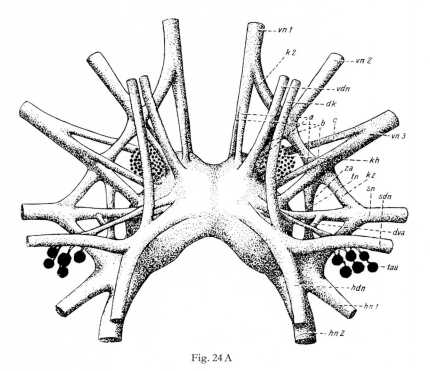

Fig. 24 A

Figure 24. Cerebral ganglion of the polyclad turbellarian Notoplana. (After HADEN-FELDT, 1929.) *A* dorsal view of cerebral ganglion. *B* and *C* Cross sections showing different arrangements of cells and neuropilemes. aukh and kh: external granule group; tau: eyes. The additional designations refer to HADENFELDT's detailed systematization of peripheral nerves and intracerebral fiber systems.

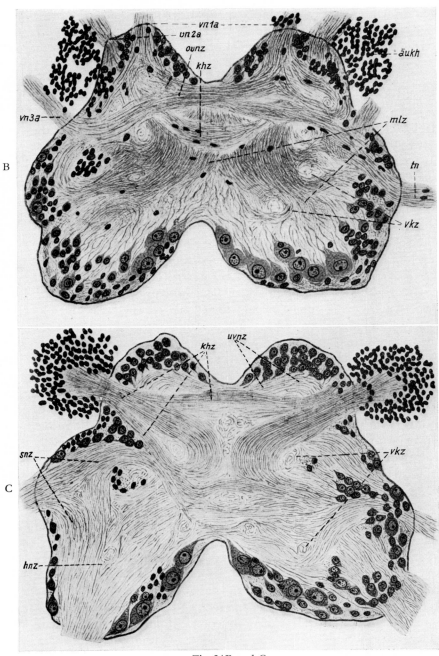

Fig. 24B und C

would then represent the homologa of pars intercerebralis of the two cited 'higher' invertebrates groups. In addition, HADENFELDT (1929) has described, within the brain of Notoplana, an inner group or cluster of granule cells.

While 'primitive' groups of Turbellaria such as Acoela display a simple configuration of nerve strands, and a poorly developed cerebral ganglion, the order Triclada, including Planaria, and the order Polycladidae, to which Notoplana and Stylochoplana belong, show the more 'advanced' types of nervous system and 'brains' within the class Turbellaria. Yet, among the polyclads, forms such as Planocera possess nerve net arrangements similar to those of coelenterates, and a rather small brain. Also, a very 'primitive' structure of the brain can be seen in Planaria. A comparison of the Figures 24 and 25 will clearly show the wide range of differentiation obtaining in one and the same platyhelminth class, namely Turbellaria, with respect to brain (cerebral ganglion) development. The differences concerning the pattern of longitudinal and transverse nerve strands are also substantial, and are well illustrated in HANSTRÖM's (1928) summary of data on this group of worms. HADENFELDT (1928) likewise emphasized the considerable diversity displayed by the development and configuration of the nervous system in different groups of Turbellaria.

Platyhelminthes as represented by turbellarians are of significance to the morphologist because, in conformity with conditions obtaining in coelenterates, an archenteron with single opening (archistoma, derived from the blastopore) is present. The ventral archistoma varies greatly from species to species with respect to its particular location. It may be (a) quite near the rostral end of the animal, (b) approximately midway between rostral and caudal body end, or (c) well within the caudal third of the body. This variable or, as it were, fluctuating behavior of the archistoma can (but not must) be interpreted in favor of the view that both protostome and deuterostome metazoa might have originated, by divergent evolution, from primordial forms similar to some Platyhelminthes.

If Nemerteans are subsumed under the phylum Platyhelminthes, we have, within that phylum, a protostome class in which the digestive canal is provided with both mouth and anus, in contradistinction to the archistome Turbellaria. Whether the recent Nemerteans are regarded as related to the 'direct line of protostome evolution' or not, is here quite irrelevant with respect to the possibility that protostome as well as deuterostome 'lines of evolution' could have arisen from corre-

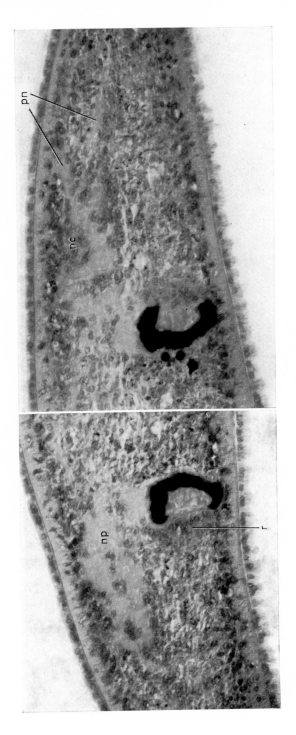

Figure 25. Cross section through anterior end of Planaria, showing left and right cerebral ganglion with pigment eyes; hematoxylin-eosin, × 450, red. $^2/_3$. (Original.)
nc: nerve cells; np: neuropileme; pn: peripheral nerves; r: retinal cells.

sponding, divergent modifications of turbellarian-like forms. Again, in Turbellaria, the Acoela have no true enteric cavity, but only a mouth-and pharynx-like structure derived from the blastopore. The embryonic development of present-day Platyhelminthes seems to be essentially of the so-called spiral and presumably 'determinate' type characteristic for protostomes (e. g. annelids and arthropods), but a number of differences obtain which cannot easily be interpreted from a phylogenetic viewpoint.

Some turbellarians such as Planaria are likewise particularly interesting because of their normally asexual reproduction by fission in a transverse plane. The separated posterior portion becomes a new animal, and regenerates a new brain, while the anterior portion develops a new posterior end. Even if experimentally cut in three or more parts, the middle parts may regenerate both ends. Fragments near the anterior end of the worm will regenerate more rapidly than those from posterior parts; this is interpreted as a manifestation of the axial metabolic gradient postulated by CHILD. Turbellarians, however, also possess a reproductive system, which is hermaphroditic, and the animals may or may not be self-fertilizing.

Cytological findings in the brain of a planarian, during the period in which the posterior body portion regenerates, have been interpreted as evidence of 'increased neurosecretory activity' (LENDER and KLEIN, 1961). This is believed to indicate that, as in annelids, regenerative growth depends on a stimulating hormonal factor originating in the central nervous system. An opposite, inhibitory effect of central nervous tissue on regeneration might also be inferred on the basis of some other observations (cf. the review by SCHARRER and SCHARRER, 1963).

The phenomenon of 'neurosecretion', apparently fairly well substantiated, as far as invertebrates are concerned, in annelids, arthropods, and mollusks, will again be considered further below in its appropriate relation to the various neural configurations under discussion[7].

The regenerative capacities of planarians have been used in performing experiments concerning 'memory'-functions. Thus, 'conditioned' planarians were transected and allowed to regenerate in a

---

[7] 'Neurosecretory' activity is also suspected in echinoderms; within this phylum, elements suggesting 'neurosecretory cells' have been described in ophiurids and asteroids (FONTAINE, 1962). UNGER (1960) has interpreted a few observations as indicating some sort of neurosecretory activities in radial nerves and circumoral ring of certain Asteroids.

ribonuclease solution or in pond water: 'Heads which had regenerated in ribonuclease displayed a retention level equal to that of head and tail sections which had regenerated in pond water. However, tails regenerated in ribonuclease performed randomly although they could be retrained to criterion' (CORNING and JOHN, 1961). 'Retention of training' in the tail end of planarians, if actually statistically significant, would suggest that some 'storage processes' or 'memory phenomena' are not restricted to the rostral part of the nervous system.

Again, planarians were conditioned, by subsequent electric shocks, to contract or 'turn' upon short illumination. This 'conditioned' response is said to persist after cutting and regeneration. Moreover, it is claimed that this response is transferable from one planarian to another (not previously 'conditioned' one) by way of 'cannibalistic' ingestion (McCONNELL, 1962).

Now, more than 35 years ago, in one of the first elaborations of a neurologic theory of memory (K., 1927, cf. also K., Brain and Consciousness, Basel 1957), I pointed out two separate sorts of postulated processes concerned, and presumably combined, in long-term memory mechanisms, namely the modification of synapses in a network pattern, and the biochemical (autocatalytic or enzymatic) changes. Since nerve cells, containing cytochromatin (*Nissl*-substance) are rich in RNA, the recent experimental findings suggesting that this substance has relationships with mnestic activities (storage or engraphy as well as ecphory) are in essential agreement with the aforementioned theory.

The difference between regenerating heads and regenerating tail does suggest a number of additional still unknown significant variables. As regards the claim that 'learning' seems to be transferable by 'ingestion' one might, however, point out that, even if the somewhat dubious data are essentially true, the transfer concerns merely the tendency toward a certain type of reaction, already present in non-'conditioned' planarians, rather than the 'learning' of a specific task. Thus, assuming that the reports are reasonably accurate, the data so obtained can be evaluated as referring merely to a very elementary phase of the biochemical events involved in the far more complex neurological memory mechanisms. It does not seem surprising that, in these processes, nucleic acids, known to be of paramount importance for vital cell functions, might likewise play a basic role.

It should be added, moreover, that experiments undertaken by BENNETT and CALVIN (1964) resulted in 'failure to train planarians reliably'. Yet, the discrepancy between this last series of experiments and that cited above rests essentially on a difference of interpretation as regards (a) what should be considered 'learning', and (b) the criterion of statistically significant or 'reliable' figures. The problems concerning the 'memory' of planarians may thus be assessed as still *sub judice*.

Studies on behavioral activities of planarians, undertaken by BROWN (1962), have disclosed that Dugesia responds not only to very weak horizontal electrostatic fields, but also to weak magnetic fields. In protozoa, various sorts of responses pertaining to galvano-taxis are well known since about 1885 and have been concisely summarized by VERWORN (1922). The cited investigations of BROWN, however, involve additional aspects of this general kind of taxis, and seem to indicate that the sensitivity of a protoplasmic system to an electric or a magnetic field may represent an important and still poorly understood type of behavioral manifestation, presumably not restricted to planarians. BROWN (1962) believes that these response mechanisms may play a role in connection with 'animal navigation', 'biological clock systems', and various thereto related aspects of temporal or spatial orientation displayed by organisms. In this connection, it might also be mentioned that the peculiar and puzzling retinal structure of the bird's eye, known as the *pecten*, recently has been suspected to represent a 'magnetic sensor' registering strength and directional components of the earth's magnetic field. This interpretation, however, has not been generally accepted at the present time.

Another interesting behavioral peculiarity reported in the turbellarian Microstoma by KEPNER (1925) has been discussed by LASHLEY (1938). Microstoma, by capturing and ingesting the coelenterate (cnidarian) fresh water polyp Hydra, is said to provide itself with nematocysts for its own predatory and defense activities. Undischarged nematocysts, remaining in the enteron of Microstoma after the eaten hydra is digested, are reportedly then picked up by ameboid processes of enteric cells, pass through the mesoderm, and are carried into the ectoderm, where they are lined up in the proper direction and become part of the worm's functional equipment.

It is claimed that when Microstoma has no supply of stinging cells, it captures and eats hydras voraciously. When a small supply of nematocysts is available, these cells are distributed uniformly over the surface of the body. As more such cells are obtained, they are inserted at uniform intervals between those already present. When a certain concentration of nematocysts is reached, it is reported that the worm 'loses its appetite for hydras and, in fact, will starve to death rather than eat any more of the polyps, which are apparently not a food but only a source of weapons'.

LASHLEY (1938) remarks that the naturalistic literature contains many such descriptions, made by careful and accurate observers, of 'instinctive behavior' so complex and precise in its execution that we can only stand aghast at the inadequacy of our concepts of its mechanism. He then adds that the relevance of this sort of behavior to the problems of 'psychology' is 'well illustrated by the classical definition of instinct as the faculty which animals have instead of intellect which yet makes their behavior seem intelligent'.

According to LASHLEY (1938) 'all the major problems of dynamic psychology' are encompassed in this behavior: 'there is a specific drive or appetite, satisfied only by a very indirect series of activities, with the satisfaction of the appetite dependent upon the concentration of nettles in the skin'. Moreover, 'there are recognition and selection of a specific object, through the sensory-motor activities of the animal. Later, there is recognition of the undischarged stinging cell by the wandering tissue cells, and some sort of perception of its form, so that it may be aimed. The uniform distribution of the nematocysts over the surface of the body is a splendid illustration of Gestalt, food for speculation concerning vectors and dynamic tensions'.

LASHLEY justly points out the close parallelism between some phenomena of behavior and those of growth, and remarks that it is impossible to draw a sharp line between them. Now, although LASHLEY, in his further comments, and in my opinion quite appropriately, brushes aside what he calls KEPNER's postulate[8] of a 'group mind among the cells of the body' as well as similar irrelevant animistic and 'mentalistic' hypotheses, his own formulation, as just quoted above, appears to me not only semantically awkward, but actually illegitimately men-

---

[8] LASHLEY (1938, p. 446) states: 'KEPNER, in fact, postulates a group mind among the cells of the body to account for the internal behavior of Microstoma, to me a *reductio ad absurdum* of mentalistic hypotheses, whether applied to worms or man.' Upon checking KEPNER's publication, which indeed displays a rather naive animistic attitude, I failed, however, to find any specific reference to a 'group-mind'. In fact, KEPNER hardly uses the word 'mind' which is not even included in his rather complete index. On the other hand, that author employs the term 'consciousness' (which he conveniently fails to define), and distinguishes 'consciousness' from 'self-consciousness'. He actually does assume a 'racial consciousness' dominating the beehive.

talistic as well as anthropomorphic, and displays considerable lack of what I would call rigorous logical judgment.

Clearly, in analyzing such behavior of turbellarians, one must confine oneself to the observed and observable facts in terms of natural sciences and strict behaviorism (I may add that I am definitely not a 'behaviorist', but that I adhere to a justifiable behavioristic approach where such procedure is indicated). How, then, can LASHLEY possibly talk about a 'drive' or an 'appetite' that must be satisfied, moreover, about 'recognition', and, particularly, about 'perception'?

Mentalistic terms of this sort refer to human experience and their use is here unwarranted as well as anthropomorphic, that is, implying the attribution of human consciousness phenomena to non-human conceptual 'entities' or 'events'. While this may be possibly justifiable in some sorts of discussion (e. g. perhaps about behavioral manifestations of primates or dogs), such extrapolation is definitely illegitimate in the aspect under consideration. Since I am well aware of LASHLEY's behavioristic views, I can merely surmise that his here inconsistent verbal behavior was conditioned by unconscious cerebration remaining under the influence of repressed 'mentalistic symbolism'.

Evidently, a sceptical and cautious formulation should be restricted to this: there is a specific tendency to ingest hydras. This behavior is regulated by the concentration of nettles in the ectoderm. The sequence of events includes registration and selection of a specific structure by the neural input-output mechanisms of the worm, moreover registration and selection of undischarged stinging cells by the wandering tissue cells. In this latter process, registration of some form invariants, namely polar differentiation, and directed, that is, vectorial displacement with respect to the body surface are manifested, resulting in an uniform distribution.

Clearly, although the effective variables pertaining to this pattern of events, and their significant interrelations, cannot be adequately

Moreover, he makes use of the terms 'psychosis' and 'neurosis' in a manner formerly adopted by some psychologists, but striking the medically trained neurologist as rather quaint. 'Neurosis' means here any neural process, and 'psychosis' any 'psychic' process (whatever that may be). Thus, he writes (1925, p. 69–70): 'It is hard to think, for example, that in Microstoma no psychosis can take place without neurosis.' He then adds '"No psychosis without neurosis" must be altered to read no psychosis without endodermosis and mesodermosis '. This passage, I take it, represents what LASHLEY interprets (not without some justification) as KEPNER's 'postulate' of a 'group mind'.

defined or described, the total set of events is no more and no less obscure than the phenomena of organic growth, or for that matter, than some of the phenomena of physics.

Because, in this general survey of invertebrate comparative neurology, references to various behavioral aspects become expedient, it is perhaps here appropriate again to stress my opinion concerning the use of the ill-defined term 'instinct'. Traditionally, as for instance defined toward the end of the 19th century by JAMES, instinct is regarded 'as the faculty of acting in such a way as to produce certain ends, without foresight of the ends, and without previous education in the performance'. Subsequently, some behavioristic psychologists have attempted to dispense entirely with the instinct concept, while others have retained it as subsuming complex, unlearned, or 'innate', i.e. 'inherited' patterns of behavior. According to LASHLEY, this 'unlearned' behavior differs from 'reflexes', because 'instincts' depend on the 'pattern of organization of the stimulus', while reflexes are elicited 'by stimulation of localized groups of sensory endings'. I do not feel that these explanations by LASHLEY are particularly enlightening. Brief discussions of instinct from the viewpoint of neurologic epistemology are included in my monographs of 1957 and 1961. Instinct was tentatively defined (1957, p. 107) as a configuration of unlearned or unconditioned directed activities not controlled by conscious understanding and reasoning, but possibly accompanied by a vaguely conscious desire or urge, that is, by affectivity. This, of course, is only observable by introspection *sensu strictiori*, and applies only to experienced human behavior. Thus, while conscious instincts might occur in some animals, such possibility remains entirely unobservable. If unconscious instinct, or instinctive behavior regardless of presence or absence of any phenomena of consciousness is deemed to be an admissible concept, then considerable difficulties still remain. It is hardly possible to make a clear-cut distinction between 'learned' and 'unlearned', and to define, in a rigorous manner, what is 'inherited' or 'innate' in contradistinction to acquired. Certainly, 'acquired habits' depend upon a mechanism whose ontogenetic development was controlled by 'genes'.

Although, with proper qualifications, and depending on the context as well as on circumstances, the use of the debatable concept instinct can be justified, it is perhaps advisable to avoid, as much as possible, employing this term, particularly where animals and behavior very dissimilar to man and his behavior are concerned.

The morphologic features of the nervous system in the parasitic *Trematodes* (flukes) and *Cestodes* (tapeworms) represent topological transforms of the features obtaining in turbellarians. In most cestodes, a segmentation of the body into ribbon-like sequences (proglottids) is a prominent characteristic. The longitudinal strands and the transverse connectives vary in number (e. g. reportedly 14 longitudinal strands in ligula, 8 in taenia and botriocephalus).

It is of interest that apparently all cestodes are characterized by a complete loss of the digestive tract (enteron, gut, including mouth). These worms, being intestinal parasites in the mature stage, directly absorb the digestive juices of their host. Yet, in contradistinction to the gut, the nervous system not only has been preserved in cestodes, but may even manifest a rather complex pattern of longitudinal connectives and commissures. The diversified and complicated life cycles of cestodes, involving, in many instances not only intermediate hosts ('transfer hosts') but also a change of habitat (connective tissue of musculature or parenchymatous organs of host, in addition to gastrointestinal tract) can be said to pose interesting problems with regard to the biological behaviors subsumed under the *clichés* 'adaptation and evolution'.

The free living, mostly marine *Nemerteans* or *Nemertines* ('proboscis worms') are characterized by a dorsal, ectodermal proboscis, which, as a rule, is a blind tube not connected with the ventral gut. The caudal part of the proboscis is imbedded in a mesodermal proboscis sheath with rhynchocoel. The nervous system is, as a whole, rather similar to that of turbellarians (Fig. 21 B). Groups of granular cells ('inner granular masses') somewhat similar to those mentioned above as occurring in polyclads are likewise found in the cerebral ganglion of nemerteans, and could perhaps be evaluated as primordia homologous or at least analogous to the corpora pedunculata of annelids (polychaetes) and arthropods. Parts of the gut are innervated by a branching strand connected with the compound cerebral ganglion. Complex and by no means entirely clarified systems of taxonomic subdivision have been elaborated for Nemerteans. Some features of the brain of these worms have been studied by B. SCHARRER (1941), who compared different forms that can be arranged in a sequence showing the various steps leading to an incorporation of a group of 'gland cells' into the cerebral ganglion, and involving the formation of a 'cerebral canal' (Fig. 26). These cell clusters within the brain were long known as 'cerebral organ' and formerly regarded as a sense organ, while B. Scharrer assumes an endocrine function. Moreover, as B. Scharrer (1941) points out, this association of 'glandular' and nervous elements in the 'cerebral organ' is of interest in view of the occurrence of 'neurosecretion' by true nerve cells of 'higher' invertebrates and of vertebrates.

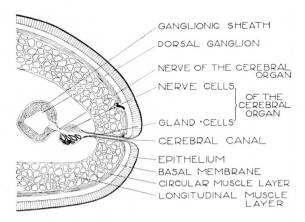

Figure 26. Section through the head region of the nemertean Drepanophorus albo-lineatus, showing cerebral canal. The ganglion cells of the cerebral organ are separated from those of the dorsal ganglion. (Modified after Bürger from B. Scharrer, 1941.)

In the nemertean nervous system, a paired fairly large neurochord cell may be present in the ventral cerebral ganglion, and a few additional ones may be located in the ventral nerve trunks. Large nerve fibres or neurochords originate from these cells and run, with apparently few collateral connections, almost through the whole length of the central nervous system. The details of these neurochord-structures are less well demonstrable, and also much less well understood in nemerteans than in annelids. Further comments on the neurochords will be found on page 80.

As regards other Platyhelminthes in the wider sense (namely including archistome and protostome forms), it seems uncertain whether some of the larger nerve fibers described in 'true' (archistome) flatworms could or could not be evaluated as 'giant fibers'.

The *Nemathelminthes* might be considered as a phylum comprising Nematoda (roundworms), Nematomorpha (hairworms), and Acanthocephala ('spine-headed worms') as classes. Many forms are parasitic,

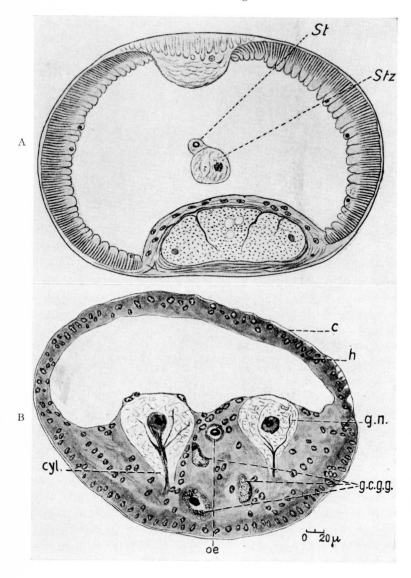

Figure 27. Aspects of nervous system in the nemertean Nectonema. *A* Section showing location of nerve chord ventral to pharynx. (From Bürger, 1891.) St and Stz: pharyngeal structures. *B* Section through 'cerebral' mass showing two giant cells and the origin of their axons. (From Feyel, 1939.) c: cuticle; cyl: origin of giant cell axon; gcgg: nerve cells; gn: giant cell; h: epidermis ('hypodermis'); oe: pharynx ('oesophagus').

and the nematodes have a very wide distribution with an abundant number of individuals. Free-living nematodes occur in soil, fresh water, or sea water. Several millions of these small worms, pertaining to several different species, may be found, in some instances, within one square meter of mud or soil. Various nematodes, somewhat like rotifers and tardigrads, can withstand extreme desiccation as well as very low temperatures. On the other hand, the habitat of nematodes includes hot springs of more than 50°C.

The morphologic features of the nemathelminth nervous system are more or less similar to those obtaining in plathelminths. Nematodes and Nematomorpha (Gordiidae, e.g. Gordius, not to be confused with the annelid Polygordius) display a rather conspicuous pharyngeal ring surrounding the gut near its rostral end.

The nematomorph pelagic marine worm Nectonema is free-living in the adult stage, but parasitic in earlier ones. Its nervous system, described by BÜRGER (1891) and FEYEL (1936), consists of an anterior pharyngeal ring and a single, unpaired ventral cord. This nervous system remains intimately connected with the ectodermal epithelium of the epidermis, from which it originated (Fig. 27). This is also essentially the case in Gordius. Such permanently remaining close connection of nervous system and epidermal epithelium is an interesting feature displayed by numerous widely differing invertebrate forms, including coelenterates, echinoderms, some annelids (Sigalion), and various 'minor' chordates (e.g. Balanoglossus). Although presumably related to the phylogeny of the nervous system, this feature appears to be unspecific and therefore of dubious value for theoretical speculations concerning the presumptive phylogenetic derivations. FEYEL (1936) depicted giant cells and neurochord-like fibers in Nectonema.

The nervous system of the nematode roundworm Ascaris is of particular interest because it was studied in great detail by R. GOLDSCHMIDT (1908, 1909) and others. In Ascaris, a number of short rostral, and long caudal ganglionated strands extend from the pharyngeal ring in a longitudinal direction. The caudal strands have interconnecting transverse commissures manifesting some right-left asymmetry (Fig. 28 A).

The nervous system of ascaris exhibits a noteworthy instance of numerical cell constancy, such that number, relative size, shape and position of nerve cells as well as of fibers are constant. According to GOLDSCHMIDT (1908, 1909) the central nervous system, of which the

pharyngeal ring represents the essential ganglionated structure, contains 162 nerve cells. At least 77 of these elements were definitely
identified as efferent (motor), and 22 as presumably internuncial.
At least 50 were regarded as afferent, and the proper functional classification of the remaining ones was somewhat less certain. In his
third paper on the central nervous system of ascaris, GOLDSCHMIDT
(1910) stated that, in the female, one pair of nerve cells is missing, so

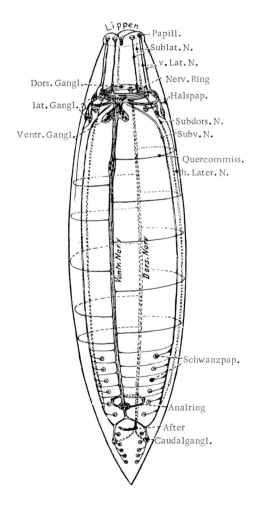

Figure 28 A. Nervous system of (male) Ascaris. (Simplified after VOLZENLOGEL, 1902,
and GOLDSCHMIDT, 1908/09, according to BÜTSCHLI, 1921, from HANSTRÖM, 1928.)

that a sex difference obtains in this respect, 162 nerve cells being thus present in the male, and 160 in the female.

GOLDSCHMIDT (1909) succeeded in tracing complete and elaborate circuit diagrams, of which Figure 28B is an example. The most painstaking and minute analysis of this nervous system failed, however, to yield the expected clarification of its working mechanism beyond the disappointing realization that everything was connected with everything else[9]. These connections, moreover, are described, with few exceptions, as direct (and hence apparently unpolarized, asynaptic) anastomoses. It is evident that, since a supplementary undefined

---

[9] Ultimately, of course, this conclusion also applies to the more complex synaptic vertebrate and human nervous system. Nevertheless, localized specific and restricted activities take place, presumably due to the threshold of synaptic resistance and its fluctuations as a result of the intricate discharge patterns collectively designated as central excitatory and central inhibitory states. GOLDSCHMIDT's frustration clearly shows that a detailed knowledge of structural arrangements may not be sufficient for an understanding of function without a corresponding understanding of relevant 'functional factors'. Two additional circumstances are here perhaps worth of notice: (1) ascaris has a highly specialized, 'endoparasitic' mode of life, with variables and parameters that are poorly understood, and not easily amenable to detailed analysis; (2) complicated circuit-systems involve, with regard to their interpretation, the particular logical difficulties intrinsic to 'complex systems, richly cross-connected internally', as emphasized by ASHBY, and briefly discussed above in the introductory chapter (vol. 1, p. 10).

In my monograph 'Brain and Consciousness' (1957), I had referred to GOLDSCHMIDT's investigations on the CNS of ascaris. In a letter of October 1957, only a few months before his death, GOLDSCHMIDT, with whom I became personally acquainted in Japan about 1925, made the following remarks with respect to these studies, as briefly mentioned in my monograph: 'I am also grateful that you dug up my old work, which, otherwise is completely unknown to neurologists. For example nowadays the neurofibrils are considered of unknown function, certainly not "das leitende Element". But nobody knows about my analysis 50 years ago. I am also surprised that nobody among present day neurophysiologists ever looked at my pictures. I think that such a nerve "net" as pictured should point to definite ideas. If one compares (only an analogy) this to a system of connecting tubes of different diameters, etc. a good simile would be: if a ganglion cell compares to a rubber ball a squeeze would produce a hydraulic pressure which would propagate in this system according to its resistances, etc. in a perfectly orderly though complicated way which would parallel the happenings to a nervous impulse. It should be possible to translate this analogy into electric and chemical features in accordance with modern tenets of neurophysiology. Strange that nobody noticed that. (I am speaking of the big reconstructions of the minimal connections in the nerve ring.)'

In view of the late Professor GOLDSCHMIDT's accomplishments and standing as a biologist, it is perhaps appropriate to quote these remarks which I am bringing here without further comments.

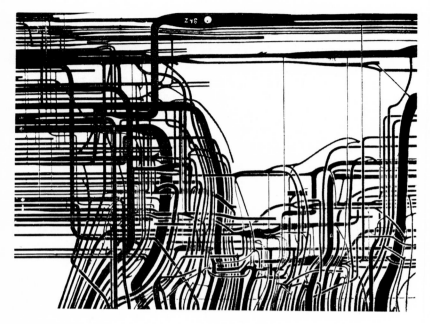

Figure 28 B. One of the elaborate diagrams of fiber connections in the central nervous system of Ascaris, traced by GOLDSCHMIDT on the basis of his reconstructions. Association cell no. 48 is shown on top. (From Z. wiss. Zool. *92*: 1909, Tafel 3.)

variable is hereby introduced, considerable uncertainty obtains with regard to a functional interpretation[10].

Additional instances of *numerical cell constancy* occur in the cerebral ganglia of other Nemathelminthes. Thus, the following characteristic brain cell numbers for different Acanthocephala have been reported: 86, 80, and 73 ganglion cells, respectively (BRANDES, 1899; HANSTRÖM, 1928; HARADA, 1931; KILIAN, 1932).

---

[10] In contradistinction to GOLDSCHMIDT, DEINEKA (1908), who likewise described anastomosing connections, found also connections by contiguity that could be regarded as synaptic. There are also a number of additional discrepancies between GOLDSCHMIDT's and DEINEKA's findings as well as interpretations. HANSTRÖM (1928) maintains a sceptical and impartial attitude toward the blistering polemic directed by GOLDSCHMIDT against DEINEKA's investigation. As regards the number of 162 to 160 cells in the central nervous system, it should, moreover, be added that this does not include enteric and pre-anal neural structures, nor some other peripheral elements which can be considered to represent neurosensory or 'nerve' cells. These receptor cells, as described by DEINEKA, seem to be fairly numerous, and may perhaps exceed the number of cells in the 'central nervous system'.

5. Miscellaneous 'Minor Groups'

The *Rotifera (Rotatoria)* or wheel-animalcules possess a cerebral ganglion and several nerve strands with some further small ganglia. Again, various instances of numerical cell constancy have been noted. Thus, in the case of Hydatina senta, the entire animal is said to be always composed of 959 cells, with a constant number of 183 ganglion cells in the brain (MARTINI, 1912). Since many of the structures in the rotifer body are syncytial, that is, without distinguishable cell boundaries, the number of 'cells' determined by the very meticulous investigation of MARTINI (1912) refers, as far as the body *in toto* is concerned, to the number of nuclei. According to NACHTWEY (1925), about 225 ganglion cells are found in the brain of Asplanchna, and 50 nerve cells each in two additional ganglia of that minute organism (mastax-ganglion of muscular pharynx, and caudal ganglion). Several small nerves extend from the brain to anterior sense organs. The cerebral ganglion is also connected with the mastax ganglion; a dorsal

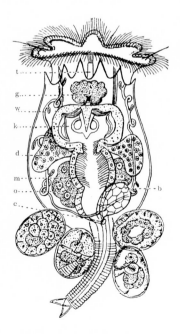

Figure 29. General aspect of the rotifer Brachionis urceolaris. (After R. HERTWIG, 1912.) b: bladder; c: anal opening; d: digestive glands; g: cerebral ganglion with eye spot; k: mastax; m: stomach; o: ovary; t: tentacle ('antenna'); w: protonephridial duct.

as well as a ventral nerve strand, running through the length of the body, arise from the brain. The ventral strand connects with the caudal ganglion (Figs. 29 to 31).

Some taxonomists consider the rotifers as related to the annelids, and, phylogenetically, as perhaps representing descendants or modified remnants of an ancestral annelid form. The resemblance of rotifers to

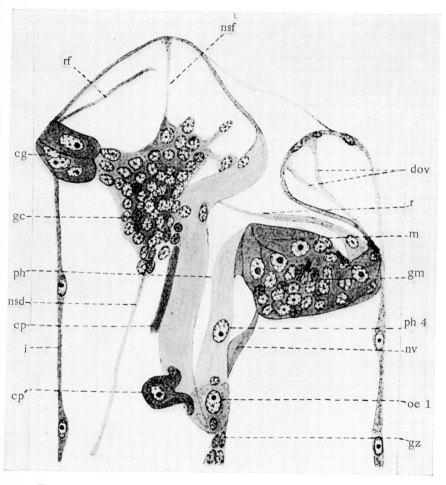

Figure 30. Cerebral ganglion and mastax ganglion of rotifer Asplanchna. (From NACHTWEY, 1925.) cp: muscles of pharynx; gc: cerebral ganglion; gm: mastax ganglion; gz: nerve cells; m: mastax; ph: pharynx. The other abbreviations are not relevant in the present context.

trochophore larvae of annelids is rather striking (Fig. 32), although the arrangement of the ciliated band (the corona of Rotifera) shows evident differences. Yet, even within the group of rotifers, very

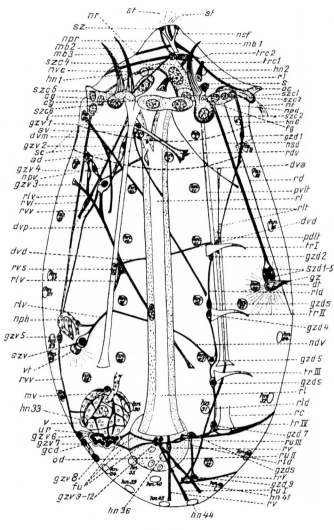

Fig. 31A

Figure 31. Organization of the rotifer Asplanchna. *A* Reduced reproduction of NACHTWEY's (1925) colored plate XIV, showing the complexities of details analyzed by this author. The constant cell (nuclear) number in Asplanchna is 900.

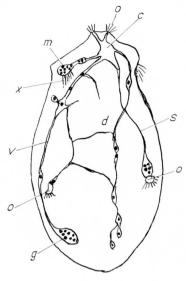

Fig. 31 B

Figure 31. B Simplified diagram indicating essential features of the nervous system in Asplanchna. (Based upon Nachtwey's findings. Some use has been made of the interpretation by Hyman, 1951, and its adaptation by Barnes, 1963.) c: cerebral ganglion; d: dorsal nerve cord; g: caudal ganglion; m: mastax ganglion; o: sense organs (apical, dorsal, ventral); s: dorsal sensory nerve; v: ventral nerve cord; x: visceral nerves. The nerves d, s, and v are paired.

different types of corona and of so-called buccal field are found. Nachtwey (1925), however, stresses some peculiarities of embryonic development distinguishing rotifers from trochophore larvae. Because of certain features displayed by protonephridia, and considering various other details, this author, in agreement with Martini (1912), regards the rotifers as phylogenetically closely related to the turbellarians.

Considerable sexual dimorphism obtains in rotifers, particularly with respect to relative size, the male being always smaller than the female. In some species, this size relation may be of the order of one to ten while in others a less pronounced difference may be manifested. In still other rotifers, males are lacking, and reproduction is parthenogenetic. The resistance of rotifers to desiccation and low temperature is considerable, and the animals can remain in a dormant state for several years. Barnes (1963) reports that some species have been placed in liquid helium (–272 °C) without damaging effect.

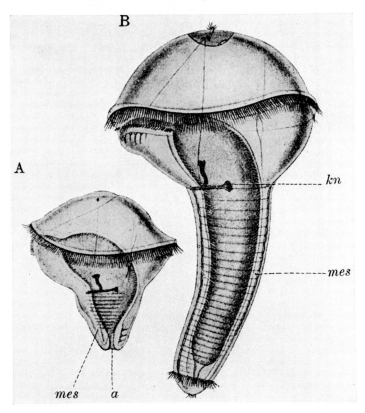

Figure 32. Trochophore larvae of the annelid Polygordius. (After HATSCHEK from R. HERTWIG, 1912.) *A* Earlier stage. *B* Later stage. kn: nephridial apparatus; mes: mesoderm. Anal opening at bottom.

Gastrotricha constitute another small group of aquatic animalcules resembling rotifers (Fig. 33), but with a number of distinctive features (cf. REMANE, 1927). Little is known about the details of their nervous system. HANSTRÖM (1928) agrees with the taxonomists regarding this form and some other dubious ones as distantly related to annelids. The brain of these minute ciliated animals represents in cross-sections a crescent-shaped mass with very few nerve cells, closely adjacent to the esophagus (Fig. 34). In some forms, the brain remains in continuity with the ectodermal surface epithelium, while in other species some separation has taken place. A paired lateral or ventrolateral nerve strand connects the brain with the caudal parts of the body.

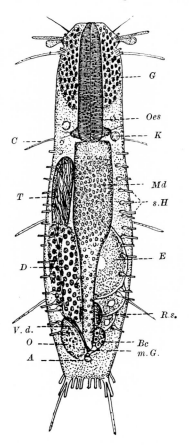

Figure 33. General organization of gastrotrich Thaumastodera. (After REMANE, 1927, from HANSTRÖM, 1928.) G: cerebral ganglion; Md: gut; Oes: esophagus; other designations not relevant to present context.

Rotifera, Gastrotricha, and Tardigrada (discussed further below in section 7) include some of the smallest metazoan organisms. The size of various species of rotifers remains within an order of magnitude corresponding to that of most ciliate protozans, namely within fractions of a millimeter, although other species may reach a length of about 2 mm. The size of gastrotrichs corresponds approximately to that of rotifers.

Chaetognatha (arrow-worms), 1–5 cm long, displaying three segments and a true celomic cavity, are active, transparent pelagic

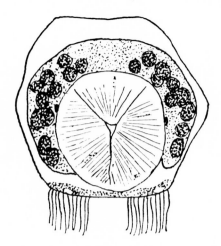

Figure 34. Cross section through cerebral ganglion of gastrotrich Chaetonotus. (After Zelinka and Remane from Hanström, 1928.)

organisms of questionable 'taxonomic status' (cf. vol. 1, chapt. II, p. 54). The elegant body, comparable to a glassy arrow, shows two pairs of lateral stabilizing fins and a transverse (horizontal) tail fin, closely similar in shape to the 'stabilizer' in the tail assembly of some early airplane designs. The nervous system includes here a small, but well-organized cerebral ganglion (Figs. 35, 36), and a larger unpaired abdominal ganglion. A thin pharyngeal ring is present. The cerebral ganglion is connected with sense organs (eyes, bristles). About ten or more branching lateral nerves extend on each side from the abdominal ganglion, and a paired, main, branching strand continues caudalward. The peripheral nerves are connected with a subepithelial nerve plexus.

Chaetognatha, Brachiopoda, Bryozoa (to which, perhaps, Phoronidea are related), Enteropneusta and Pterobranchia have been grouped together, e.g. by Bütschli, in a sort of super-phylum *Oligomera*, which is, for practical purposes, tentatively adopted by Hanström (1928). Chaetognaths are, however, deuterostome metazoans.

In the tentative and rough taxonomical interpretation adopted in chapter II of the present treatise, Bryozoa, Brachiopoda and Phoronidea were loosely grouped together as Molluscoida (cf. vol. 1, p. 54). Enteropneusta and the perhaps related Pterobranchia became then subsumed as Hemichorda under the phylum Chordata.

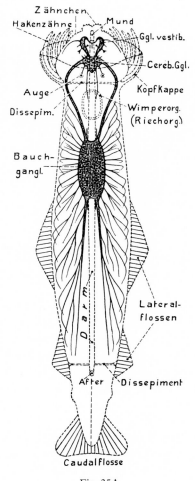

Fig. 35A

Figure 35. General aspect of Chaetognatha. *A* Diagrammatic ventral view of Sagitta. (After Bütschli and other authors from Hanström, 1928.) *B* Ventral view of Sagitta preserving body proportions. Head with cerebral ganglion shown on right in dorsal view. (From R. Hertwig, 1912.)

Bryozoa are sessile, colonial marine and also fresh water animals giving the impression of seaweed or moss because of their delicate tentacles. The gut has a siphon-shape, such that anus and tentaculated mouth lie side by side in the opening of the calcareous or horny

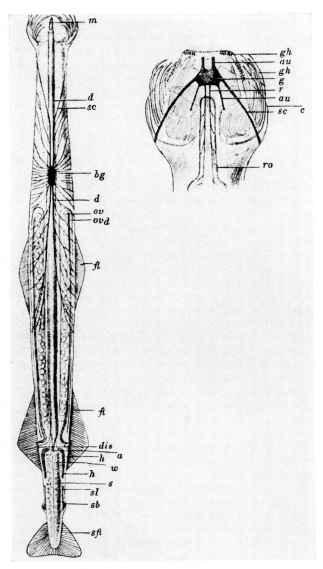

Fig. 35 B

tubular protective case. The tentacles are attached to a circular or U-shaped ridge designated as the lophophore. The motile ciliated bryozoan larvae resemble the trochophora larvae of annelids and molluscs. In ectoprocta bryozoans the anus opens outside the ring of

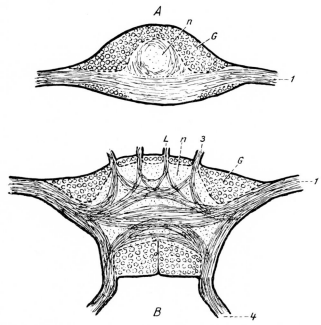

Figure 36. Cross-section (A) and combined horizontal sections (B) through cerebral ganglion of chaetognathe Krohnia hamata. (From HANSTRÖM, 1928.) G: nerve cell layer; n: neuropil; other designations refer to peripheral nerves.

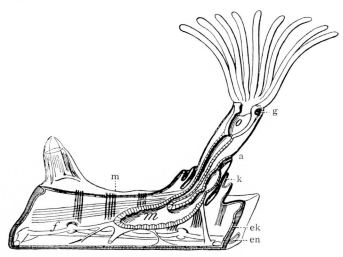

Figure 37. Ectoproct bryozoan Flustra membranacea. (After NITSCHE from R. HERT-WIG, 1912.) a: anus; g: cerebral ganglion; o: oral opening; other designations not relevant in this context.

tentacles, and in endoprocta within that ring (Figs. 37, 38). Several thousands of extinct bryozoan species have been recorded from the Ordovician period of the Paleozoic era, to, and throughout, the subsequent spans concluding with the Cenozoic era.

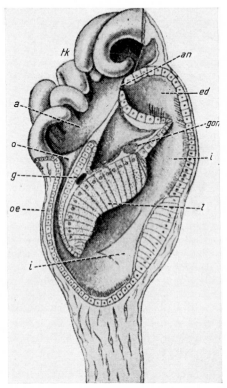

Figure 38. Endoproct bryozoan Loxosoma. (After Nitsche from R. Hertwig, 1912.) an: anus; g: main ganglion; i: gut; o: oral opening; other designations not relevant in present context (a: tentacular ring).

A cerebral and a subesophageal ganglion are found in Bryozoa. Nerve rings with complicated radiating tentacular nerves are connected with the main ganglionic mass, and other strands form a nerve net surrounding the looped gut. It seems of particular interest that the cerebral ganglion of Ectoprocta is known to develop by invagination from the ectoderm as a hollow vesicle, and the brain thus shows a ventricle-like cavity (Fig. 39), which however, becomes greatly reduced.

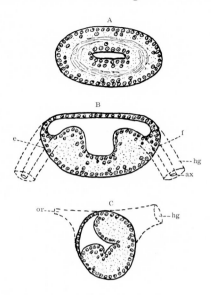

Figure 39. Sections through cerebral ganglion of ectoproct bryozoan Cristatella. (After GEWERZHAGEN, 1913, from HANSTRÖM, 1928.) A Cross-section through the level indicated by e and f in B. B Horizontal section. C median sagittal section. ax: so-called axial canal, communicating with 'cerebral ventricle'; hg: so-called 'ganglionic horns' to lophophore arms; or: oral nerve ring.

Ectoprocta possess only a cerebral ganglion, although a subesophageal ganglion may be indicated by strands and a ring structure connected with the brain (Fig. 40). In Endoprocta the central ganglion is believed to be represented by the subesophageal ganglion, while the changes in the course of ontogenetic metamorphosis are interpreted to show a reduction and disappearance of the anlage representing the cerebral ganglion. Because of the peculiar morphologic pattern, cerebral and subesophageal ganglia asume closely related positions. E. MARCUS (1926) has investigated various aspects of bryozoan behavior.

Present-day taxonomists have split the 'phylum' Bryozoa into two separate 'phyla', the coelomate Ectoprocta and the pseudocoelomate Entoprocta. The former are supposedly manifesting a 'higher level of structure'. Also, the Rotifera, Gastrotricha, Nematoda, Nematomorpha, Kinorhyncha, and Priapulida, each group considered as a 'class', have been subsumed under the 'phylum' Aschelminthes. This latter, again, together with the 'phyla' Acanthocephala and Entoprocta, is subsumed under the concept or 'superphylum' Pseudocoelomates.

The above-mentioned Kinorhyncha and Priapulida, which were not previously discussed in the text, require perhaps a brief explanation, since they may be unfamiliar even to the neurologist with extensive general biological interests. Kinorhyncha (or Echinodera; not to be confused with Echinodermata) are a small group of animalcules (of less than one millimeter length), similar to gastrotrichs, but lacking cilia; the integument shows segmentation.

The 'class' with the amusing designation Priapulida includes only three known species of faintly phallus-like shaped animals living in the bottom sand of coastal oceanic waters. Their distribution, however is world-wide (northern and southern hemisphere). The nervous system, consisting of a pharyngeal ring and a ganglionated cord, can here be regarded as highly 'reduced'. In fact, early developmental stages of Priapulus are said to display ganglia which disappear at later stages

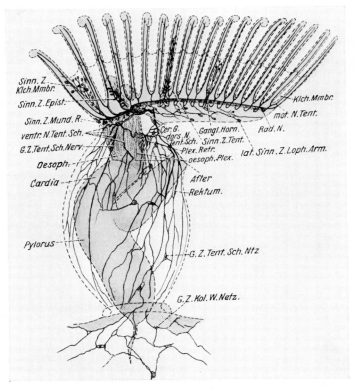

Figure 40. Nerve plexus of ectoproct bryozoan Cristatella. (After GEWERZHAGEN, 1913, from HANSTRÖM, 1928.) Cer. G.: cerebral ganglion; G. Z.: nerve cells.

(HANSTRÖM, 1928). In this, and perhaps also other respects, Priapulida display similarities with Echiurida (cf. footnote 12, p.72). Moreover, it is not impossible that the body cavity of Priapulida represents a 'regressive' true coelom.

In contradiction to a number of zoologists, I am, furthermore, much less impressed with the significance of a celomic cavity in phylogenetic speculations (cf. also section 14, p. 310). It cannot be ruled out that celom-formation might have quite independently occurred in numerous unrelated forms. Also, it is not impossible that, in view of the marked tendency toward a peculiar type of heteromorphous polymorphism in many invertebrate groups, celom-formation may have both occurred or not occurred in various closely related forms. Within one and the same circumscribed taxonomic subset, suggesting a presumptive phylogenetic relationship on the basis of some fundamental pattern manifestations, considerable structural or even configurational differences in the development of some systems, including also some of the fundamental ones, can be displayed.

Thus, in taxonomically closely related forms, the central nervous system may remain connected with the ectodermal surface epithelium, or may have become entirely separated (cf. section 4, p. 51; section 6, p. 73; section 13, p. 292). Again, metameric segmentation might likewise have originated quite independently in various, phylogenetically entirely unrelated groups of organisms. Inferences concerning ancestry, based on such features, or other ones of comparable sort, although perhaps permissible, remain exceedingly uncertain. Unfortunately, in many instances, such very dubious clues represent the only ones available.

Brachiopoda superficially resemble bivalve molluscs such as clams; the brachiopod shells[11], however, are dorsal and ventral, while in molluscs, the pelecypod shells are bilateral (i.e. right and left). Within the brachiopod shells lie the tentacular arms or lophophores, similar to those of Bryozoa (Figs. 41, 42). A caudal muscular peduncle, attaching the animal e.g. to rocks, may be provided. A celomic cavity is present, and the digestive tract is either a blind sack, or provided with an anus.

---

[11] The shells may be of a horny texture (e.g. in Lingula) without a hinge structure, and merely held together by muscles. Such shells are also of equal size. In the more differentiated groups, however, the shells are calcareous, hinged together, and of unequal size, such that the ventral one is larger than the dorsal one.

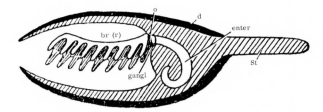

Figure 41. Simplified diagram of brachiopod organization. (From a sketch by F. MAURER after BOAS and other authors.) br. r.: right tentacular arm; d: dorsum; enter.: gut; g: ganglion; o: oral opening; St: stalk.

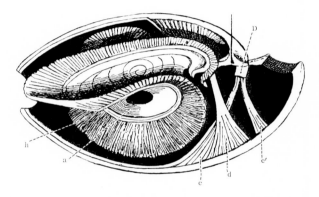

Figure 42. Tentacular arms and shells of brachiopod Waldheimia. (After ZITTEL from R. HERTWIG, 1912.) a: tentacular arm; d, c, and c': musculature; h: tentacles; D: part of shell hinge, which is also indicated by a black line.

The nervous system (Fig. 43) displays a cerebral ganglion and a larger subesophageal ganglion, connected with each other by a thin paired strand forming a pharyngeal ring. From both ganglia the nerves, also containing nerve cells, extend to the periphery. The paired cerebral ganglion and the pharyngeal connectives innervate the lophophores, and the paired subesophageal ganglion provides nerves for the shells as well as other parts. The nerves form peripheral plexuses including some nerve cells. On the whole, this organization is rather similar to that obtaining in Bryozoa.

While the recent brachiopods, with not much more than 200 different species, can be regarded as a rather minor group (either phylum or subphylum, or superclass), these animals represent, from

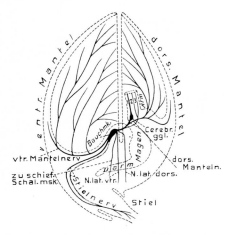

Figure 43. Nervous system of Brachiopod. (Diagram by Bütschli, 1921, from Hanström, 1928.)

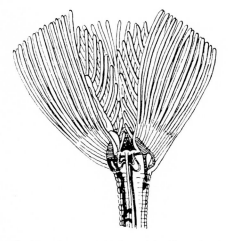

Figure 44. General view of anterior body end in Phoronis. (From Selenka-Gold-schmidt, 1919.

the paleontologic viewpoint, one of the major groups, with perhaps 3000 species already recorded from the Paleozoic era. The earliest brachiopods are present in the Cambrian. The genus Lingula, of which recent species exist, has persisted in essentially unchanged form since the Cambrian. Brachiopods provide the bulk of various rock strata. Shells of Terebratula are, in some regions, particularly common fossils. A gradual decline of brachiopods set in, from about 450 genera in the Paleozoic to about 180 in the Mesozoic and about 75 in the Cenozoic, including present survivors.

Phoronidea are marine, sedentary, coelomate wormlike animals dwelling in a tube, from which the lophophore may protrude (Fig. 44). The intestine is U-shaped, and the larva is of the trochophore type. The phoronideans thus resemble bryozoans, although differing from these latter in several other respects. Only about a dozen species are known.

The nervous system (Fig. 45) consists of a postoral ring, from which the lophophore nerves arise, and of a single asymmetric left

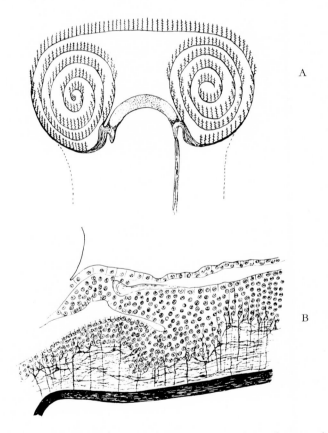

Figure 45. Nervous system of Phoronis pacifica. *A* Postoral ring (between the two lophophores), and (on right) asymmetric longitudinal cord. (After HILTON, 1922, from HANSTRÖM, 1928.) *B* Lophophore ganglion and 'brain' (right) at higher magnification. (From HILTON, 1922.)

aboral longitudinal strand. The nervous nature of this cord is suspected, but not quite certain (HILTON, 1922). The short rudiment of a right cord is recognizable. The nervous system is only partly separated from the epithelium. Histologically, the nervous elements resemble those of echinoderms.

SILÉN (1954) has demonstrated paired lateral cords in several species of phoronids. According to this author, the lateral cords (or 'lateral nerves'), at least in some instances, could be interpreted as single 'giant fibers'.

6. Annelida

These animals, sometimes also designated as *Annulata*, represent an important group[12] of Metazoa with genuine segmentation, and with a rather typical pattern of central nervous system, from which that of the multitudinous arthropods can easily be conceptually derived.

In Polychaeta, such as Sabella, two longitudinal cords, ventral to the gut, display in each segment a ganglion connected by a transverse connective or commissure. Rostrally, these cords form a subesophageal or subpharyngeal ganglion, and then surround the gut or pharynx by a pharyngeal ring which contains the paired dorsal suprapharyngeal ganglion, interconnected in the midline. This pattern is known as the 'ladder-type' of nervous system (German: 'Strickleiternervensystem'),

---

[12] If small marine worms such as Polygordius are separated from the Polychaeta, and regarded as forming the class Archiannelida, six additional annelid classes may be assumed. The Echiurida are marine worms, unsegmented in the adult stage. The Gephyrea (e. g. Phascolosoma, Bonellia and Sipunculus) are likewise marine worms, without segmentation (except a few borderline instances of barely suggested external segmentation) in the adult. Some taxonomists regard the Gephyrea as a separate phylum. BARNES (1963) has adopted an at present not infrequently used classification in which sipunculids and echiurids are considered two distinct phyla, and the notion of a special phylum Gephyrea is discarded.

The Myzostoma are parasites of echinoderms, and not distinctly segmented. The Polychaeta, such as Nereis, are practically all marine. The Oligochaeta are mostly fresh water or terrestrial worms, such as lumbricus. The Hirudinea are terrestrial, marine, or fresh water worms (such, e. g., as the leech). The celomic cavity of Hirudinea becomes obliterated by connective tissue. The annelid *trochophora larva*, with a ciliated band, is of considerable theoretical interest for phylogenetic speculation, since this type of larva occurs also in molluscs. The likewise very similar larvae of flatworms and nemerteans, and those of Bryozoa as well as Phoronidea can also be considered to represent the trochophore type. Yet, among the annelids, Oligochaeta and Hirudinea do not seem to have trochophore larvae.

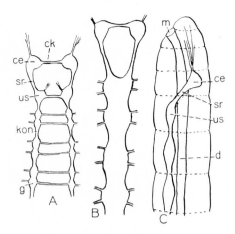

Figure 46. Diagram showing the general configuration of the central nervous system in annelids. (From K., 1927.) *A* Rope-ladder pattern in Sabella (polychaete), modified after B. HALLER, 1904. *B* Lumbricus terrestris. *C* Topographic relationship of ventral nerve cord and brain to gut in lumbricus. ce: cerebral ganglion; ck: cerebral commissure or connective; d: gut; g: ganglion of ventral nerve cord; kon: connective; sr: pharyngeal ring; us: subesophageal ganglion. In B are shown only the two paired nerves arising from the middle portion of the ganglia, but not the single paired nerve arising from the anterior portion merging with the longitudinal cord or connective (cf. Fig. 47).

which displays features comparable to a reduced orthogon (cf. Fig. 233). In other annelids, these paired structures may fuse in the midline to form an unpaired, but bilateral-symmetric system with a ring for the pharynx (Fig. 46). The suprapharyngeal ganglion is customarily designated as cerebral ganglion or brain. The peripheral nerves are connected with this ganglionated central nervous system, such that, generally speaking, and discounting special instances, as e. g. that of the stomatogastric system, each ganglion is connected with the organs of its own segment or segments. Thus, in lumbricus, two paired nerve arises from the segmental ventral ganglia (cf. Fig. 46 B), while one anterior paired nerve arises from the nerve cord in each segment (cf. Fig. 47). Each pair of ganglia or each bilateral symmetric unpaired ganglion represents thus, to some extent, a control and communication 'center' for its corresponding segmental region.

In the polychaete marine worm Sigalion, the ventral nerve cord remains in close connection with the ectodermal epidermis (Fig. 48), thereby displaying relationships similar to those manifested by the

radial nerve strands of echinoderms or the nervous cord of Nematomorpha (cf. p. 51).

The cutaneous nerves end in a subepithelial plexus. Some of the
sensory elements are primary sensory cells having the function or
value of a nerve cell, that is, of a neuron. Other sensory endings are
free endings of nerve fibers (Fig. 49, cf. also Fig. 65). Plexus-like nets

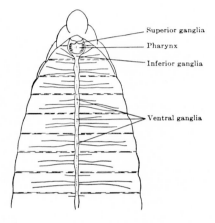

Figure 47. Segmental nerves in lumbricus. (From HERRICK, 1931.)

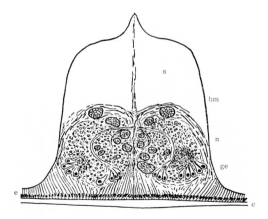

Figure 48. Cross section through the ventral nerve cord of the polychaete marine
annelid Sigalion. The nerve cord retains here a close connection with the epidermis.
(After HATCHEK from PARKER, 1919.) bm: basement membrane; c: cuticula; ge: nerve
cells; s: supporting tissue (omitted); n: nerve fibers and neuropil; e: epidermis.

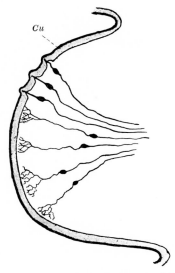

Figure 49. Sensory elements and sensory endings in the skin of the polychaete annelid Glycera dibranchiata. (From HANSTRÖM, 1928.) Cu: cuticula.

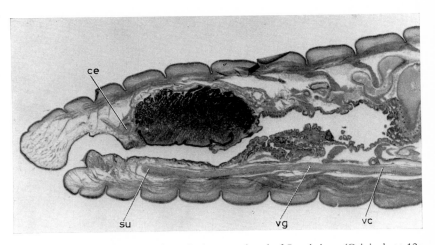

Figure 50. Sagittal section through the rostral end of Lumbricus. (Original; × 12; red. ²/₃; hematoxylin-eosin.) Three parts of the gut can be seen: mouth, pharynx, and esophagus. Dorsal to pharynx the dark, musculo-glandular pharyngeal pad is shown, rostral to which the brain (intracerebral commissure) is located. Several intersegmental septa are recognizable. ce: cerebral ganglion; su: 'subesophageal' ganglion; vc: ventral cord connective; vg: ventral cord ganglion.

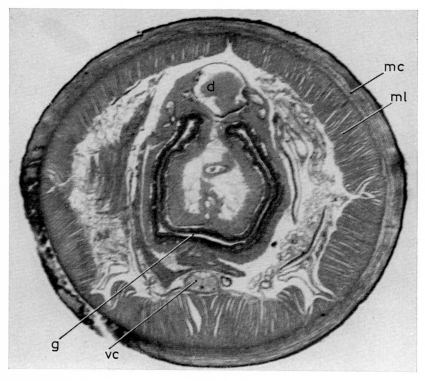

Figure 51. Cross section through the body of Lumbricus near an intersegmental septum. (Original; × 25; red. $^9/_{10}$; hematoxylin-eosin.) d: dorsal blood vessel; g: gut; mc: circular musculature; ml: longitudinal musculature; vc: ventral nerve cord. The deep fold in the dorsal wall of the gut is designated as typhlosole. It significantly increases (almost doubles) the epithelial surface lining the lumen of the gut.

of nerve fibers innervate musculature as well as intestinal tract, and contain minor ganglia or scattered nerve cells. These plexuses are connected by nerves (e. g. 'stomatogastric nerves') with the esophageal ring and the segmental ganglia. The extensive, peripheral, nerve cell containing plexuses of annelids, especially under the skin and between the muscular layers of the body wall, are regarded by some authors, and from a phylogenetic viewpoint, as a 'survival' of the diffuse nerve nets displayed by coelenterates (DAWSON, 1920). However, data obtained and interpreted by COONFIELD (1932) did not indicate the presence of a functionally significant diffuse peripheral network. Thus, there remain some doubts with respect to the evaluation of the peripheral plexuses in lumbricus.

In the ganglia and large nerve cords of the annelid central nervous system (Figs. 50 to 56), the nerve cells display essentially a peripheral arrangement, while the interior region contains nerve fibers and their terminal arborizations, including the synaptic junctions. These central masses of interlacing fiber systems constitute the neuropil (or neuro-pilemes) mentioned above (p. 38), and characteristic for the nervous centers of all 'higher' invertebrates. The arrangement of this neuropil displays, in the series obtained by means of the comparative anatomical approach, patterns of increasing complexity, ranging, e. g. from the brain of turbellarians to that of bees or ants. The neuropil is the structural basis for the switching, combination, permutation and transformation of the variety transmitted and processed by the network of nervous connections. The nerve cells are frequently of a peculiar unipolar type, with a vesicular nucleated cell body from which one main or stem process originates. This process, again, displays various branches, some of which receive the transmitted impulse, that is, the input variety, while one main branch functions as transmitter of

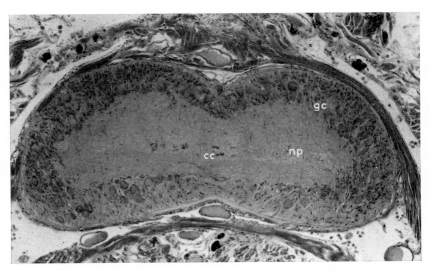

Figure 52. Cross section through cerebral ganglion of Lumbricus. (Original; × 140; red. ²/₃; hematoxylin-eosin.) cc: intracerebral commissure; gc: nerve cell layer; np: neuropileme.

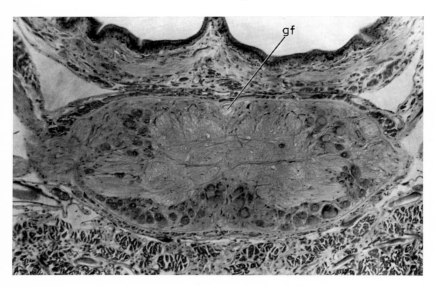

Figure 53. Cross section through 'subesophageal' (subpharyngeal) ganglion of Lumbricus. (Original; × 140; red. $^3/_4$; hematoxylin-eosin.) In the dorsal part of the ganglion, the giant fibers are of small caliber, and barely recognizable. gf: middle giant fiber.

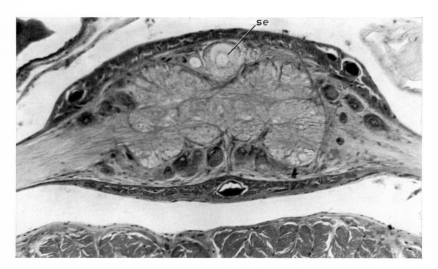

Figure 54. Cross section through one of the rostral ventral cord ganglia of Lumbricus. (Original; × 190; red. $^2/_3$; hematoxylin-eosin.) The giant fibers have not yet reached their full size. In two of the dorsal giant fibers, the neurofibrillar bundles appear in form of a central dot. se: septum in median dorsal giant fiber.

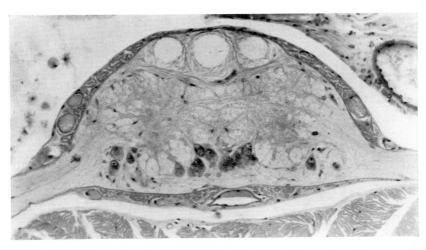

Figure 55. Cross section through a ventral cord ganglion of Lumbricus. (Original; × 210; red. ²/₃; hematoxylin-eosin.) This ganglion is located several segments caudal to that of Fig. 54. The dorsal giant fibers have approximately reached full size, and the ventral giant fibers are well recognizable.

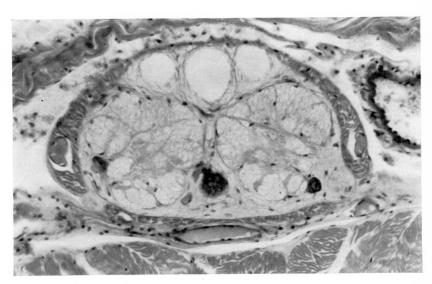

Figure 56. Cross section through transitional zone between longitudinal connective and ventral cord ganglion. (Original; × 220; red. ³/₄; hematoxylin-eosin.) This section lies caudal to the segment of Fig. 55. Giant fibers are prominent. Figs. 53 to 56 should be compared with the diagrams as shown in Fig. 57 and some of the following figures.

output variety (Figs. 57, 58). This latter branch may be designated as the neurite, while the input receiving branches would represent dendrites. In addition, there are various types of multipolar and bipolar cells. Basophil *Nissl*-granules (or tigroid substance) as well as neurofibrils are conspicuously displayed in various types of annelid nerve cells. Neurofibrils seem 'already' to be present in nerve cells of coelenterates and plathyhelminthes, but the available data are here more uncertain. Further comments on these structural components of nerve cells will be found in chapter V (volume 3).

The nervous system of the earthworm lumbricus has been extensively studied both from the anatomical and the functional viewpoint. The older essential data, which still remain valid, have been critically reviewed by Hanström (1928) and Herrick (1924). In conjunction with the diagrammatic sketch of Figure 46, the morphologic and structural arrangements of that nervous system are shown in Figures 50 to 58.

In addition to local segmental reflexes, which may easily be inferred from the connections shown in Figures 57, 58, and 64, and which are presumably of a sort as discussed in the introductory chapter I, longitudinally arranged intersegmental chains of conductors provide for a compounding of reflexes in Sherrington's sense.

In this respect, a peculiar mechanism seems to be provided by a number of giant fibers or *neurochords*, which run through almost the whole length of the central nervous system (Figs. 54 to 58). These large fibers arise in 'giant' neurochord cells. Although a true myelin sheath, such as is widely characteristic for nerve fibers of vertebrates, appears to be typically lacking in the invertebrate nervous system, these neurochords seem to be provided with a lipid substance somewhat resembling myelin (Hanström, 1928). In taxonomically lower worms, such as some nemertines and cestodes, a few neurochord cells are likewise present, as mentioned further above in the discussion of

Figure 57. Three diagrams of ventral nerve cord in Lumbricus. *A* Ganglion and peripheral nerves as seen on the basis of *Golgi* preparations. (After Retzius, 1892, from Hanström, 1928.) e: cutaneous epithelium; g: vessels; hn (and In): lateral extension of peripheral nerve (n); l: longitudinal musculature; r: circular musculature. *B* Neuropil diagram. (From K., 1927.) ko: dorsal giant fibers (neurofibrillar bundle according to Cajal, 1904); kof: commissural fibers; mo: motor neuron; np: neuropil; se: afferent fiber; st: supporting tissue; sz: internuncial cell. *C* Diagram based on *Golgi* preparation, showing some relationships with a minimum of additional details. (After Retzius, 1892, from Hanström, 1928.) bg: blood vessel; mg: motor neuron with contralateral axon; mt: thick motor fibers, not displaying cells or origin; rf: giant fibers; sf: afferent fibers.

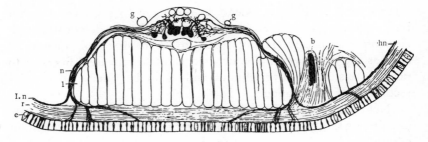

Fig. 57A

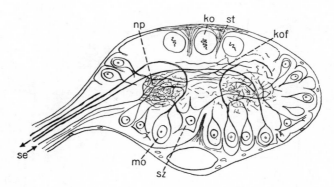

Fig. 57B

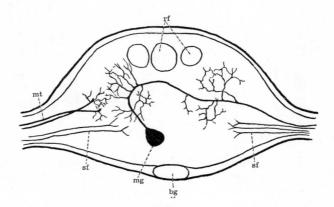

Fig. 57C

these forms. Their 'giant fibers' do not seem to exhibit the distinct but somewhat loosely wound myelin-like layers demonstrated by electron microscopy (HAMA, 1959) in the neurochords of annelids such as the earthworm. The occurrence of 'myelinated' fibers in the nervous system of invertebrates will again be briefly discussed in section 12 of this chapter.

Neurochord cells of annelids may be represented bilaterally, that is as pairs, or singly, unilaterally and, alternatingly one on the right and one on the left side, in successive segments. In addition, such cells are

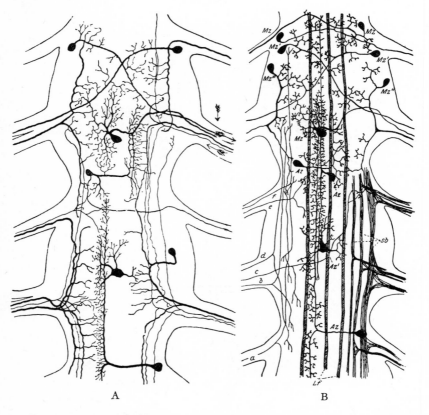

A   B

Figure 58. Two semidiagrammatic drawings of horizontal sections through the ventral cord of Lumbricus showing the variety of connections seen in *Golgi* impregnations by RETZIUS (1892). *A* From a diagram by L. EDINGER, 1912. *B* From a diagram interpreted by ZAWARZIN, 1925, and HANSTRÖM, 1928. Az: various internuncial cells; Lf: dorsal giant fibers; a–f: afferent fibers; sb: afferent bundles.

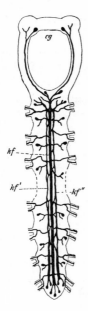

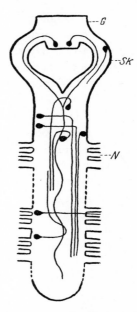

Figure 59. Neurochords of Lumbricus in the interpretation of B. HALLER, 1904. (From PLATE, 1922.) cg: cerebral ganglion; kf: giant fibers.

Figure 60. Neurochords of polychaete Sthenelais in the interpretation of ROHDE. (After FORTUYN, 1920, from HANSTRÖM, 1928.)

located in the brain of many annelid groups[13], as will be discussed further below.

Generally speaking, the neurochords or giant fibers found in the nervous system of some, but not all representatives of various animal groups, such as cestodes, nemerteans, annelids, crustaceans, insects, cephalopods, enteropneusts, cephalochordates, and vertebrates, display a variety of different structural organizations. Some remain in the central nervous system, while others become peripheral. Again, some

---

[13] Analogous large cells, from which large fibers arise and run through almost the whole length of the neuraxis, are found in the brain stem of some vertebrates (Ichthyopsida), namely *Müller's* cells in Petromyzonts, and the paired *Mauthner* cell in ganoids, teleosts, dipnoans and some amphibians (urodeles, and at least some anuran larvae).

Again, roughly summarizing their occurrence in non-chordates, 'giant fibers' might be said to be present in various species of Platyhelminthes (including Nemerteans), Annelida, Arthropoda, Mollusca (Cephalopoda, Gastropoda, e. g. Aplysia), and Phoronidea.

are very large single neurites, while others are composite fibers formed by the fusion of neurites pertaining to several nerve cells.

Three particularly conspicuous dorsal giant fibers can be seen in the ventral nerve cord of lumbricus (Figs. 55, 57, 59), and an additional paired fiber lies in a ventral position. Connections as well as structural relationships of these fibers may vary in different annelids, and a complete understanding of the various questions pertaining to that arrangement has not yet been reached.

According to STOUGH (1926), the neurochords of lumbricus are compound structures, consisting of a number of closely joined, or fused, parallel axons which originate from different nerve cell bodies. The giant fibers are said to be strictly segmental, and each segmental component originates from its own group of ganglion cells in its corresponding ganglion. The various components or 'segmental elements' are separated from each other by oblique septa, connected with neurochord sheath, and formed by membranes of a lipoid character, presumably representing synaptic structures. Moreover, the neuro-chords send processes into the neuropilemes of each segment. Thus,

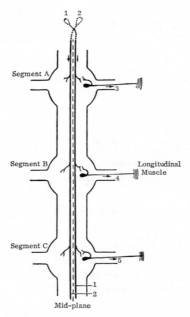

Figure 61. Diagram of neurochords in the polychaete Halla according to ASHWORTH (1909), in HERRICK's interpretation. (From HERRICK, 1924.)

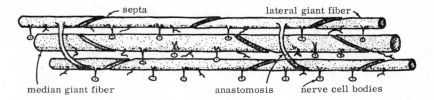

Figure 62. Diagram of dorsal giant fiber connections in Lumbricus according to BULLOCK's interpretation. (From BULLOCK, 1945.)

the neurochords of lumbricus would not be continuous, uninterrupted fibers, but rather chains of short compound axons. Figure 62 shows BULLOCK's interpretation of the three dorsal neurochords in that oligochaete worm. Extensions from the neurochords into the peripheral nerves have been described by some authors. In addition, the two lateral fibers are said to be interconnected by frequent anastomoses.

It was assumed that the median fiber conducted in a posterior direction, while the lateral ones transmitted the impulse toward the cephalic end of the animal. BULLOCK (1945), who investigated the functional organization of the giant fibers of Lumbricus, found, however, that conduction in all three fibers (paired lateral and unpaired median) could take place in both directions. This author believes that the apparent polarization of the system noted by earlier workers 'is due to regional localization of sensory connections capable of firing the giant fibers'. Yet, BULLOCK (1945) regards the septa as 'synaptic' structures, and adds the comment 'that the synapse is not inherently polarized nor delaying, but is only so as a result of the particular anatomical relations prevalent in vertebrates'. According to the cited author, said properties 'should not be a part of the definition of the synapse'. I am inclined to disagree with BULLOCK and to regard irreversibility of conduction, i.e. polarization, and the hereto related characteristics, as the significant 'synaptic' properties. If the network is not polarized, but nevertheless displays histologic discontinuities between conducting elements, I would prefer to use the term 'asynaptic' connections, or, at most 'protosynapses'. If the term 'ephapse' (cf. further below p. 121), used by a certain highly 'sophisticated' group of neurophysiologists, were not rather exclusively referring to some particular sorts of 'electric events', one could also use said designation as possibly equivalent to 'protosynapse'. BULLOCK's observation

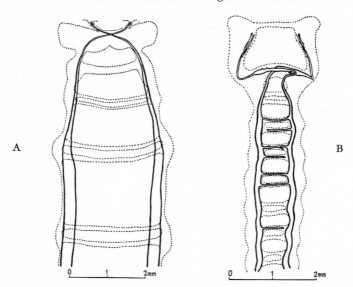

Figure 63. Giant fibers in two polychaetes according to BULLOCK. (From BULLOCK. 1953.) *A* Arrangement in Protula. *B* Arrangement in Spirographis.

(1945) that nicotine in concentrations as high as 1:10 000 did not abolish conduction over the giant fibers within 30 min, would, in my opinion, corroborate the validity of a synapse-concept in the formulation which I have chosen to retain.

As regards functional interpretations, it is assumed that a transmission from rostral levels to more anal levels and vice-versa may be effected by chains of short neurons, such that an impulse is passed onward from segment to segment. In each segmental ganglion the path may divide, one impulse passing to the next segment, and another reaching the periperal effector. Yet, the ordinary movements imply a rather complex sequence of activities, and presumably involves some, either proprioceptive or exteroceptive feedback action[14] (cf. Fig. 64). The neurochords, which appear to have a much greater velocity of conduction than other fiber systems, are believed to trigger sudden 'avoiding reactions' ('Zuckreflex') particularly, but not

---

[14] The feedback assumed by HERRICK (1924) is believed to result from a traction exerted in the skin and underlying tissues by the elongation of the body. This elongation occurs through contraction of circular muscle and relaxation of longitudinal muscle (cf. Fig. 57A).

exclusively initiated at the rostral end by the 'dominant' cerebral ganglion. Figures 60, 61, and 63 show some of the assumed neurochord connections in polychaetes.

E. v. HOLST (1932, 1933) reached the conclusion that, in lumbricus, peristaltic body movement, startling excitation ('Zuckerregung'), switching effects ('Umschaltung'), and undulating movements ('Schlängelbewegung') are performed by means of different tracts or 'channels' ('Bahnen'). Conduction velocity, in some particular instances, was measured at 5 mps, and was found to be independent of the actual state of length of the animal concerned ('Erregungsleitung unabhängig von der jeweiligen Länge des Tieres'). The cited author also demonstrated a 'rhythmic automatism' in the central nervous system of lumbricus. He adds (1933): 'Die 3 im Ganglion entspringenden Nervenpaare enthalten die gleichen Bahnen; ihre Wirkung addiert sich lediglich.'

BULLOCK (1945), however, reported a much higher conduction velocity. He states that 'the overall, effective speed of conduction (not counting any utilization time or synaptic delays at the segmental septa) is very high—up to 45 meters or more per second (24 °C)—

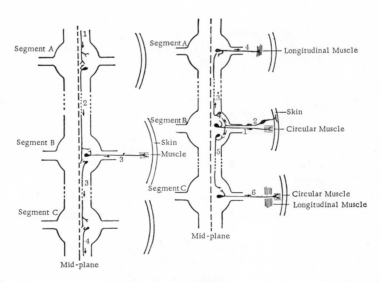

Figure 64. Diagrams of impulse correlation within the ventral nerve cord of Lumbricus according to HERRICK's interpretation. Left: longitudinal conduction of nervous impulse. Right: proprioceptive effect originating from skin, mediated by neuron 2 in segment B.

probably the fastest conducting fibers yet recorded among invertebrates, although they are far from the largest. The time for conduction
from head to tail increases as the worm is stretched, but not proportion-
ately, so that the rate also increases. This is a normal, reversible phenomenon'.

In addition, BULLOCK (1953) has investigated, with respect to his
concepts of 'synaptic' activities, the giant fibers of some polychaetes,
namely Eudistylia, Spirographis (Sabella), and Protula (cf. Fig. 63),
and recorded unpolarized transmission of the neural impulse. An
arrangement of neurochords and giant cells is also present in the
polychaete Nereis (NICOL, 1948, and other authors).

In the polychaete Myxicola only one single (unpaired) neurochord
is found, which is believed to control the longitudinal muscles
drawing the animal in its tube. A single neurochord is likewise
reported in Eunice (cf. e. g. BARNES, 1963).

Again, in some polychaetes, the cell bodies of motor cells innervating the parapodia may not be located in the ventral ganglia of the
central nervous system, but in separate peripheral pedal ganglia.
These, in turn, may be joined longitudinally by connections, which
form a bilateral peripheral cord (e. g. in Hermodice). Such 'tetraneural'
pattern can be interpreted as corresponding to that of the multiple
longitudinal cords founds in various platyhelminths (cf. BARNES, 1963).

As regards the giant fiber reflex of the oligochaete Lumbricus,
the strength of the contraction depends upon the number of impulses
in the burst, and this, in turn, upon the intensity and duration of the
stimulus. Rapid failure of transmission ('accommodation') occurs
between the sensory neurones and the giant fibers, and between the
giant fibers and the motor neurones (ROBERTS, 1962).

The afferent neurons of annelids are to a large extent represented
by the peripheral primary sensory cells mentioned above (p. 74),
which are located in the epithelium. The long central fiber ends with
terminal arborizations in the neuropil of the ganglia. Other sensory
nerve cells in less superficial position are likewise assumed (cf. Figs. 49
and 65).

The slower crawling motions of the earthworm are of the peristaltic
type, whereby a contraction wave runs from the rostral to the posterior
end (Fig. 64), while marine worms such as Nereis display the faster
undulating swimming movement ('Schlängelbewegung').

Memory mechanisms are provided in the nervous system of
annelids, since experiments with Lumbricus as well as Nereis have

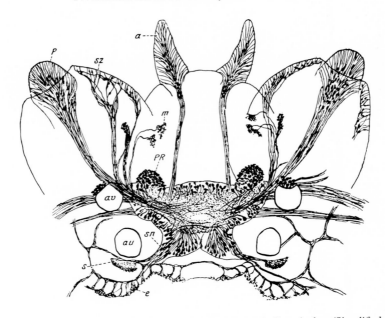

Figure 65. Brain and part of head of polychaete Nereis diversicolor. (Simplified after RETZIUS from HANSTRÖM, 1928). a: antenna with sensory cells; au, av: eyes; e: free nerve endings; m: motor endings; p, s: sensory organs; sz: primary sensory cells; PR: granule groups (corpora pedunculata); sn: bipolar afferent neurons.

demonstrated conditioned responses, habituation, and a few elementary associations. These 'higher' functions, at least in lumbricus, do not always require the activities of the brain and most rostral ganglia, but can also be performed by some of the other anterior ganglia of the ventral nerve cord. HANSTRÖM (1928) as well as HERRICK (1924) bring a fairly detailed critical review of the relevant experimental data obtained by a number of different authors. STEINER (1898), on the basis of his experimental work, expresses the opinion that the metameric ganglia of annelids have a substantial degree of autonomy in representing a segmental 'Bewegungszentrum'.

OGAWA (1934, 1939) has computed the number of ganglion cells found in the central nervous system of the oligochaete earthworm Pheretima during succeeding developmental stages. In the adult cerebral ganglion, about 12800 nerve cells were counted, and about 5150 in the subesophageal ganglion. In the segmental ganglia of the ventral cord, the cell number is said to vary between about 4470 and

930, depending on the complexity of organisation of its segment. Since about 100 segments are present, the total number of nerve cells is within the order of magnitude of 10^5 (I have rounded all numbers, which the author has given with 'precise' figures in the 10^9 range).

The brain of polychaetes is relatively well differentiated, and may, in some forms, consist of three delimitable portions, although such subdivision is not displayed in all worms of that group. Figures 65 and 66 show some aspects of the brain in Nereis. Densely arranged groups of cells, capping stalk-like, or 'pedunculated' special regions of neuropil, represent the so-called pedunculated bodies or mushroom bodies *(corpora pedunculata)*, which are regarded as association and correlation centers. These structures are particularly developed in the brain of arthropods, and will be discussed further below in connection with this latter group of invertebrates. According to reliable authors,

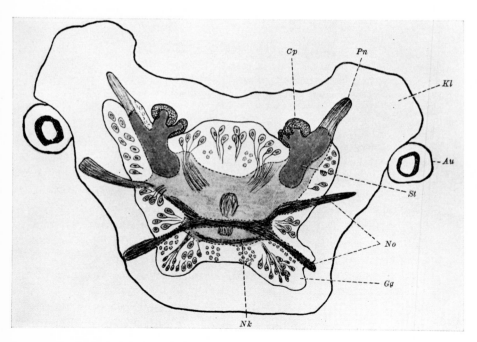

Figure 66. Horizontal section through head of Nereis virens. (From Hanström, 1928.) Au: eye; Cp: corpora pedunculata; Gg: nerve cell layer; Kl: lobe of head; NK: nuchal commissure; No: optic nerves with commissure; Pn: nerves of sensory tentacles; St: stalk or corpora pedunculata.

the corpora pedunculata are not present in the brain of all representatives of the polychaete class. Again, in various polychaetes, the nerves pertaining to the sensory palps may be connected with circumscribed clustered or globular condensations of neuropil designated as glomeruli. The arrangement of the neurochords in some polychaetes is illustrated by Figures 60, 61, and 63, referred to above on page 87. These figures (Figs. 60, 61) indicate the 'cerebral' location of a few neurochord cells, and the approximate location of other such elements in the ventral nerve cord.

CLARK (1955) has studied the centripetal migration of epidermal mucous cells into the brain; this sequence of events is quite similar to that displayed by the evolution of the nemertean 'cerebral organ' (cf. above, section 4, p. 48).

The brain of Oligochaeta, such, e.g., as lumbricus, apparently does not contain corpora pedunculata, nor does the brain of Hirudinea. In these latter forms, the cerebral ganglion, if compared with that of lumbricus, has undergone an aboral displacement, namely from the third segment (lumbricus) to the fifth (hirudo).

In Hirudo medicinalis, altogether 23 ganglia, joined by connectives, have been described. Each segmental ganglion contains about 350 to 400 monopolar nerve cell bodies. The connectives between successive segmental ganglia consit of three longitudinal strands, enclosed in a common sheath, namely one pair of larger lateral ones, and a smaller and more dorsal median one, also known as FAIVRE's nerve.

Supporting cells, perhaps homologous (in the sense not of special, but of general morphologic homology) to the neuroglial cells of vertebrates, have been described in annelids by various authors (CAJAL, 1904; HAVET, 1916; HANSTRÖM, 1928; COGGESHALL and FAWCETT, 1964; KUFFLER and POTTER, 1964). Such glia cells, fibrous as well as protoplasmic, are distributed in ganglia and nerve trunks. In the ganglia, the neuroglia may form septa separating groups of nerve cells, fiber tracts, and neuropilemes. On the whole, the available data on neuroglia of annelids and other invertebrates still remain fragmentary and uncertain. Concerning the leech hirudo, however, some recent detailed observations, including electron-microscopic and electrophysiological studies, have been published (COGGESHALL and FAWCETT, 1964; KUFFLER and POTTER, 1964). Three different sorts of glia cells were pointed out: (1) packet glial cells, six in each ganglion, each of these cells is said to envelop about 60 monopolar nerve cell bodies; (2) a pair of large glial cells, the processes of which 'permeate' the neuropil in the ganglia; (3) the connective glial cells, one pair in the connectives between adjacent ganglia, each cell enveloping, with its processes, several thousand axons. The glia cells are believed to make up approximately half of the volume of the central nervous system (KUFFLER and POTTER, 1964). Figure 67 illustrates the interpretation, by KUFFLER and POTTER (1964), of their findings in hirudo. Some additional remarks on glial elements of invertebrates will be found below in section 12 (p. 258) of this chapter.

It is generally recognized that, with some exceptions, blood vessels do not enter the nervous 'tissue', that is, the nervous system of invertebrates. Among the best known exceptions to this rule are the annelid lumbricus (HAVET, 1916; E. SCHARRER, 1944), and the mollusk cephalopods (CAJAL, 1929; E. SCHARRER, 1944).

The capillary blood vessels of the well-vascularized central nervous system of the earthworm are of the so-called loop type, found, among

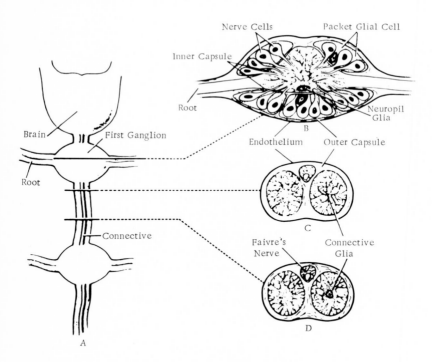

Figure 67. Glial elements in nervous system of Hirudo according to KUFFLER and POTTER. (From KUFFLER and POTTER, 1964.) *A* Brain and first two ganglia. *B–D* Diagrammatic sections showing arrangement of glia.

vertebrates, e.g. in marsupials, some reptiles, some amphibians, and some cyclostomes. On the other hand, the capillary blood vessels in the well-vascularized brain of the squid (cf. also further below p. 216) are of the so-called network type, found, among vertebrates, in some cyclostomes, most fishes, anuran amphibians, most reptiles, birds, and placental mammals (cf. E. SCHARRER, 1944). In a few vertebrates (lung-fish Epiceratodus, urodele Amblystoma), E. H. CRAIGIE found a combination of both, as a rule mutually exclusive patterns.

The regenerative capabilities of annelids such as lumbricus are well known. Amputated anterior segments may be restored, including a typical functional head with brain, and removed portions of the ventral cord can likewise regenerate. SCHWARTZ (1932) reported replacement of ablated cerebral ganglia of lumbricus within approximately three weeks. According to this author, however, such worms with regenerated brains, of seemingly quite normal histologic structure, did no longer burrow, and crawled with the anterior end raised. In addition, SCHWARTZ (1932) reached the conclusion that the new brain arose from a differentiation of 'connective tissue cells'. This interpretation, however, does not appear fully convincing and the relevant questions might be regarded as still unsettled. While a relative specificity of 'germ layers' can be reasonably maintained, and the nervous system, on the whole, qualifies as a neuroectodermal configuration, there are some indications that such specificity should not be considered absolute. In section 2 of this chapter, brief references were made to entodermal components of the coelenterate nervous system, and to assumed mesodermal as well as entodermal components of the echinoderm nervous system. Thus, a regeneration of nervous tissue from mesodermal elements, although rather unusual and perhaps doubtful, cannot 'a priori' be dismissed as 'impossible'.

The annelids exhibit well substantiated evidence of neurosecretory activity, which is, however, also suggested in some nemerteans (cf. p. 49). In the free and sessile polychaete annelids, neurosecretory cells manifesting possible cyclic secretory activity have been found in the ventral nerve cord. Although there are no definite sex differences, the neurosecretory activity is seen to undergo changes correlated with reproductive activity.

In the oligochaete earthworm lumbricus, neurosecretory cells have been observed in the cerebral and esophageal, as well as in both (peripheral) anterior gastric ganglia; the cerebral ganglion, in particular, contains aggregations of conspicuous neurosecretory cells in its dorsal part (E. and B. SCHARRER, 1937). In lumbricus, functional relationships between neurosecretory activity and reproductive as well as regenerative phenomena have been established. In Gephyreans (sipunculids) neurosecretory extracts were shown to slow down the contraction of nephridia[15].

7. Tardigrada

In the synopsis on taxonomy presented in chapter II, the tardigrades were tentatively considered a dubious arthropod class. HANSTRÖM (1928) cautiously regards the tardigrades as 'related to the annelids'[16].

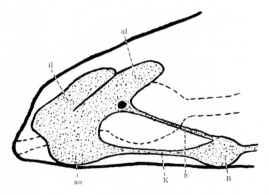

Figure 68. Lateral view of brain in the tardigrad Macrobiotus hufelandi. (Simplified after PLATE, 1922, from HANSTRÖM, 1928.) B: first ventral ganglion; K: connective between subesophageal ganglion and first ventral ganglion; S: dorsal pharyngeal connective; al: lateral lobe of cerebral ganglion with eye spot (connected to first ventral ganglion); il: internal lobe of cerebral ganglion; so: subesophageal ganglion; digestive canal indicated by dotted line.

The tardigrades or water bears are very small transparent animals living in fresh or salt water, or in damp terrestrial environment. The body displays some segmentation. The central nervous system

[15] Various pertinent data on neurosecretion, including its manifestation in the different invertebrate groups, have been critically reviewed and evaluated by ORTMANN, 1960.

[16] Merely for the sake of convenience, HANSTRÖM (1928) discusses Tardigrada subsequently to the parasitic Linguatilida, which are likewise of dubious taxonomic status, but might be distantly related to the Arachnida, particularly to the mites or Acarina. Recent authors (e. g. BARNES, 1963) classify the tardigrades as a separate 'phylum'.

(Figs. 68, 69) is of typical 'rope-ladder' pattern; in addition to the usual pharyngeal ring, there exists an accessory connection of lateral cerebral lobe with first ventral ganglion. The cerebral ganglion (brain) shows an external subdivision into five portions, namely into paired lateral and medial (internal) lobes, and unpaired median one. A subesophageal ganglion, partly fused with the brain, and four segmented ganglia, fused in the midline, are present. Small ganglia are scattered within the peripheral nervous system (E. Marcus, 1928). Sensory cirri, and

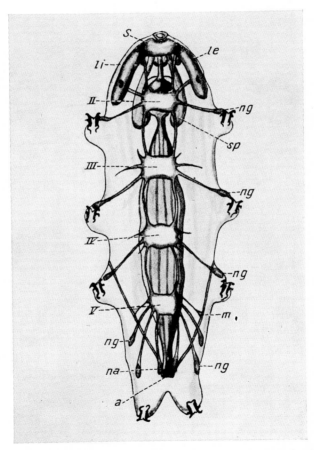

Figure 69. Central nervous system of Macrobiotus hufelandi. (After E. Marcus, 1928, from Hanström, 1928.) S: subesophageal ganglion; a: anus; le, li: external (lateral) and internal lobe of cerebral ganglion; na, ng: accessory ganglia; sp: gland; m: Doyère's eminence; II–V: ventral ganglia.

a pair of rudimentary eyes are provided. These latter are connected with the lateral lobe of the brain, near the origin of the dorsal (or accessory) 'pharyngeal ring'. Like Rotifera, these animalcules show marked resistance to dessication, and survive for a considerable time in the dried condition; the name of one species, Macrobiotus hufelandi, refers to this behavior[17]. Because of their transparence, LOUIS DOYÈRE (1811–1863) chose these animals in order to study the connection of nerve fibers with individual muscle fibers, and discovered the motor endings ('DOYÈRE's eminence'). The total length of a fully grown tardigrade remains, generally speaking, within the range of one millimeter, and may be less than 0.5 mm.

8. Arthropoda

The nervous system of this very polymorphous phylum can easily be conceptually derived from that of the annelids, both as regards morphology and histologic structure.

If, for the sake of convenience in a generalized treatment, the *Onychophora* are included as arthropods, this procedure becomes clearly justified by the fact that the brain of onychophores, such, e. g., as Peripatus, is evidently a brain of arthropod type, despite some similarity with that of polychaetes, and despite its lack of typical segmentation.

Onychophora are rare animals, with few species and individuals, that can perhaps all be subsumed under one family. Its representatives, commonly designated by the term Peripatus (the name of one genus), live under moist debris in the tropical forests of Africa, Asia, Australia and South (including Central) America. Their scattered distribution in widely separated continents is interpreted as indicating that this

---

[17] CHRISTOPH WILHELM HUFELAND (1762–1832), an eminent clinician who played a significant role in the evolution of medical thought in Germany at the transition from 18th to 19th century, had published a once widely known treatise under the title Makrobiotik (1796), i. e. 'die Kunst, lange zu leben'.

The survival of tardigrads, rotifers and at least diverse nematods in a dried state of, as it were 'suspended animation', is known as *'anabiosis'* (literally: 'resuscitation' or 'reviving'). This state is characterized by water loss and contraction or shriveling into a non-descript spherical mass. Specimens of tardigrads have been revived after immersion in liquid helium (near absolute zero), brine, ether, absolute alcohol, and other substances (BARNES, 1963). Also, resistance of the anabiotic metazoa to high temperatures has been reported.

group was formerly more widespread and is now gradually disappearing. Peripatus is thus considered as a good approximation to a 'missing link' between annelids and arthropods. It appears of interest that ciliated epithelium, which has not been shown to occur in arthropods but can be found in annelids, is present in at least one of the visceral structures of Peripatus.

Yet a number of difficult and undecidable questions arise as regards the specific phylogenetic implications. Because of their tracheae similar to those of myriapods, insects, and some arachnids, the onychophores were also designated as protracheates. Again, protracheates, myriapods, and insects seem, in many respects, more closely related to each other than to crustaceans, which are provided with gills; the air-breathing arachnids likewise stand somewhat apart. It has been

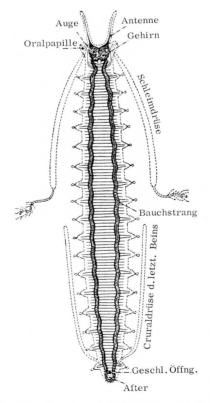

Figure 70. Central nervous system of Peripatus capensis in dorsal view. (After BALFOUR, 1883, simplified by BÜTSCHLI, 1921, from HANSTRÖM, 1928.)

assumed by some authors that crustaceans on one hand, and tracheates, including onychophores, on the other hand, might have derived from a different annelid stem form. Moreover, arachnids and their kin could possibly have arisen from a third, different ancestral annelid form.

The central nervous system of onychophores (BALFOUR, 1883; FEDOROW, 1926) is a topologically typical, but nevertheless in some respects peculiar 'rope-ladder' nervous system with a paired faintly sinuous[18] longitudinal cord interconnected by very numerous transverse commissures (Fig. 70). The two rather widely separated longitudinal cords join by fusion at the posterior body end, behind the anal opening. Nerve cells are fairly evenly distributed along the ventral part of the longitudinal strands (Fig. 71), with very slight indications of segmental condensations.

The peripheral nerves originate from the longitudinal cords, six pairs to a segment; as in many arthropods, the motor nerves are dorsal roots of the longitudinal cord, and the sensory roots ventral ones.

The brain (Fig. 72) consists of an anterior and posterior subdivision. The anterior part innervates a pair of primitive vesicular eyes, one pair of antennae, and part of the 'head'-integument. This part of the cerebral ganglion contains small, but well-defined corpora pedunculata, forming a tripartite group on each side. It also displays a neuropileme known as central body, and characteristic for the arthropod brain, but lacking in that of annelids. Another neuropil-structure, which, however, can likewise be seen in some polychaetes, is provided by the glomeruli formed by connections of the antenna-nerves.

The posterior part of the brain, designated as mandibular ganglion, innervates the mandibles, the oral cavity, and, through the mediation of the stomatogastric nerves, esophagus, pharynx and portions of the oral region. HANSTRÖM (1928) assumes, from a phylogenetic viewpoint, and in general agreement with previous views of HOLMGREN, that this posterior part of the cerebral ganglion represents the first ventral ganglion of the longitudinal cord; the ganglion is believed to have been 'cephalized', that is, displaced forward, and fused with the primordial brain. The origin of the stomatogastric system from that first ventral ganglion, secundarily fused with the primary brain,

---

[18] The lateral convexities of the faintly sinuous, wavy course of the two cords are interpreted as corresponding to the ganglionic swellings of annelids and arthropods (HANSTRÖM, 1928).

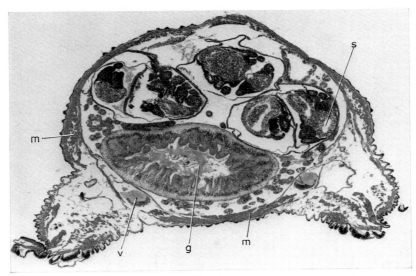

Fig. 71 A

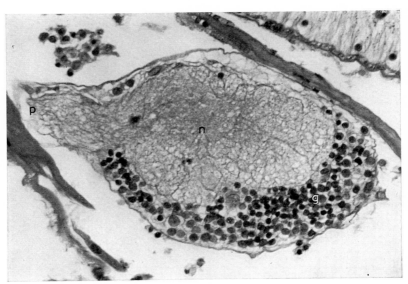

Fig. 71 B

Figure 71. Ventral nerve cord of Peripatus. (Original.) *A* Cross section through body, showing topographic relationships. ($\times$ 25; red. $^2/_3$; hematoxylin-eosin.) g: gut; m: musculature; s: slime glands and their duct; v: nerve cord. *B* Left nerve cord in higher magnification ($\times$ 250; red. $^3/_4$). g: nerve cell layer; n: neuropil and fibers of different caliber; p: origin of peripheral nerve.

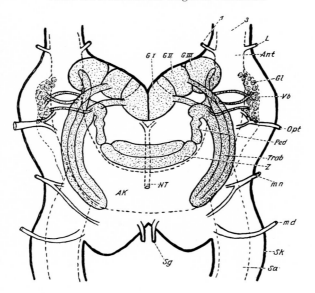

Fig. 72 A

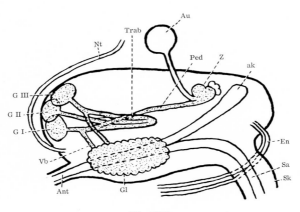

Fig. 72 B

Figure 72. Diagram of brain of Peripatus. (Modified after HOLMGREN, from HAN-STRÖM, 1928.) *A* Dorsal view. *B* Lateral view. Ak: antennal commissure; Ant: antennal bundle; Au: eye; En: visceral nerves; GI, II, III: globuli of corpora pedunculata; Gl: antennal glomeruli; L (1, 3): antennal nerves; md: mandibular nerve; mn: labial nerve; NT: integumentary nerve; Opt: optic nerve. Ped: pedunculus; Sa: subantennal strand; sg: stomatogastric nerve; Sk: pharyngeal connective; Trab: stalk of corpora pedunculata; vb: globulo-glomerular connections; Z: central body.

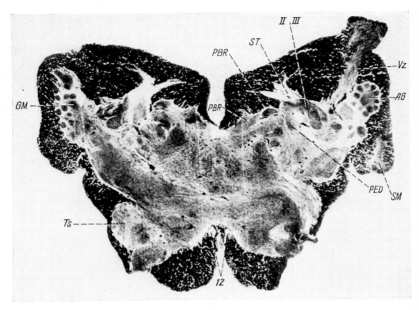

Fig. 72 C

Figure 72C. Horizontal section through the brain of the Australian onychophore Peripatoides occidentalis (from HANSTRÖM, 1935). Ag: antennal glomeruli; Gm: glomerular region; Pbr: protocerebral bridge (conjectural identification); Ped: origin of pedunculus; Sm: optic neuropileme; St: stalks of medioventral globulus-region of corpora pedunculata; Ts: tractus subantennalis; Vz: ventral branch of nervus antennalis; II, III: fused trabeculae of stalk; 12: nervus stomodealis. There is some doubt whether the cell masses of the globuli should be considered tripartite or quadripartite.

is considered a common feature for polychaetes, onychophores, and arthropods.

Detailed information on sense organs and brain of onychophores, with comments on possible phylogenetic relationships, were published by HOLMGREN (1916), FEDOROW (1929) and HANSTRÖM (1935). Further general data about onychophores, including various still unsettled questions, can be found in papers by HENRY (1948) and by MANTON (1949).

In a short survey of the nervous system of arthropods, it is convenient to group arachnids (including the horse-shoe crab limulus) as chelicerates, and insects, crustaceans, and myriapods (diplopods and chilopods) as antennates.

Arachnids are characterized by a cephalothorax and an abdomen. The cephalothorax is provided with six pairs of appendages, of which the four posterior ones are usually walking legs. The anterior pair represents the chelicerae or jaws, and the second the pedipalps, sensory in spiders, and an instrument for seizing prey in scorpions. The abdomen has no locomotor appendages. Arachnids, moreover, lack compound eyes and antennae.

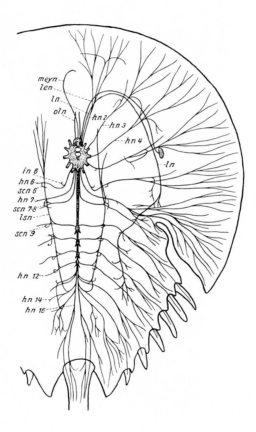

Figure 73. Nervous system of Limulus, ventral view. (Simplified after PATTEN-REDENBAUGH from HANSTRÖM, 1928.) hn 2–16: so-called haemal nerves; in 6: intestinal nerve; len: nerve of complex eye; ln: lateral nerve; lsn: lateral sympathetic nerve; meyn: nerve of lens-eye; oln: olfactory nerve; scn 6–9: segmental cardiac nerves.

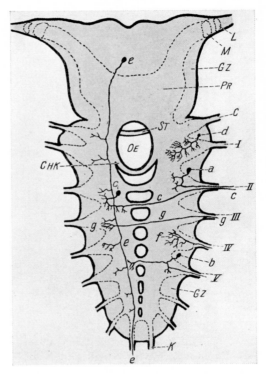

Figure 74. Brain and ventral cord in the so-called 'trilobite'-larva of Limulus. (After Hanström, 1928.) C: cheliceral nerve; Chk: cheliceral commissure; Gz: ganglion cell layer; L: lamina; M: medulla; K: connective to separate abdominal ganglia; Oe: esophagus; Pr: protocerebrum; St: stomodeal bridge; I–V: nerves to walking legs; a–g: neurones of ventral cord.

The horse-shoe crab[19] or king crab, here loosely included with the arachnids, is the only surviving representative of a large paleontologic

---

[19] The king crab is, of course, not a 'crab'. Larval stages of limulus lack the long, sword-like (Xiphosuran) tail of the adult, but display an abdomen plainly subdivided into 8 segments, which subsequently fuse into a single part. Because of a superficial similarity with trilobites, this larval stage was called the trilobite stage of Xiphosura. The extinct trilobites, which derive their name from the tripartite subdivision of the dorsal surface of their body by two longitudinal furrows, seem most closely related to the crustaceans, while the definite morphologic relationship of Xiphosura to Arachnida is quite evident. Trilobites appeared in the Cambrian and died out in the Permian. Limulus appeared in the Triassic, and has changed little since its first appearance, presumably about 200 000 000 years ago.

group (Gigantostraca, Palaeostraca), with perhaps not more than five living species, all pertaining to the genus Limulus, subsumed, by some taxonomists, under the class Merostomata and subclass Xiphosura.

Since limulus may be regarded as a 'living fossil', this animal is, despite its very minor general importance, of considerable morphologic and biologic interest[20]. The arrangement of the nervous system of

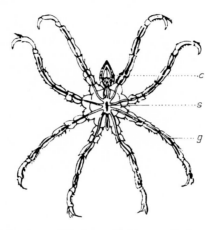

Figure 75. General aspect of Pycnogonid (Pantopod) Ammothea pycnogonoides. (After Selenka-Goldschmidt, 1919.)c: chelicerae; g: gut diverticles in legs; s: stomach.

Xiphosura is shown in Figures 73 and 74. It can be seen that a considerable concentration of the segmental ganglia is manifested.

In the brain, corpora pedunculata are present, and located in an unusually ventral position related to the caudal displacement of the oral opening. This configuration, in turn, is associated with modifications in the topography of the cerebral ganglion.

The central nervous system of limulus is said to contain neurosecretory elements. The active neuroendocrine substance obtained from limulus produces, in bioassay on crustaceans, an effect on the chromatophores (Scharrer and Scharrer, 1963). Neurosecretory cells are also described in the nervous system of Araneae or true spiders (Kühne, 1959).

---

[20] Thus, Patten (The Evolution of the Vertebrates and their Kin. Philadelphia 1912) has elaborated a phylogenetic hypothesis, in which Arachnida (including here particularly limulus) play a key role in the evolution of vertebrates ('*Arachnid Theory*'). Various views on the origin of vertebrates will be discussed further below on page 318-346.

The nervous system of *Pycnogonida (Pantopoda)* includes a cerebral ganglion, a pharyngeal ring, and four to five more or less fused abdominal ganglia (Figs. 75, 76). The central nervous system of these animals, although corresponding rather closely to that of Xiphosura and Arachnida, is, on the whole, poorly differentiated (HILTON, 1916; HANSTRÖM, 1928).

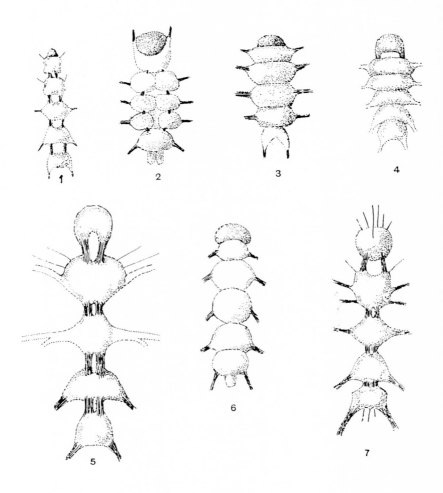

Figure 76. Configuration of central nervous system in seven different species of California Pycnogonids, seen from ventral side. The supraesophageal ganglion ('brain') is shown at the upper end. (From HILTON, 1916.)

The class *Arachnida* in the narrower sense can be subdivided into various orders, of which, for the present purposes, only the Araneae and the Scorpionida need be briefly considered[21].

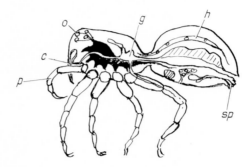

Figure 77. Simplified diagrammatic sketch illustrating the organization of a 'generalized' Aranea or true spider. (After a blackboard drawing by PLATE in his 1919 lecture course.) c: chelicera with poison gland and fang; g: gut with various diverticula ('sucking' stomach); only one of the diverticula extending into the legs is indicated (in fourth leg); the hatched part in the abdominal portion of the gut represents the 'liver'; h: heart with ostia; o: ocelli; p: palp; sp: spinneret with silk glands; rostral to these structures ovary and 'book' lung; the central nervous system is indicated in black; a conspicuous constriction separates the body into anterior cephalothorax and posterior abdomen.

The *Araneae* are true spiders (Fig. 77), with spinnerets (spinning tubes, connected with silk glands) on the abdomen. The respiratory organs consist of air sacs ('lungs'), and of air tubes comparable to those of tracheates such as insects. With regard to the 'lungs', Dipneumones and Tetrapneumones can be distinguished.

In Dipneumones the whole central nervous system is fused into a single mass, which is perforated by the esophagus. From this mass, which is located in the cephalothorax, the nerves for the locomotor

---

[21] Other orders of that class, as commonly distinguished by present-day taxonomists, are the following. Pseudoscorpionidae (small, superficially scorpion-like animals, such, e.g., as the harmless Chelifer living in houses), Solpugidae ('sun-spiders', or 'wind-scorpions'), Palpigradi (small, poorly known animals), Uropygi (e. g. 'whip scorpions'), Amblypygi, Ricinulei, Opiliones (or Phalangides, 'harvestmen' or 'daddy longlegs'), and Acarinae (mites and ticks). Some biologists consider the parasitic Linguatulida (Pentastonum) as related to the Acarina. The Pycnogonida (sea-spiders, of between 10 mm and 2.5 cm or more in body length) are now usually considered to represent a separate class of the subphylum Chelicerata (cf. e. g. BARNES, 1963).

extremities arise in radiating strands (Figs. 78 A and B). The nerves for the ocelli, for the chelicerae, and for the pedipalps arise anteriorly. Posteriorly, there is a paired nerve strand designated as 'cauda equina', which distributes nerves to various parts of the abdomen.

In Tetrapneumones, a free posterior abdominal ganglion has been reported (HANSTRÖM, 1928).

The corpora pedunculata in the brain of Araneae consist, on each side, of a single group of globuli cells in a rather anterior position. In these animals, the pedunculate bodies are considered to represent essentially a 'secondary optic center' (HANSTRÖM, 1928). In sedentary

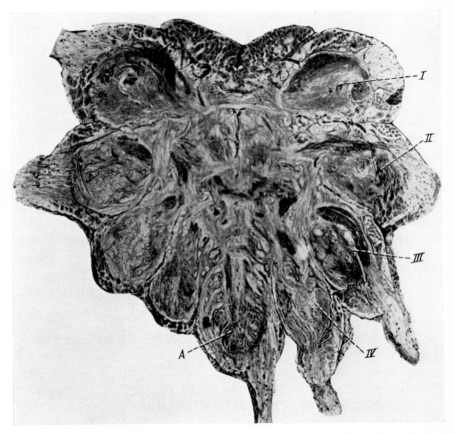

Figure 78 A. Horizontal section through the central nervous system in the Aranea Tegeneria domestica. (From HANSTRÖM, 1928.) A: caudal complex with so-called cauda equina; I–IV: ganglia of walking legs.

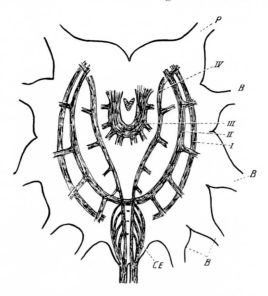

Figure 78 B. Diagram of tracts on central nervous system of Araneae. (From HAN-STRÖM, 1928.) B: nerves to four walking legs; Ce: so-called cauda equina; P: nerves to pedipalps; I–IV: main longitudinal tracts (within the concavity of III: cross section of stalk pertaining to corpora pedunculata).

forms, lacking eyes, the corpora pedunculata are wanting. It is believed that they 'disappeared' in the course of phylogenetic changes.

In *Scorpionida* (Fig. 79) there is a fused ganglionic mass, similar to that of Araneae, located in the cephalothorax, but with a posterior extension in form of a nerve cord, containing several smaller segmental ganglia in the so-called praeabdomen and in the tail-like postabdomen. As in Araneae, the brain displays paired corpora pedunculata with a fairly large single group of globuli cells.

The sensory equipment of Arachnida in general includes tactile hairs, eyes, and slit sensory organs. Some authors assume that certain types of tactile hairs might also register sound waves. The eyes contain a combined cornea and lens, frequently a layer of hypodermal cells designated as 'vitreous body', and a retinal layer. The neurosensory photoreceptor cells may, in some instances, have the photosensitive ending directed toward the light ('direct eye') or away from the light ('indirect eye', 'inverted eye'). In some spiders, both sorts of eyes are present. The 'slit organs' consist of covered pits in the cuticle, and

hypodermal sensory cells. Chemoreceptor (olfactory) as well as mech-
anoreceptor functions ('auditory', 'kinesthetic') have been attributed
to these organs.

Crustacea can be subdivided into numerous subclasses and orders[22].
The Phyllopoda, which include the Branchiopoda, display a 'rope-
ladder' nervous system more typical than that of most annelids. In
other groups, various degrees of fusion and concentration can be
noticed (Fig. 80). The distribution of peripheral nerves is exemplified
by Figure 81, showing the nervous system of the decapod crayfish
Astacus. The nervous system of the isopod Porcellio scaber is illustrated
in Figure 82.

The brain of Crustacea usually shows the three main parts characteristic for 'higher' arthropods, and particularly for insects. These
three parts are protocerebrum, deutocerebrum, and tritocerebrum.
In arachnids, including pantopods (pycnogonids) and limulus, on
the other hand, a deutocerebrum is, apparently, not developed. The
protocerebrum is mainly connected with the eyes, while the *deutocerebrum*
is related to the first antennae. The *tritocerebrum*, which is connected

---

[22] From an overall macrotaxonomic viewpoint as adopted in this treatise, three major
groups might be very roughly circumscribed. The subclass Branchiopoda comprises small
crustaceans that are mainly fresh-water inhabitants. The subclass Copepoda includes the
small, abundant members of the plankton in lakes and seas. The subclass Malacostraca
includes most of the better known crustaceans such as crabs, lobsters, and shrimps. The
two first groups were formerly believed to represent the 'lower crustaceans', characterized
by a Nauplius-larva, and the Malacostraca were regarded as 'higher crustaceans', predominantly developing through a more complex Zooëa-larva stage.

Peculiar crustaceans are the Cirripedia (barnacles), a sessile and very 'aberrant' group,
of which some forms are stalked and superficially resemble Brachiopods (not to be
confused with Branchiopods as mentioned above). A mantle, or shell, encloses the body.

Another, recently discovered, very 'primitive' group, with some distant resemblance
to trilobites, comprises three (at the time of this writing) known species. Their length does
not exced 3 mm. The first specimen of this group, regarded as the subclass Cephalocarida,
was discovered in 1954 in the floor of Long Island Sound. This newly found crustacean,
that can actually and easily pass through the proverbial eye of a needle, was called Hutchinsoniella.

Although Crustacea, generally speaking, are aquatic organisms, breathing by means
of gills (connected with the appendages), or, in groups of very small body size, by direct
cutaneous gaseous exchange, some terrestrial forms occur. Here, a modified structure of
the gills preserves the necessary moisture; as an alternative, so-called pseudotracheae or,
again, lung-like cavities may be present.

On page 56, chapter II, in the general survey of taxonomy, an estimate of 9000 known
crustacean species was given, based on data available less than ten years ago with respect
to the time of writing (1963). A more recent estimate has now reached the figure 26000+.

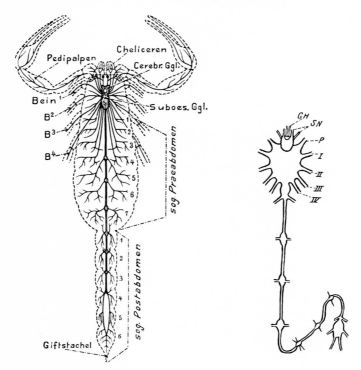

Figure 79. Nervous system of Scorpion. *A* Dorsal view. (After NEWPORT from BÜTSCHLI, 1921, and HANSTRÖM, 1928.) *B* Outline of dissected nervous system. (Simplified after DUFOUR from HANSTRÖM, 1928.) Gh: chelicerate nerves; Sn: optic nerves; P: pedipalp nerves; I–IV: nerves of walking legs.

with the chelicerae in arachnids, is concerned with the second antennae of crustaceans. It also is connected with the stomatogastric nervous system.

The protocerebrum displays, as a rule, corpora pedunculata, and two peculiar neuropilemes, namely the central body, and the protocerebral bridge, which will again be briefly discussed further below in connection with the insect brain.

From a comparative viewpoint, it is assumed that the protocerebrum corresponds to the simpler primordial cerebral ganglion (archicerebrum) of polychaetes, to which, by additional differentiation, a deutocerebrum (HANSTRÖM, 1928) has been added (I am here using HANSTRÖM's application of that term, although the term deuterocerebrum may appear preferable). The tritocerebrum is believed to represent the

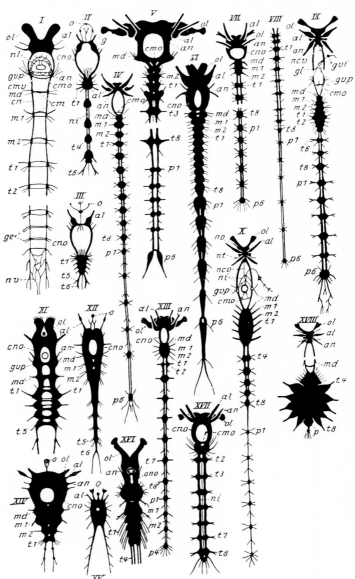

Figure 80. Variety of configurations manifested by the Crustacean central nervous system. (After GIESBRECHT from HANSTRÖM, 1928.) I: Phyllopoda; II, III: Cirripedia; IV: Dichelopoda; V: Apseudidae; VI: Leptostraca; VII: Anomostraca; VIII: Sympoda; IX: Stomatopoda; X: Decapoda macrura; XI: Cladocera; XII, XV: Copepoda; XIII: Gammaroidea; XIV: Ostracoda; XVI: Branchiura; XVII: Oniscoidea; XVIII: Decapoda brachiura.

first postoral ganglion, which, even in some polychaetes and in onychophores, may fuse with the archicerebrum, to form a syncerebrum. Figure 83 provides a diagrammatic illustration of the relationships between the subdivisions of the polychaete and the arthropod brain.

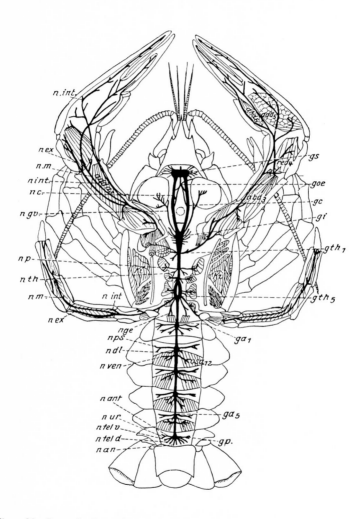

Figure 81. General view (dorsal aspect) of nervous system in crayfish Astacus fluviatilis. (After KEIM, 1915, from HANSTRÖM, 1928.) ga: abdominal ganglia; gc (and nc): pharyngeal connective; gi: infraesophageal ganglion; gp: postabdominal ganglion; gs: cerebral ganglion (brain); gth: thoracic ganglia; Ki: gills (branchia); additional structures not relevant in this context.

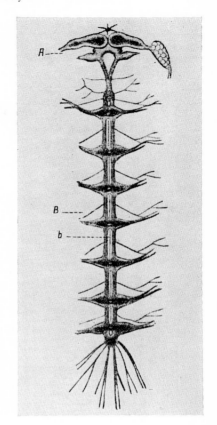

Figure 82. Rope-ladder nervous system of isopod Porcellio scaber. (After LEYDIG, 1857, from R. HERTWIG, 1912.) A: brain; B: ventral cord; b: unpaired median accessory connective.

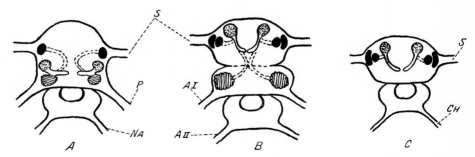

Figure 83. Diagram of brain configuration in Polychaetes (A), antennate Arthropods (B), and chelicerate Arthropods (C) according to HANSTRÖM (1928). AI: nerve of antennulae; AII: nerve of antennae (in Crustaceans); Ch: nerve of chelicerae; Na: nerve of appendages pertaining to first somatic ganglion; P: nerve of palps; S: optic nerve; optic centers black, corpora pedunculata dotted, glomeruli of antennae and palps indicated by cross hatching.

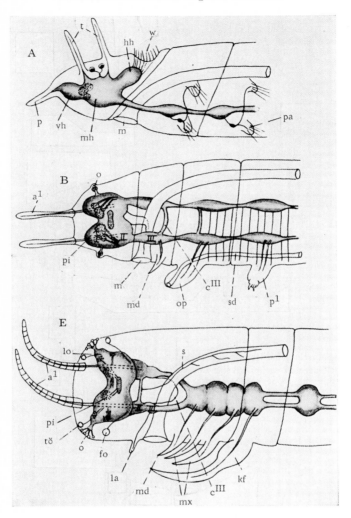

Figs. 84 A, B, E

Figure 84. Diagrams of rostral end of central nervous system in Annelida and Arthropoda. (After PLATE, 1922). *A* Annelida. *B* Peripatus. *C* Phyllopod Crustacea. *D* Malacostraca (Crustacea). *E* Chilopoda. *F* Insecta. *G* Araneae.

Central body, horizontal hatching; protocerebral bridge vertical hatching; corpora pedunculata dotted; a^1 and a^2 first and second antenna; c III: commissure of tritocerebrum;

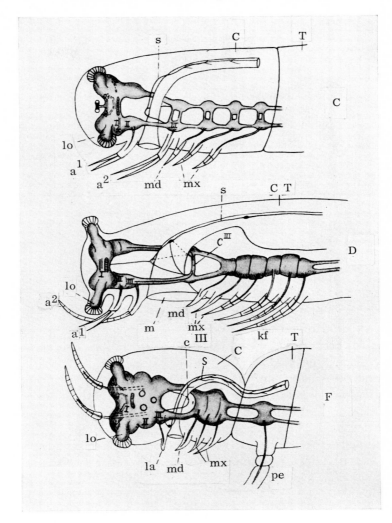

Figs. 84C, D, F

C: head; ch: chelicera; CT: cephalothorax; fo: frontal organ; hh: posterior cerebral lobe of annelid; kf: appendages; la: labrum; lo: lobus opticus; m: mouth; md: mandible; mh: middle lobe in annelid; mx: maxilla; o: ocelli; op: oral papilla; p: palpus; pa: parapodium; pe: foot; pi: corpora pedunculata; pp: pedipalps; S: 'sympathetic' (stomatogastric) nerve; sd: slime gland; t: tentacle; T: thorax; tö: TÖMÖSVARY's organ; vh: rostral lobe of brain; w: ciliated organ of annelid.

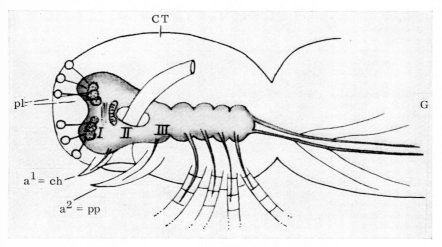

Fig. 84 G

Figure 84 brings an interesting comparison concerning the rostral differentiation of the central nervous system in various groups of articulates according to PLATE's (1922) interpretation. This author, in contradistinction to HANSTRÖM and HOLMGREN, regards the deutocerebrum as a derivate of the first postoral ganglion. I am inclined to favor HANSTRÖM's interpretation. This latter author also pointed out that the so-called stomodeal bridge occurring in diverse forms may be evaluated as a differentiation of the stomatogastric nervous system rather than as the manifestation of a definite neuromeric segment.

FERRIS (1947) has emphasized some difficulties (which he calls 'contradictions') in the evaluation of brain and head 'segmentation' of insects. Taking into consideration the great variety of segmental differentiation among even presumably 'closely related' vertebrates, and leading to the concept of allomeric kathomologies (cf. vol. 1, chapter III of this series), I believe that FERRIS may have overstressed the significance of such 'segmentation' and of the therefrom resulting 'contradictions'. Many of the problems pertaining to a correlation of mesodermal 'head segmentation' and of 'brain segmentation' in annelids and arthropods as well as in the vertebrates seem to represent 'undecidable questions' of secondary significance which, at least for the present, may be ignored in a conveniently simplified and yet sufficiently rigorous and consistent presentation of invertebrate and vertebrate configuration adapted to the needs of vertebrate comparative neurologists.

Yet, regardless of the 'segmentation' problem, FERRIS' argumentation concerning 'protocerebrum' and 'deutocerebrum' has some definite merits, as can easily be seen if, e.g., Figure 98 is scrutinized. It is evident that a good point can be made for designating the antennal lobe (deutocerebrum) as protocerebrum, and the brain region connected with the compound eyes and optic neuropilemes (protocerebrum) as deutocerebrum in the rostro-caudal sequence (cf. also Figs. 72 B, C, 83 A, and 90). However, being essentially a *'vertebrate'* neurologist, I prefer not to entangle myself into a knotty issue of (more or less arbitrary) terminology and evaluation that concerns primarily *invertebrate* neurobiologists and morphologists.

In some crustaceans, although protocerebrum and deutocerebrum are present, no fusion of these parts with tritocerebrum has taken place. Such crustacean forms have thus no syncerebrum. Most other crustaceans, however, have a syncerebrum consisting of the three parts.

Some crustaceans, such as Isopoda ('wood lice', 'sow bugs', Oniscus, Porcellio, or the aquatic Asellus) and Amphipoda ('beachflea', Gammarus) do not possess corpora pedunculata. This lack may be interpreted as a secondary reduction.

In decapods with normal eyes the corpora pedunculata are located within the lobus opticus or eye stalk (Fig. 85 II), in a position somewhat different from that in insects (Fig. 85 I)[23]. In decapods with rudimentary eyes, however, the corpora pedunculata assume their usual position between the lobus opticus and the pars intercerebralis (Fig. 85 III). HANSTRÖM (1928) suggests that the displacement of the corpora pedunculata into the eye-stalks of some Malacostraca, and their withdrawal from the rest of the protocerebrum, is related to their increasingly intimate connections with the optic system of these animals. When the role of the corpora pedunculata for optic 'associations' decreases *pari passu* with a reduction of the visual sensory apparatus, and, on the other hand, the olfactory centers manifest a higher degree of development, the corpora pedunculata, by a secondary displacement, may have migrated back into the main portion of the brain.

---

[23] Because of this peculiar location, some authors failed to recognize the presence of corpora pedunculata in such decapods. However, BELLONCI (1882) had already properly identified these structures, and HANSTRÖM (1928 and previous publications) thoroughly clarified the relevant morphologic relationships.

In these latter forms with rudimentary eyes, the corpora pedunculata would then, to a larger extent, represent secondary olfactory centers, since olfactory neurons of the second order end in their neuropileme. The peduncular synaptic glomeruli provide a connection, or an exchange, between olfactory and optic system, e.g. between olfactory neurons of the second order, and optic neurons of the fourth order.

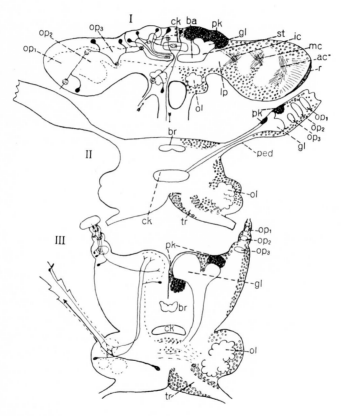

Figure 85. Comparison of decapod crustacean brains with an insect brain. (From K., 1927). I. Frontal section through insect brain (Hymennoptera) simplified after VON ALTEN, 1910, and ZIEGLER, 1920. II. Similar section through brain of decapod crustacean with normal eyes (Carcinus maenas). III. Corresponding section through brain of decapod (Calocaris McAndreae) with rudimentary eyes. II. and III. simplified after HANSTRÖM, 1925. ac: external chiasma; ba: stalk of corpora pedunculata; br: protocerebral bridge; ck: central body; gl: globulus; ic: inner chiasma; lo: optic lobe; lp: lobus protocerebralis; mc: middle chiasma; ol: olfactory lobe; op 1, 2, 3: optic centers; ped: pedunculus lobi optici; pk: corpora pedunculata; r: retina; st: stalk; tr: tritencephalon.

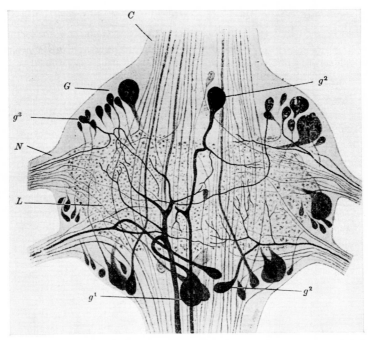

Figure 86. Third abdominal ganglion of crayfish Astacus, as seen with methylene-blue technique. (After Retzius, 1890, from R. Hertwig, 1912.) C: longitudinal connective; G, g: various types of nerve cells; L: neuropil; N: peripheral nerve.

This, of course, is an oversimplification, since numerous other connections and circuits are doubtless involved. A 'center' such as the corpora pedunculata, correlating and processing input from at least two important senses (photoreceptors and presumably chemoreceptors), must evidently be of considerable significance for the animal's behavior[24].

---

[24] The sense organs of crustaceans consist of eyes, statocysts, proprioceptive receptors, general tactile receptors, and chemoreceptors. The eyes are of two types, simpler median eyes, and compound eyes. A median eye is formed by three or four small pigmented ocelli of the inverse type (that is, with photoreceptors whose nerve fibers originate on the side exposed to the light). A median eye characterizes the nauplius larva, and is thus frequently called a nauplius eye. It may either degenerate or persist in the adult. Chemoreceptors are present in appendages, such as antennae, antennules, and others, and might be loosely called 'olfactory'. It is possible that additional receptors (e. g. thermoreceptors, and receptors to water pressure) are present at least in some crustaceans (cf. the summary by Barnes, 1963).

The ventral nerve cords of crustacea and their ganglia have been particularly studied in decapods. The ganglia usually give origin to three pairs of peripheral nerves, of which an anterior and a posterior one are lateral, and a ventral one, which originates from the connective at the caudal end of the ganglion. All three nerves are mixed, that is, contain afferent and efferent components.

Figures 86 and 87 show the general structure of an abdominal ganglion in the crayfish Astacus. Although the nerve cells are predominantly of the unipolar type described above (p.77), bipolar as well as multipolar neuronal elements have been found.

Motor fibers may leave the ganglia through the homolateral or, crossing the midline, through the contralateral nerves. Giant cells and neurochords (cf. Figs. 86 to 88) are likewise present in crustaceans. Such neurochords can be medial longitudinal, lateral, and segmental,

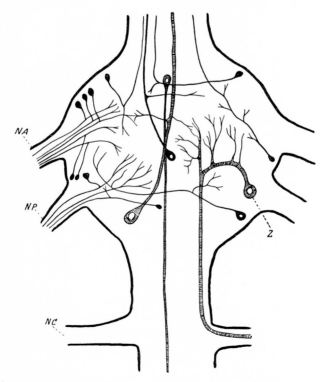

Figure 87. Second abdominal ganglion of crayfish Astacus. (Simplified after methylene-blue preparations depicted by Retzius, 1890, from Hanström, 1928.) Na and NP: anterior and posterior nerve; NC: nervus ventralis; Z: large ganglion cell with extensive dendrites.

as well as primary motor, leaving the central nervous system through a peripheral nerve.

JOHNSON (1924) has described some significant features displayed by the peculiar arrangement of the neurochords or giant fibers of decapod crustaceans. This system was subsequently studied in great detail with respect to the physiologic processes of nerve impulse transmission (ADELMAN and DALTON, 1960; WATANABE and GRUND-FEST, 1961, and many other authors). The term 'ephapse', supposedly supplementing the concept 'synapse', is here used by some neurophysiologists to designate all such functionally significant neural 'discontinuities' where exclusively 'electric events' are presumed to be involved in the process of excitation-transmission.

The medial pair of neurochords originates in the brain. These giant fibers decussate, whereby the two axons come in direct 'ephaptic' contact with each other, and then run, without branching, from the brain to the caudal ganglion. In the various thoracic and abdominal ganglia, motoneurons have presumably polarized contact with said giant fibers.

The lateral giant fibers display a segmental arrangement (Figs. 88 A, B) which may somewhat differ in accordance with the various crustacean forms. Commissural antimeric intrasegmental connections by means of axonal fibers have been described. Again, these neurochords have synaptic or perhaps merely protosynaptic connections with motoneurons. As regards the segmental arrangement, the metameric units are separated by septa (Fig. 88 B) which, roughly speaking, are presumably similar to those found in the neurochords of Lumbricus (cf. above p. 80), and may represent inherently 'protosynaptic' structures.

The perhaps essentially glial septa have a thickness of about 2μ and display a lamellated structure, as well as an 'ultrastructural' fenestration. Within these fenestrations, the axoplasmic components of the two separated units may reach a propinquity of about 100 Å (DE LORENZO, 1960; ROBERTSON, 1961).

A third group of giant fibers, as mentioned above, is represented by the axons of large motoneurons reaching the peripheral effectors.

With respect to the total number of nerve cells in the crustacean central nervous system, WIERSMA (1957) assumes, on the basis of his calculations, $9 \cdot 10^4$ as the order of magnitude obtaining for the decapod Procambarus clarkii. Of this number, about 75 000 nerve cells may be located in the brain (without peripheral optic ganglia), perhaps 1000 large cells in the subesophageal ganglion, and the

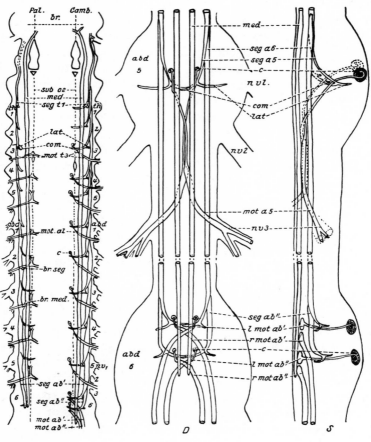

Fig. 88 A

remainder in the thoracic and abdominal ganglionic chain. In a pharyngeal connective, about 2000 fibers were counted, in a thoracic connective
approximately 3000 fibers were found, and about 1000 in an abdominal
connective. HUBER (1963) remarks: 'Kennzeichnend für das ZNS der
Arthropoden ist die geringe Zahl der Neurone.' Yet, relatively little
is known with certainty about cell numbers in other crustaceans and
in the insect CNS. Some preliminary data on these latter arthropods
will be discussed further below (p.174), but, because of considerable
methodologic difficulties in obtaining satisfactory counts of the
crowded and compact cell populations in the insect brain, the reliability
of these figures remains questionable. The overall range of my own

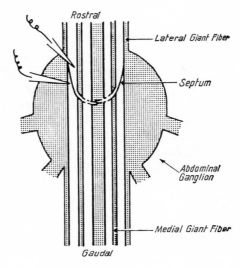

Fig. 88 B

Figure 88. Diagrams of neurochord arrangements in the crustaceans Palaemonetes, Cambarus (A), and Procambarus (B). *A* on left, general aspect in Palaemonetes (Pal.) and Cambarus (Camb.); D: dorsal view in Cambarus; S: lateral view in Cambarus; abd 5 and 6 refers to the corresponding abdominal ganglia; com: commissural branch; other abbreviations not relevant in present context. (After JOHNSON, 1924, from HANSTRÖM, 1928.) *B* Giant fiber system in Procambarus, as it appears in transilluminated preparations. The two lateral giant fibers (about 100 μ in diameter) are distinguished from the medial ones by the presence of septa which are interpreted as dividing these axons into autonomous segmental units. The commissural branches have been drawn on the basis of combined histologic and electrophysiologic data. Microelectrodes are shown as inserted on both sides of the septum in a lateral giant fiber. (After WATANABE and GRUNDFEST, 1961.)

crude first approximation in some insects might, roughly speaking, be regarded as corresponding to the figures suggested by WIERSMA.

Concerning peripheral innervation, TONNER (1933) has described a peripheral network of multipolar nerve cells in the crayfish Astacus fluviatilis; this net, designated as integumental nervous system ('Hautnervensystem'), is said to extend over the whole body of the animal ('das sich über den ganzen Krebs hinzieht').

The innervation of the viscera is provided from the tritocerebral pharyngeal connectives through the nerves of the stomatogastric system, as well as from the thoracic ganglia by nerves for the heart, and particularly from the last abdominal ganglion by nerves for the posterior part of the intestinal tract. These nerves are connected with a plexus located in the wall of the gastrointestinal tract, and containing nerve cells. Many of the relevant data are still insufficiently clarified.

The heart ganglion in a variety of crustaceans has been studied in great detail, particularly as regards functional aspects (MAYNARD, 1960; HAGIWARA, 1961). In Decapoda, this ganglion is located within the dorsal wall of the myocard, and contains 9 nerve cells (5 larger ones, and 4 smaller ones). If the ganglion is extirpated, the heartbeat comes to a standstill. Thus, the myocardial heart activity of these crustaceans is said to be 'neurogenic'. The activity of the heart ganglion, in turn, becomes modulated by the extracardial nerves.

In crustaceans, hormones are present in some parts of the central nervous system, and HANSTRÖM (1931) discovered in decapods the first neurosecretory cells recorded in invertebrates. Besides some neurosecretory cells in the brain, two glandular structures, HANSTRÖM'S, x-organ (1934), and the sinus gland, likewise described by that author, are related to neurosecretory activity. The sinus gland is usually found within the eye stalk and is associated with a central blood cavity; the x-organ, likewise in the eye-stalk, is believed to be formed by cells of a displaced and modified eye-papilla. Sinus gland and x-organ are considered components of a neuroendocrine system (cf. also HANSTRÖM, 1937a, b).

After transection of the tract from the x-organ to the sinus gland, there occurs initially a depletion of neurosecretory material at the site of the cut, followed later by a complete regeneration of the sinus gland. Removal of the entire eye stalk leads to increased respiration, a fall in respiratory quotient and water intake. These changes do not occur when the sinus gland alone is removed, thus leaving intact and functional those neurosecretory cells in the brain, which produce the effective hormones. There are perhaps at least three different types of secretory nerve cells, and at least three chromatophoric hormones and other substances exerting an influence on the pigments of the eye are said to be formed in the optic centers. In addition there are neurosecretory substances regulating molting[25], and calcium as well as water metabolism (cf. ORTMANN's review, 1960).

Generally speaking, the significant functions controlled by hormones in crustaceans are: color change, retinal pigment migration,

---

[25] The molting of arthropods is considered further below, in connection with a discussion of insects, on pages 130 and 200.

growth and molting, metabolism, and maintenance of secondary sex characters. The metabolic changes observed after experimental interference with the normal pattern of endocrine activities concern sugar, calcium, phosphorus, water metabolism, and rate of oxygen consumption. Some of these activities appear interrelated and, moreover, controlled by additional non-endocrine factors. It is obvious that, because of this complexity, certain effects observed after experimental disturbance of the endocrine system, e. g. alteration of heart rate, of locomotor activity, and of 'viability', defy attempts at a proper abstract, semantic formulation, and are therefore 'not yet clearly understood' (B. SCHARRER, 1953).

Diplopoda (millipedes), *Chilopoda* (centipedes), as well as the smaller groups[26] *Pauropoda* and *Symphyla* represent four 'classes' comprising the arthropod subphylum *Myriapoda*.

Diplopoda (also known as Chilognatha), of which about 8000 species have been described, display doubled trunk segments with two pairs of legs each. These animals, living in dark places beneath stones, leaves or logs, are slow and, 'mechanically', relatively defenseless. Some species can roll up into a ball, or coil, while others, however, secrete, when disturbed, a poisonous, repellent fluid or spray containing a mixture of hydrogen cyanide and benzaldehyde, ejected through lateral gland openings called foramina repugnatoria. Additional components of these 'chemical warfare' combat substances may be quinone, and iodine, the secretion being whitish or brown. This defense mechanism causes attacking ants to withdraw in a state of considerable excitement, and the ants can then be seen to perform cleansing movements. If the secretion has been exhausted by repeated previous stimulations, the millipedes become very susceptible to attack by ants[27].

---

[26] Pauropoda are minute animals, about 0.5 to 2 mm long, found in soil and forest debris, and of widely scattered geographical distributions. About 60 species may have been described.

Symphyla, a 'class' with a likewise small number of species, and similar type of habitat, are slightly larger (up to 10 mm), and resemble centipedes. Eyes are missing. Some biologists believe that symphylans may be related to an 'ancestral' insect form.

[27] Repellent substances secreted as a defense mechanism, are, of course, not restricted to Diplopoda, and, as is well known, can even be found in mammals (skunk: Mephitis mephitis, etc.). Defensive secretions are not uncommon among insects. About thirty different chemical compounds, particularly benzoquinones, have been reported as present in these secretions of insects and related arthropods (ROTH, L. M. and EISNER, T.: Chemical defenses of arthropods. Ann. Rev. Entomol. 7: 107–134, 1960).

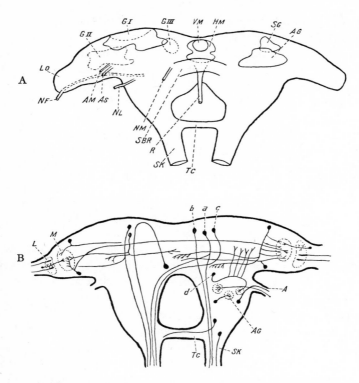

Figure 89. Brain of the diplopode Julus. (After HOLMGREN from HANSTRÖM, 1928.) *A* Brain viewed from the rostral and inferior side. Ag: antennal glomeruli; Am, As: efferent and afferent antennal nerves; GI-III: globuli; Hm: posterior median body; Lo: lobus opticus; Nf: nerve of frontal organ; Nl and Nm: labral nerves; R: recurrent nerve; Sbr: so-called stomodeal bridge; Sg: stalk glomeruli; Sk: pharyngeal connective; Tc: tritocerebral commissure; Vm: anterior median body. *B* Neuronal connections as seen in GOLGI pictures. A: antennal nerve; L: lamina optica; M: medulla optica; a, b, c, d: various neurons; other abbreviations as in Fig. 89 A. It should be noted that, in contradistinction to crustaceans and insects, the hitherto examined myriapods are provided with only two optic centers (L and M, cf. also Figs. 90 and 91). The internal optic neuropileme (op₃ Fig. 85) is apparently lacking.

The brain (Figs. 89, 90) is relatively well developed, although less differentiated than that of insects, and is provided with large antennal glomeruli. The antennae are supplied with at least tactile receptors and chemoreceptors. The animals tap the surrounding ground with their antennae as they move along. Eyes may be entirely lacking or be represented by two or even many (up to 80) ocelli. In Julus, the ocelli

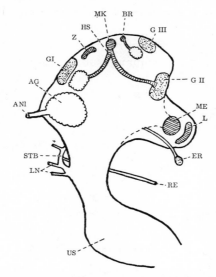

Figure 90. Diagram of diplopod brain (Julus) seen in lateral view. (After HOLMGREN from HANSTRÖM, 1928.) Ag: antennal glomeruli; ANl: antennal nerve; Br: protocerebral bridge; GI-III: globuli; ER: frontal organ; HS: main peduncle of globuli; L: lamina; Ln: labral nerves; Me: medulla; Mk: median body; Re: nervus recurrens; Stb: stomodeal bridge; Us: subesophageal ganglion; Z: central body.

are clustered into a sort of approximation to a compound eye, with a common layer of 'cornea'[28].

As regards the ventral nerve cord, there is a rope-ladder system with two pairs of ganglia (each pair fusing in the midline) within each diplosegment.

Chilopoda (centipedes) may have rather long, slender antennae, and the appendages of this first trunk segment become a large pair of poison claws, used in feeding. Tropical centipedes of the genus Scolopendra can reach the length of one foot and are dangerous to man. Scolopendridae have four small ocelli on each side, Lithobiomorphae and others display a bilateral group of ocelli resembling a compound eye. Various forms are eyeless. On the whole, the brain (Figs. 91, 92) appears

---

[28] Many diplopods (but not Julus), as well as some chilopods and symphylans possess a pair of sensory pits, located behind the base of each antenna, and containing a cluster of sensory cells. The significance of this structure, designated as TÖMÖSVARY's organ, is unknown. Its nerve has been traced to the medullae of the lateral 'optic lobe'. Julus possesses a group of cutaneous sensory cells located behind the eye, and connected with pars intercerebralis (HANSTRÖM, 1928).

somewhat similar, but perhaps less differentiated than that of the diplopod Julus.

The ventral nerve cord is of the rope-ladder type with a fusion of the first three ganglia to a common subesophageal ganglion in Scolopendra.

The cerebral ganglia of *Symphyla* (Scolopendrella) appear reduced particularly because of the lack of eyes. *Pauropoda* may be more closely related to the diplopods than to the other myriapods, and possess a nervous system roughly similar to that of all myriapod groups in general.

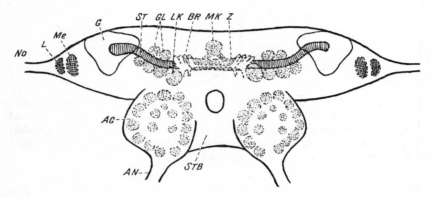

Figure 91. Brain of chilopod Lithobius as seen from the anterior side. (From HAN-STRÖM, 1928.) Ag, An, Br, L, Me, Mk, Stb, Z, as in Fig. 90. G: globulus; Gl: glomeruli; Lk: lateral body; No: optic nerve.

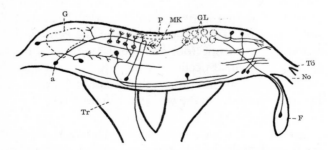

Figure 92. Neuronal connections in brain of Lithobius as seen in GOLGI preparations. (Simplified after HOLMGREN from HANSTRÖM, 1928.) F: frontal organ; P: protocerebral bridge; Tö: TÖMÖSVARY's nerve; a: neuron of globulus with dendrites in stalked glomeruli; other abbreviations as in preceding figure (Tr: tritocerebrum).

9. Arthropoda: Hexapoda,
Including Some Remarks Concerning Various Aspects
of Insect Behavioral Activities

Insecta (Hexapoda) represent, in many respects, the most important class of arthropods. There are more kinds of insects than of all other animals, or, for that matter, of all other terrestrial organic beings ('animals' and 'plants') combined. Although somewhat less than a million insect species are now said to have been described in published biologic literature, some estimates assume several million of actually existing insect species. The orders containing the greatest number of species are Coleoptera (beetles; about 200000), Lepidoptera (butterflies, moths; about 95000), Hymenoptera (bees, wasps, ants; about 80000), Homoptera (cicadas, scale insects, aphids; about 75000), and Diptera (flies, mosquitoes, gnats; about 70000). These figures, compiled only a few years ago, may now be significantly larger. In addition, perhaps 28 to 30 further different orders can be recognized, of which Heteroptera (true bugs, 'water boatmen'; about 20000 species), and Orthoptera (grasshoppers, crickets, roaches; about 18000 species) might here be mentioned.

Insects can be distinguished from other arthropods by the presence of three pairs of legs, pertaining, one each, to three thoracic segments. Numerous insects also display two pairs of wings, connected with second and third thoracic segments. Again, one pair may be rudimentary. Head, thorax and abdomen, this latter with six to eleven segments, are quite distinct. The head displays one pair of antennae, and three pairs of very polymorphous jaw-elements, biting or sucking (labrum with mandibula; maxilla I; labium with maxilla II). A simplified diagram representing the morphologic pattern of a 'generalized' insect is shown in Figure 93.

Insects, like other Arthropoda, do not possess an internal skeleton, whose supporting function is here performed by the integument, provided with a hard cuticle (exoskeleton), containing chitin (a nitrogenous polysaccharide acetate), and other hard material. At the joints, the integument is pliable. Growth and other biologic events are correlated with periodic shedding of the cuticle; this process is called molting or ecdysis.

Ontogenetic development in what are considered 'primitive' forms proceeds directly, the young animals being only miniature adults. In other forms the larval stages differ from the adult one, but all stages are

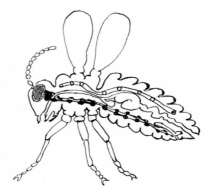

Figure 93. Diagram of a 'generalized insect'. The sketch shows, in sequence, dorsal heart tube, intermediate gut, and ventral nerve cord (black); genital opening rostroventral to anal opening. Further explanations in text.

active (incomplete metamorphosis). In 'higher' forms, with complete metamorphosis, there is an active *larval* stage, an inactive *pupal* stage, and the active adult or *imago* stage.

Insect metamorphosis is of considerable biologic interest[29]. It consists of three histological processes: total destruction of the most specialized larval structures; completely new construction of the most specialized organs of the adult from embryonic histoblasts; and reconstruction *in situ* of the less specialized and more plastic organs and cells (WIGGLESWORTH, 1954). These three processes are superimposed and intermingled in varying degree in different insects (PÉREZ, 1910; WIGGLESWORTH, 1954). Embryonic primordia for adult structures are

---

[29] Depending on non-occurrence, occurence, and type ot 'metamorphosis', insects can be classified as Ametabola, Hemimetabola, and Holometabola, with additional subdivisions (e.g. Paurometabola with 'slight' metamorphosis, and Hypermetabola with four or more distinguishable larval stages). There are thus eggs, larvae with different stages, pupae, and adults or imagines. The periods between moults are 'stadia', and the form of an insect between moults is an instar. A 'nymph' is an immature instar of a paurometabolous insect, and a chrysalis (or chrysalid) is the naked pupa of some Lepidoptera. A cocoon is the protective covering of a pupa, such, e.g., as is spun (with a single continuous thread of silk) by Bombyx mori (Lepidoptera).

Again, the external similarity between a caterpillar and an annelid worm is striking, and can be loosely regarded as suggestive of the arthropods' assumed annelid ancestry. Yet, the spectacular observable and thus actual transformation from caterpillar to imago involves a large number of highly intricate complicating aspects and factors.

present at the larval stage in the more or less compact matrices forming the so-called imaginal discs.

The destructive processes during metamorphosis are histolysis and phagocytosis; in this latter phase, the histolysing tissue elements are removed and digested by blood cells. In some forms, autolysis takes place with little or no phagocytosis.

As far as the nervous system is concerned, the metamorphic changes in the peripheral nervous system are said to proceed more rapidly than those in the central nervous system where the transitions appear to be somewhat more gradual. In the central nervous system, histolysis, particularly studied by SANCHEZ (1923, 1925, 1927), goes hand in hand with histogenetic and proliferative processes. The brain of the larvae, as a rule, is much less differentiated than that of the imagines. Central body, various glomeruli, and most components of the corpora pedunculata may be entirely lacking. However, considerable differences do, in this respect, characterize the various taxonomic groups.

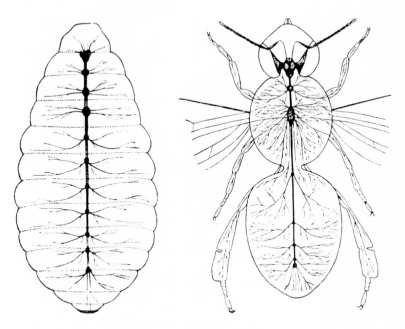

Figure 94. Nervous system in larva (left) and imago (right) of worker bee. (After BLANCHARD, 1846, from PLATE, 1922.) These instructive diagrams, however, do not adequately indicate the double aspect of the longitudinal connectives.

SANCHEZ (1925) and HANSTRÖM (1928) distinguish, in this connection, the following types of neural elements in caterpillars of Lepidoptera: (a) elements fully developed in the larva, and subserving important larval biological functions; these elements are said to disappear, through the histolytic process, during metamorphosis; (b) embryonic elements which do not form definite centers in the larva, and do not have specific functions, but represent the matrix for the formation of new centers; (c) to these two types pointed out by SANCHEZ, HANSTRÖM adds such elements which are already fully functional in the larva, and persist, without significant transitional changes, in the imago.

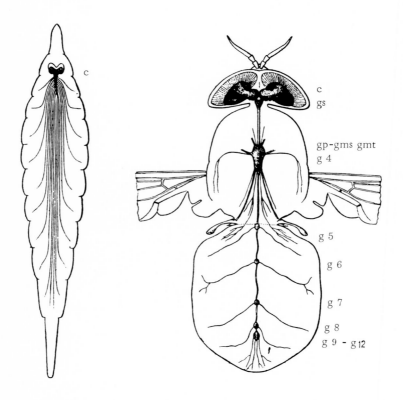

Figure 95. Nervous system in larva (left), and imago (right) of female fly Stratiomys longicornis. (After KÜNCKEL D'HERCULAIS from PLATE, 1922.) c: brain; gp, gms, gmt: ganglia of pro-, meso-, and metathorax, fused with g4; g4–12: abdominal ganglia; gs: subesophageal ganglion.

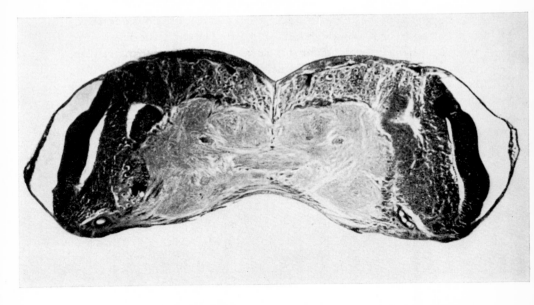

Figure 96. Cross section through the brain in a fairly advanced larva of the butterfly Pieris brassicae. (From HANSTRÖM, 1928.) On the lateral side the imaginal discs for the optic centers can be seen. Within the neuropilem vague outlines of central body and peduncular stalks are noticeable.

The gross changes occurring during metamorphosis can be visualized by comparing Figures 94 and 95. A section through a larval Lepidoptera brain with imaginal discs is shown in Figure 96. It will be noted that in one instance the imaginal nervous system is more concentrated than the larval one, while in another instance the opposite is the case. Greater concentration in the imago than in the larva, however, can perhaps be regarded as the far more common type of change.

In the course of growth and development, cessation or inhibition of these activities may occur. A period of suppressed development is designated as *diapause*, which may be temporary, prolonged, or complete. One may distinguish between growth and differentiation (combined as 'development' in the wider sense), and behavioral activity in the narrower sense, not related to 'development'. Cessation of behavioral activity *sensu strictiori* (such, e.g. as in hibernation) is called kinetopause.

The *central nervous system* of adult insects displays various degrees of concentration or fusion of ganglia (Fig. 97). The three subdivisions of the brain, namely protocerebrum, deutocerebrum, and tritocerebrum are structurally well distinguishable, although, in some forms, because of a considerable degree of fusion, the surface configuration may not display conspicuous limits.

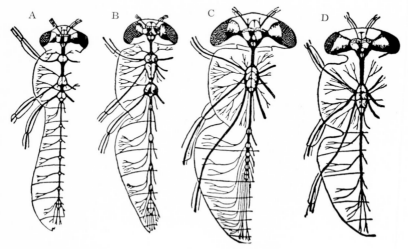

Figure 97. The nervous system of four species of flies with various degrees of ganglionic fusion. (After BRAND, and LANG's textbook, 1888, from HERRICK, 1924.) *A* Chironomus plumosus. *B* Empis stercorea. *C* Tabanus bovinus. *D* Sarcophaga carnaria.

The protocerebrum is connected with the ocelli and the compound eyes, the deutocerebrum innervates the antennae, and the tritocerebrum supplies the labrum as well as part of the integument. The stomatogastric system also originates from the tritocerebrum. The subesophageal ganglion supplies maxilla I and labium with maxilla II. The location and general shape of an insect brain in lateral view is shown by Figure 98.

HANSTRÖM (1940) has published an extensive monograph dealing with incretory organs, sense organs, and nervous structures of the head in numerous lower insect orders.

As regards the ventral nerve cord with its ganglia in various stages of fusion and concentration, the observed series can be interpreted as manifesting, in numerous instances, the tendency of a forward migration.

The overall pattern of the peripheral nerves arising from thoracic and abdominal ganglia can be seen in Figures 94 and 97. Considerable variability seems to obtain, not only among different orders and species of insects, but also among individuals of one and the same species, with regard to details in the arrangement of peripheral nerves. Thus, in one species, two bundles of motor fibers with different distribution may leave a ganglion as a single root, and as two separate roots in another, closely related species. Again, bundles of fibers to individual muscles may leave a ganglion as completely independent nerves, but may arise from a large common nerve root in other species. Finally, the remarkable degree of variability in the details of nerve distribution patterns in different individuals of the same species as well as in different segments of the same individual should again be stressed. A summarizing review on the comparative anatomy of peripheral nerves in insects was presented by SCHMITT (1962), and some additional details can be found in specific studies by MAKI (1936), PIPA and COOK (1959) and SCHMITT (1959).

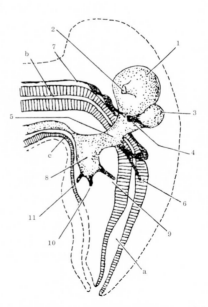

Figure 98. Diagram showing topographic relationships of brain and head in the cockroach Periplaneta; lateral view. (From BECCARI, 1947.) 1: Protocerebrum; 2: optic peduncle; 3: deutocerebrum; 4: antennal nerves; 5: tritocerebrum; 6: labral nerve; 7: stomatogastric nerve; 8: subesophageal ganglion; 9: mandibular nerve; 10, 11: nerves of first and second maxilla; a: buccal cavity; b: esophagus; c: duct of salivary gland.

Among older and pioneering studies emphasizing the functional aspects of insect and invertebrate central ganglia in general, and their relationship to peripheral innervation, the investigations of BIEDER-MANN (1891), under whom I studied physiology in Jena, and of STEINER (1898) might be mentioned.

The visceral nervous system is provided by the stomatogastric nerves which form an unpaired nervus recurrens taking its course along the dorsal wall of the esophagus (Fig. 98). A caudal system of visceral nerves originates from the last abdominal ganglion. Small ganglia and groups of nerve cells are said to be present in the wall of the intestinal tract and of other viscera.

The *insect brain*, whose essential features are rather similar to those of the crustacean brain (Fig. 85), contains a number of distinct structures which will be enumerated further below. As generally in articulates, the bodies of the nerve cells form a more or less continuous peripheral layer (in this respect somewhat 'cortex'-like), enclosing a central mass of fibers and neuropilemes. CAJAL and SANCHEZ (1915) believe that this location of cell bodies might be related to the mode of nutrition of organs in insects. Since there are no capillaries in the brain, the peripheral position of cell bodies is of 'advantage' for a close contact with the haemolymph. Various regions of this cellular layer display characteristics of cell size and to a certain extent also of shape.

The following configurations can be regarded as the main sub-divisions of the brain (Figs. 99 to 105):

(a) *Corpora pedunculata*, which may be provided with up to three globuli each. The darkly staining and crowded globuli cells usually surround the cup-like calyces or globuli, in which synaptic connections are provided. The globuli form stalks that, as a general rule, extend in different planes. One of these stalks, the inner root, is frequently referred to as 'Balken' in German terminology (e. g. HANSTRÖM, 1928). This designation, also rendered as corpus callosum, might, however, cause confusion, since it is here applied to a system of presumably synaptic connections (neuropilemes). DUJARDIN (1850) was perhaps the first author describing the mushroom bodies of insects.

According to VOWLES (1955), the corpora pedunculata of bees and ants (Fig. 104) consist of four lobes, namely two calyces, an alpha lobe, and a beta lobe. Fibers originating from cells in calyces are said to give off three branches, one to its calyx, one to the alpha lobe, and one to the beta lobe. The calyces and the alpha lobe receive tracts from all the sensory centers of the brain. The beta lobe sends tracts to the 'motor

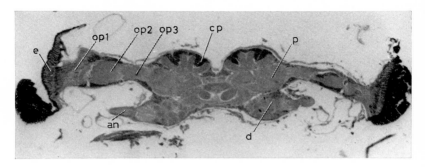

Figure 99. Cross section through the brain of the cockroach Periplaneta americana. (Original; × 38; red. $^2/_3$; hematoxylin-eosin.) an: antennal nerve; cp: corpora pedunculata; d: deutocerebrum; e: retinulae of compound eye; op 1, 2, 3: external, middle, and internal optic neuropileme; p: protocerebral lobe.

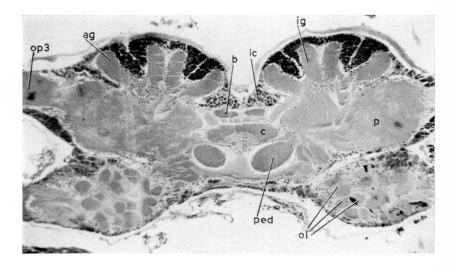

Figure 100. Cross section through the brain of the cockroach Periplaneta americana, showing additional details. (Original; × 100; red. $^2/_3$; hematoxylin-eosin.) ag: external globulus; b: protocerebral bridge; c: central body; ic: pars intercerebralis; ig: internal globulus; ol: antennal (olfactory) glomeruli; ped: stalk of corpora pedunculata; (other abbreviations as in preceding figure). Figs. 99 and 100 should be compared with the external configuration shown in Fig. 98.

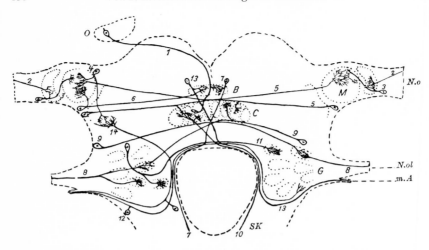

Figure 101. Diagram of neuronal connections in the brain of Periplaneta according to BRETSCHNEIDER, 1914. (From PLATE, 1922.) B: protocerebral bridge; C: central body; G: antennal (olfactory) glomeruli; M: internal optic medulla (neuropileme). ma: motor antennal nerve; N.o: optic stalk; O: ocellus; SK: pharyngeal connective; 1–14 diverse neurons.

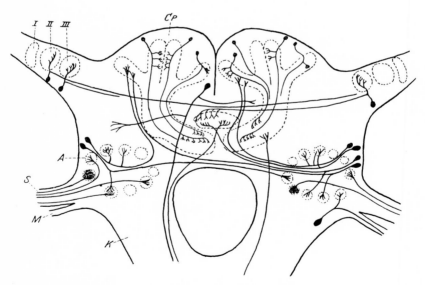

Figure 102. Diagram of neuronal connections in the brain of Periplaneta according to HANSTRÖM. (From HANSTRÖM, 1928.) I–III: optic neuropilemes; A: antennal glomeruli; Cp: corpora pedunculata with stalks; K: pharyngeal connective; M, S: motor and sensory antennal nerve; the large neuron of pars intercerebralis sending a neurite into the pharyngeal connective should be noted.

regions'. The cited author states that excitations from calyx and alpha lobe may interact, and that 'excitation passing down from beta lobe may be the result of their interaction'.

It is, in some instances, difficult to ascertain whether a terminal arborization of an insect or arthropod nerve cell should be considered presynaptic (neurite) or postsynaptic (dendrite), and the direction of the nervous pulse flow, as indicated in diagrams such as Figures 85, 101,

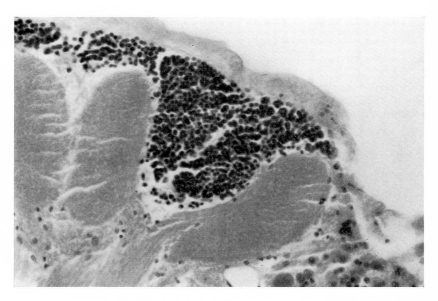

Figure 103. Internal globulus of Periplaneta. The fiber bundle forming the peduncle is recognizable; on the right, larger cells of pars intercerebralis. (Original; × 370; red. $^2/_3$; hematoxylin-eosin.)

102, 104, and others, although quite probable, can not be regarded certain. Yet, there seems to be little reason to doubt that these neuronal connections in the insect brain may, on the whole, represent true synapses. With respect to specific details of function one might agree with VOWLES' comment (1955): 'It is indeed apparent that although we have a detailed knowledge of the histology of the corpora pedunculata, our ignorance of their function remains very great'.

(b) The *central body* or *central complex* is a median, bilaterally symmetric structure and consists of several components, representing glome-

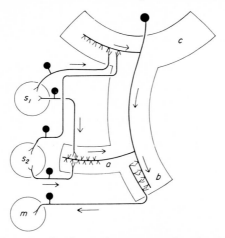

Figure 104. Connections of an insect (bee or ant) pedunculated body neuron. (After VOWLES, 1955, from ROEDER, 1963.) a: alpha lobe; b: beta lobe; c: calyx; m: motor system; s 1, 2: sensory (optic, antennal) systems.

rular synaptic connections[30]. It is an important correlation center connected with various parts of the brain. In contradistinction to insects, the central body of crustaceans is said to be a single, non-sub-divided structure.

(c) The *protocerebral bridge* is likewise a median, bilaterally symmetric glomerular structure. It is connected with the optic system, the central complex, the antennal glomeruli and other parts of the brain[31].

(d) The *lateral optic lobes* are connected with the compound eyes. The optic input from retinulae, whose sensory cells, in contradistinction to those of the retina in the vertebrate lateral eye, are directed toward the light, is transmitted over at least three additional neurons in series. Analogies with the optic system of cephalopods and with the vertebrate retina will be pointed out further below in section 12, page 263. There are three groups of neuropilemes, the outer ('lamina ganglionaris',

[30] The designation 'central body' refers to the fact that this presumably synaptic structure, which lacks a well-defined correlated cell-group, is located in the midst of fiber masses and neuropilemes. According to POWER (1943), the subdivisions of the central complex are: (1) the central body proper, also called fan-shaped body, which is the largest component; (2) the ellipsoid body (appearing circular in true transverse sections), located within the anterior concavity of the 'fan-shaped body'; (3) a pair of ventral and posterior ventral tubercles, representing spherical glomeruli.

[31] In Drosophila (order Diptera), the protocerebral bridge is said to be 'interrupted by a cleft in the median line of the animal' (POWER, 1946).

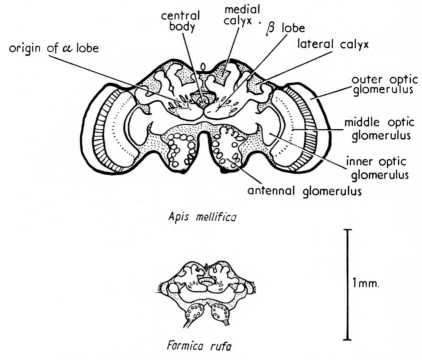

Figure 105. Diagram comparing the brain of a bee with that of an ant. (From VOWLES, 1955.)

external glomerulus), the middle (medulla externa, middle glomerulus), and the internal (medulla interna, internal glomerulus), which may show further subdivisions. Two conspicuous crossings of optic fibers, the chiasma externum and the chiasma internum, are displayed between outer neuropileme and medulla externa, and between medulla externa and interna respectively[32]. One visual fiber comes from each of the usually seven or eight retinular cells contained within a single

---

[32] In Drosophila, the external chiasma fibers cross from anterior to posterior location and vice-versa, and in the internal chiasma a crossing from ventral to dorsal location, and vice-versa, takes place, as described by POWER (1946). Again, decussating fibers between the internal glomerulus and the protocerebral lobe have been occasionally designated as internal chiasma (Fig. 85, I), whereby the internal chiasma between middle glomerulus and internal glomerulus would become the 'middle chiasma'. Including the local chiasmata, one might then, from retinulae (lateral) to protocerebral lobe (medial) enumerate altogether four chiasmata: (1) local, (2) external, (3) internal *sensu strictiori* or middle *sensu latiori*, (4) internal *sensu latiori*.

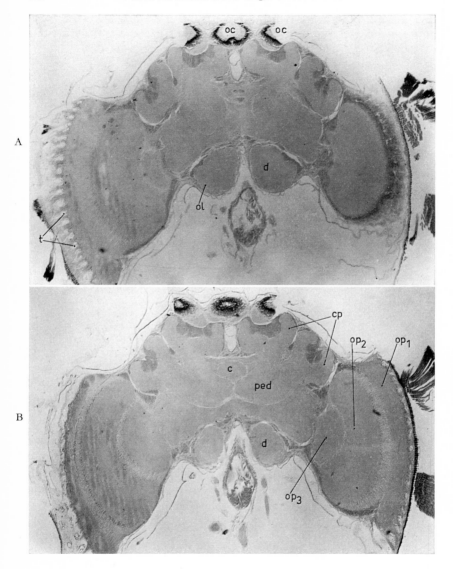

Figs. 106 A and B

Figure 106 A to *D*. Configuration of brain in Bombus (A–C) and in worker bee (D) as seen in serial transverse sections. (Original; × 65; red. $^2/_3$; hematoxylin-eosin.) an: antennal nerve; b: protocerebral bridge; c: central body; cp: corpora pedunculata;

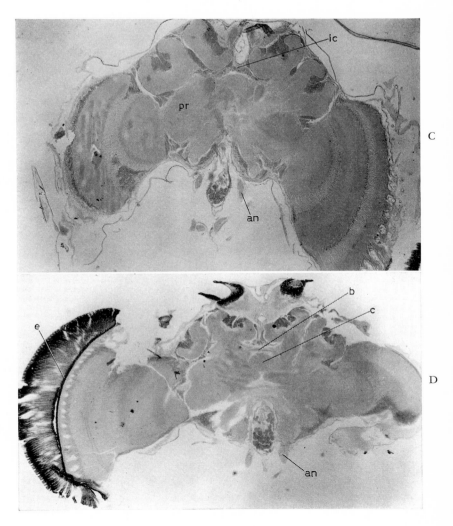

Figs. 106 C and D

d: deutocerebrum; e: retinulae of compound eye; ic: pars intercerebralis; oc: ocellus; ol: antennal glomeruli; op 1, 2, 3: external, middle, and internal optic neuropileme; ped: stalk of corpora pedunculata; pr: protocerebral lobe; t: tracheae between retinulae and external optic neuropileme.

ommatidium[33], but only one or two enter directly the external glomerulus. The others form local chiasmata with those from neighboring ommatidia before entering the peculiar synaptic structures, called 'optic cartridges' (Fig. 183), of the external glomerulus. Any ommatidium is thus connected with as many as three or four 'optic cartridges'.

(e) *Pars intercerebralis* consists of cellular elements, some of which may be relatively large, located on the medial side of the corpora pedunculata, and on both sides of the midline. In certain Odonata (dragon-flies), it has been demonstrated (HANSTRÖM, 1928) that elements of the pars intercerebralis have connections with input from the three ocelli or stemmata. These latter, moreover, are connected with ocellar glomeruli, which may be located, depending on the particular taxonomic form, in different positions within the protocerebrum. Some insects lack ocelli, and a few forms are entirely eyeless (e. g. some Thysanura such as the bristletail Japyx). According to HANSTRÖM (1928), two paired, and one unpaired nerve, which has a double root, may be connected with the three (rarely four) ocelli. In Diptera such as Drosophila, however, there is a single ocellar stalk (POWER, 1946).

(f) The *antennal glomeruli* pertain to the deutocerebrum, while all previously discussed structures (a–e) are components of the protocerebrum. The antennal glomeruli consist of synaptic connections for antennal input, and are usually located near the esophageal ring. In addition, the deutocerebrum contains motor cells for the antennae. The glomeruli are interconnected across the midline by a conspicuous supraesophageal commissure, and linked with the antennae by a rather large antennal nerve. A well-defined tractus olfactorio-globularis connects the antennal glomeruli with the corpora pedunculata. Separate fiber systems reach the other neuropileme centers of the brain.

(g) The *tritocerebrum* does not display well delimitable separate components, and, although representing a definable morphologically significant subdivision[34], may have, in various taxonomic forms, and

---

[33] The ommatidium is the basic structural and functional unit of the compound eye. It consists of a lens-like cornea, a crystalline cone (second lens), and several retinular cells, which are the neurosensory elements. These latter are arranged in a circular fashion such that the photoreceptive rhabdome portion faces toward the center (cf. Fig. 180).

[34] The three subdivisions of the insect brain (protocerebrum, deutocerebrum, and tritocerebrum) were already distinguished and named by VIALLANES (1887). Their morphologic significance, particularly with respect to a comparison of insects with other arthropods, and of arthropods with annelids, was analyzed in great detail by HANSTRÖM (1928), who adopted and adapted these terms in his systematization (cf. above, p.110).

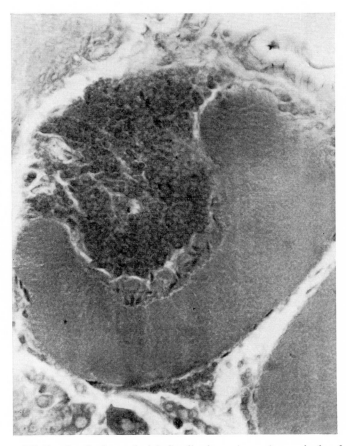

Figure 107. Details of calyx and globuli cells cluster in mushroom body of worker bee. (Original; × 460; red. $^3/_4$; hematoxylin-eosin.)

as mentioned above (p.134), only indistinct boundaries. The tritocerebrum gives origin to the system of the nervus tegumentarius, to the labro-frontal nerves, and to the stomatogastric system.

(h) *Commissures and fiber tracts.* In addition to those mentioned under (f), the following systems can be distinguished. The commissure between the medullae externae of the lateral optic lobes, with perhaps further connections, the commissure between the medullae internae, and several other commissures of the protocerebrum, which may also include, in part, some fibers from the optic lobes. Three commissures have been particularly emphasized by different authors,

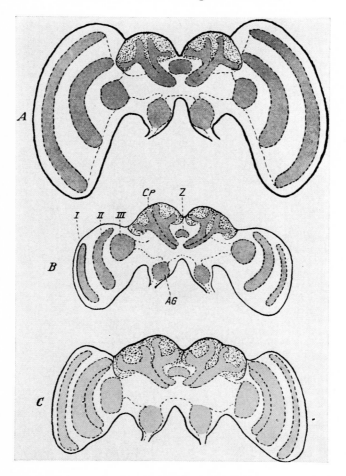

Figure 108. Diagrams of brain configuration in the three forms of the honey bee. (Modified after JONESCU, 1909, from HANSTRÖM, 1928.) *A* Drone. *B* Queen. *C* Worker. I–III: optic neuropilemes; AG: antennal glomeruli; Cp: corpora pedunculata; Z: central body.

namely dorsal or posterior, central, and anterior accessory. The tritocerebrum is provided with a subesophageal commissure.

Various, more or less distinct tracts connect the medulla interna of the optic lobe with other parts of the brain. These systems include posterior tracts of large fibers, posterior bundles of fine fibers, an

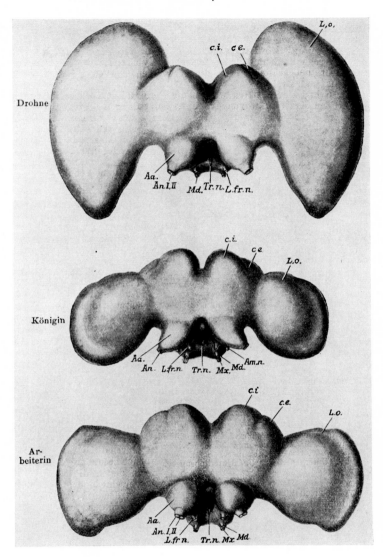

Figure 109. Reconstructions (wax models) of brains in the three forms of the honey bee. (After JONESCU, 1909, from PLATE, 1928.) Aa: antennal lobe (deutocerebrum); Am.n, An: antennal nerves; ce, ci: external and internal globuli; Lfrn: labrofrontal nerve; Lo: optic lobe; Md: mandibular nerve; Mx: maxillary nerve; Trn: tritocerebral nerve; the tritocerebrum is not distinctly demarcated.

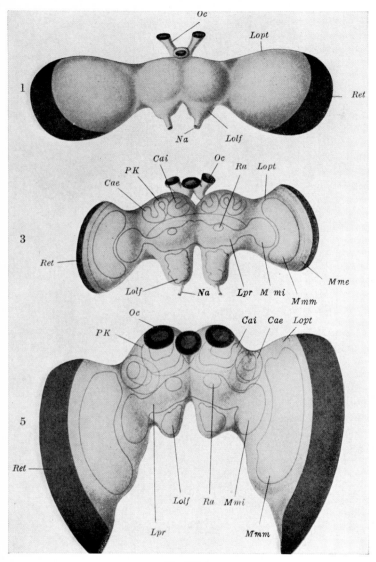

Fig. 110 A

Figure 110. Aspect of the brain in the females of different Hymenoptera. (After VON ALTEN, 1910, from HANSTRÖM, 1928.) 1: Tenthredo flava; 2: Sirex gigas; 3: Ichneumon obsessor; 4: Andrena albicans; 5: Antophora vulpina; 6: Vespa vulgaris; Cae, Cai: calyx

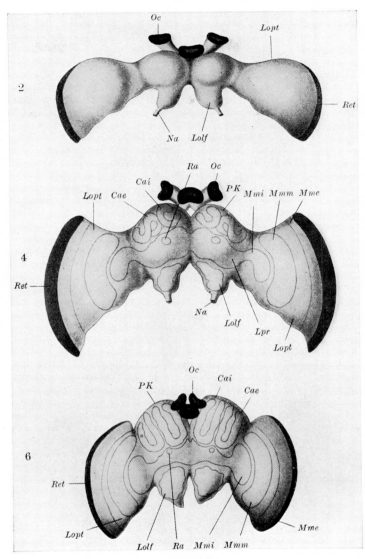

Fig. 110 B

externus and internus; Lolf: deutocerebrum; Lopt: lobus opticus; Lpr: protocerebral lobe; Mme, Mmi, Mmm: external, internal, and middle optic neuropilemes; Na: antennal nerve; Oc: ocelli; PK: mushroom bodies (corpora pedunculata); Ra: peduncle; Ret: retina.

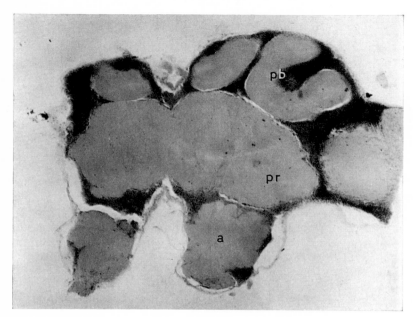

Fig. 111A

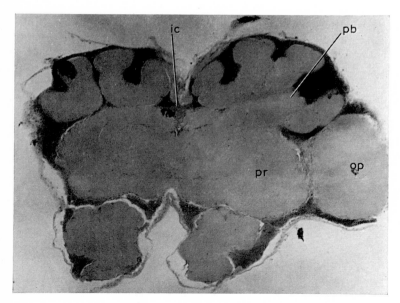

Fig. 111 B

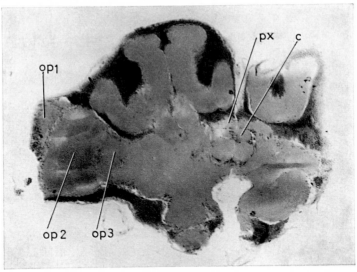

Fig. 111 C

Figure 111 A to *C*. Configuration of brain in the ant Monomerium as seen in serial, somewhat oblique transverse sections. (Original; × 190; red. $^4/_5$; hematoxylin-eosin.) a: antennal lobe (deutocerebrum); c: central body; ic: pars intercerebralis; op (1, 2, 3): optic neuropilemes; pb: corpora pedunculata; pr: protocerebral lobe; px: protocerebral bridge (111 B red. $^3/_4$).

anterior 'optic tract', and other fasciculi, such as the optic components of the above-mentioned central commissure. In addition, median unpaired bundles have been described, which course dorso-ventrally (POWER, 1943, 1946, in Drosophila). Thus, an anterior bundle extends ventrally from large cells of the pars intercerebralis, to split around the esophagus and to enter the ventral medulla. Another bundle related to the ocellar stalk extends down the posterior side of the brain to enter the ventral medulla. It is believed to pass into the thoracic ganglia.

As regards fiber tracts connected with the optic system, POWER (1946) therefore justly emphasizes that in Drosophila (Diptera) the optic glomeruli are directly and abundantly connected to the central cerebral mass through several distinct fiber bundles. Except for the commissure of the middle glomeruli, essentially interconnecting these two antimeric parts, all other optic fiber tracts are said to 'come from the two inner glomeruli', namely the anterior and the posterior ones (POWER, 1946). Again, according to the cited author, three fiber systems connect, in Drosophila, the antennal glomeruli with the other

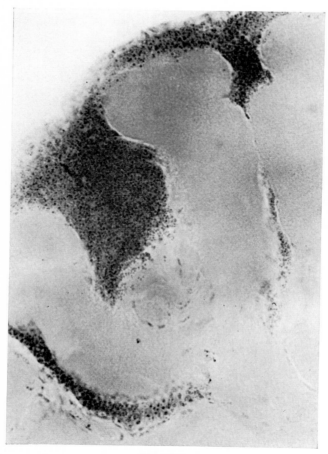

Fig. 112 A

regions of the brain: (1) the tractus olfactorio-globularis extends diagonally from each glomerulus to the dorsoposterior region of the brain and establishes direct connections with the central complex, the protocerebral bridge, the corpora pedunculata and the dorsal protocerebrum; (2) a few crossed fibers in the posterior antennal commissure run from each glomerulus to the contralateral side of the brain; (3) the broad root extensively joins each glomerulus to the main brain mass. The principal systems (tractus olfactorio-globularis and 'broad root'), connecting the antennal glomeruli with the brain mass in Drosophila melanogaster are said to be homolaterally one-sided (POWER, 1946).

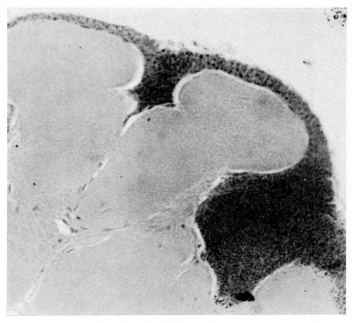

Fig. 112 B

Figure 112 A, B. Details of inner (A) and outer (B) globulus and calyx of mushroom bodies in Monomerium. (Original; × 760; red. ³/₄; hematoxylin-eosin.)

Figures 99 to 108 illustrate some of the general internal structural aspects of the insect brain, while external aspect of the brain in a few Hymenoptera is shown in Figures 109 and 110. Some structural details of the ant brain are displayed in Figures 111 to 113; the relationships of brain and head in various forms of one and the same species of ants are illustrated by Figure 114. Diverse configurational relationships and details concerning the brain of Diptera are shown in Figures 115 to 118. A rough sketch (Fig. 118) also includes the brain of Gryllus (Orthoptera). Figure 119 illustrates connections in the optic system of insects. That system, however, is again discussed further below in section 12. Concerning the bee's compound eyes it might nevertheless here be added that SANCHEZ (1920–1921) has described tactile hairs located, and protruding between, the 'corneolae' of the ommatidia. These structures, assumed to be present in a number of other insects, are

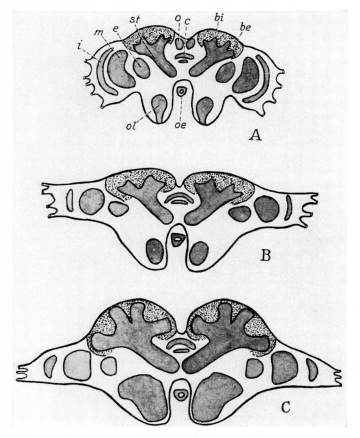

Fig. 113

Figure 113. Diagrams of brain configuration in the three forms of the ant Camponotus ligniperdus. (Modified after PIETSCHKER, 1911, from HANSTRÖM, 1928.) A: male; B: female; C: female worker; bi be: inner and outer mushroom body; c: central body; e: internal optic neuropileme; i: external optic neuropileme; m: middle optic neuropileme; o: protocerebral bridge; oe: esophagus; ol: antennal glomeruli.

Figure 114. Heads of soldier (A) worker (B) female (C), and male (D) of the ant Pheidole instabilis, drawn at identical magnification, and showing topography of brain. (After WHEELER, 1913, from HERRICK, 1924.) an: antennal nerve, oc: median ocellus; og, on: parts of optic system; ol: antennal (olfactory) lobe; pb: pedunculated bodies.

Figure 115. Diagram showing topographic relationship of head and brain in Diptera. (Adapted and modified from a diagram by POWER, 1943.) *A* dorsal aspect; *B* rostral aspect.

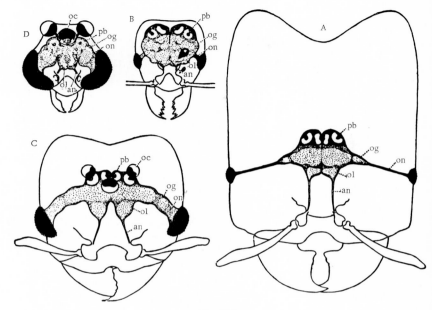

Fig. 114

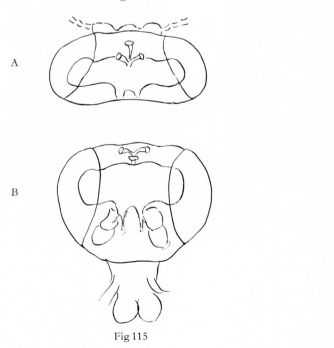

Fig 115

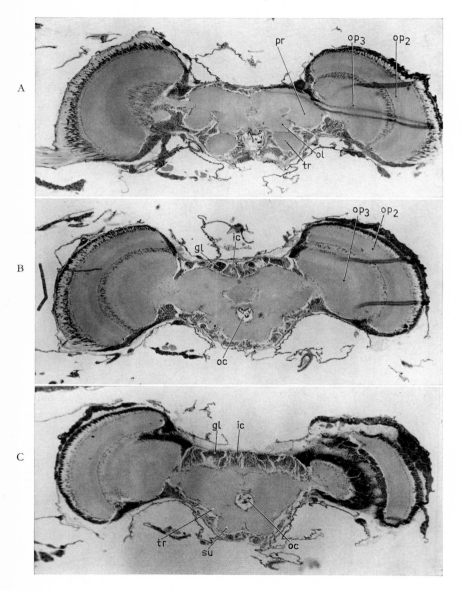

Figure 116 A to *C.* Configuration of brain in the horsefly Tabanus as seen in serial transverse sections. (Original; × 60; red. ²/₃; hematoxylin-eosin.) gl: globuli; ic: pars intercerebralis; oc: esophagus; ol: antennal lobe; op 2, 3: middle and inner optic neuropilemes; pr: protocerebral lobe; su: subesophageal ganglion; tr: tritocerebrum.

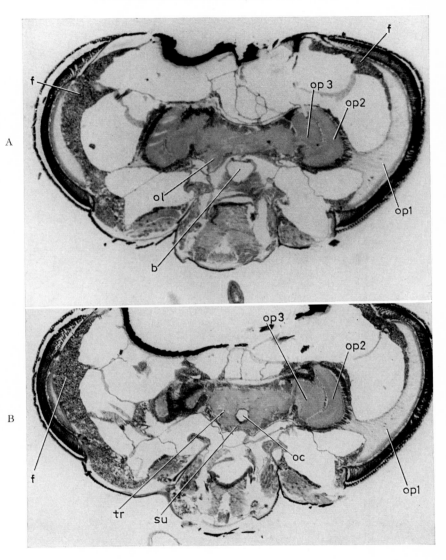

Figure 117A, B. Sections through head and brain of horsefly Tabanus. (Original; × 35; red. ³/₄; hematoxylin-eosin.) b: buccal cavity; f: fat cells; op 1: external optic neuropileme (layer of neurommatidia); other abbreviations as in Fig. 116.

interpreted as a 'protective apparatus' ('acción protectora de los pelos tactiles corneales').

As regards the *ventral ganglia*, or 'ventral medulla' (German: *Bauch-mark*) of insects, detailed data pertaining to the dragon-fly larva of Aeschna (Odonata) have been provided by the meticulous investigations of ZAWARZIN (1924, 1925, and others), who applied the methylene blue technique.

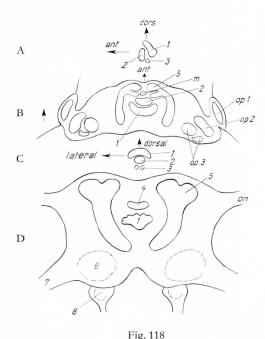

Fig. 118

Figure 118. Rough sketches of some topographic relationships in the brains of Drosophila (Diptera), and Gryllus (Orthoptera). *A* Configurational relationships of central complex in sagittal section. *B* Configurational relationships of central complex and some other structures in horizontal section. *C* Configurational relationships of central complex in transverse section. *D* Configurational relationships of protocerebral bridge, central body, and some other structures in oblique frontal section. *A* to *C* in Drosophila, simplified after POWER, 1943. *D* in Gryllus, simplified after HUBER from ROEDER, 1963. 1: central body; 2: ellipsoidal body; 3: ventral tubercles; 4: protocerebral bridge; 5: corpora pedunculata; 6: antennal glomeruli (deutocerebrum); 7: antennal nerve; 8: tritocerebrum; m: median bundle; on: 'optic nerve'; op 1, op 2, op 3: first, second and third optic neuropile.

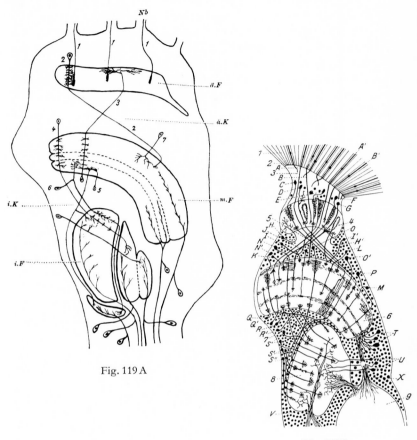

Fig. 119 A

Fig. 119 B

Figure 119. Diagrams of neuronal connections in the optic system of insects. *A* Optic lobe in a well developed larva of the dragonfly Aeschna. (Simplified after ZAWARZIN, 1914, from PLATE, 1922.) äF: external optic neuropileme; äK: external chiasma; iF: inner optic neuropileme; iK: internal (middle) chiasma; mF: middle optic neuropileme; Nb and 1: primary optic neuron (process of neurosensory retinal cell); 2–7 diverse internuncial optic neurones. Ventral side on left.

B Optic lobe of Apis mellifica. (After CAJAL and SANCHEZ, 1915, from HANSTRÖM, 1928.) 1: retinulae; 4: lamina ganglionaris (external optic neuropileme with neurommatidia); 5: chiasma externum; 6: medulla externa (middle optic neuropileme); 7: chiasma internum (also occasionally designated as 'middle' chiasma); 8: medulla interna (inner optic neuropileme); 9: protocerebral lobe; V: optic connections with other parts of brain (occasionally referred to as 'inner' chiasma); additional abbreviations not relevant to present context.

In all ganglia, the neuronal elements are symmetrically grouped on the lateral and ventral side. The neuropilemes show different, well distinguishable regions; a dorsal, efferent, and a ventral, afferent root give origin to the peripheral paired nerves, namely an anterior, middle, and posterior one. In addition, there are anterior and posterior unpaired nerves, as well as some accessory ones originating from a few ganglia. The nerve cells are of different sizes, and a few of the thick fibers can

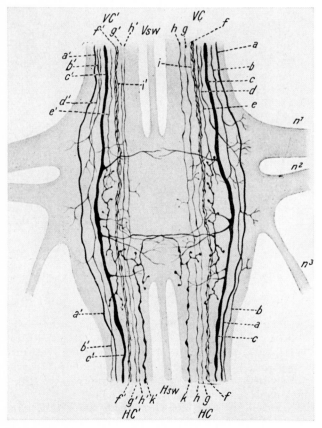

Figure 120. Domain of dorsal connective fibers in the fourth abdominal ganglion of an Aeschna larva, as shown in methylene blue preparations. (After ZAWARZIN, 1924, from HANSTRÖM, 1928.) Hc: posterior connective; Hsw: posterior root of ventral unpaired nerve; n1–3: roots of lateral nerves; Vsw: anterior root of unpaired nerve; other designations refer to various sorts of neurons and fibers.

perhaps be considered directly comparable (presumably analogous) to the neurochords of crustaceans, annelids, and other forms. Figures 120 to 123 illustrate some of the structural arrangements observed by Zawarzin (1924, 1925).

Additional details concerning the abdominal nervous system of aeschnid nymphae were recently published by Mill (1964). This author describes the diverse groups of nerve cells, and the general disposi-

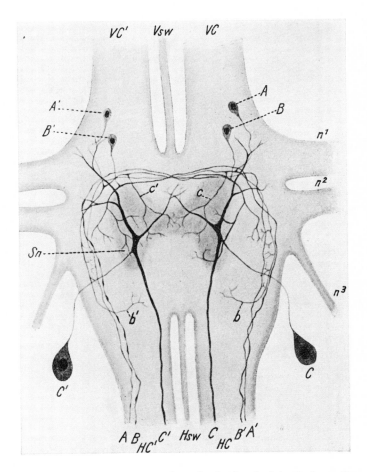

Figure 121. Ventral zone of neuropileme in the fourth abdominal ganglion of an Aeschna larva. (After Zawarzin, 1924, from Hanström, 1928.) Designations as in Fig. 120. Sn: sensory ventral neuropileme; VC: anterior connective.

tion of two pairs of giant fibers as well as of some other fairly large
longitudinal fibers. Among other reports on giant fibers in the
ventral medulla of Hexapoda are those of Cook (1951), Pipa, Cook,
and Richards (1959), Power (1948), and Roeder (1948, 1963).
Cook's observations (1951) concerned Locustae. Findings included
in the other cited papers will be considered in the following brief comments.

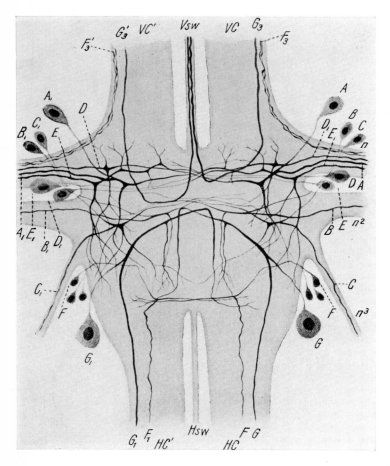

Figure 122. Region of dorsal (efferent) roots in the fourth abdominal ganglion of
an Aeschna larva. (After Zawarzin, 1924, from Hanström, 1928.) Designations as in
Fig. 120.

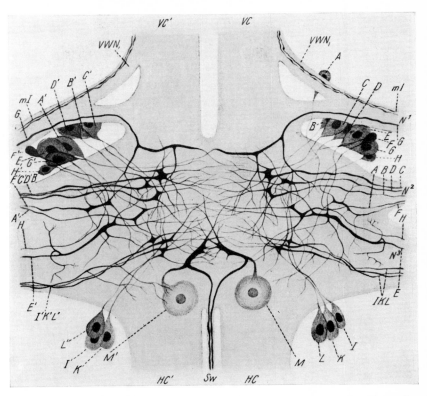

Figure 123. Domain of dorsal (motor) roots in the second thoracic ganglion of an Aeschna larva. (After ZAWARZIN, 1924, from HANSTRÖM, 1928.) N1 to N3: nerves of third thoracic ganglion; other designations as in Fig. 120; additional letters refer to various types of neurons. Sw: 'root of unpaired nerve'.

POWER (1948) made a detailed study of ventral medulla (thoraco-abdominal ganglia) in Drosophila melanogaster, using an activated protargol impregnation method. In this fly, the entire non-cephalic division of the central nervous system is concentrated into a single ganglionic mass, the thoraco-abdominal center (Fig. 124). This mass displays only very indistinct external traces of segmentation. Internally, the neuropilemes show a subdivision into pro-, meso- and metathoracic neuromeres, with an accessory dorsal mesothoracic pair. The entire abdominal nervous system is concentrated into a single, small unpaired mass attached to the posterior end of the thoracic center. One larger median, and two pairs of thin lateral nerves are connected with this

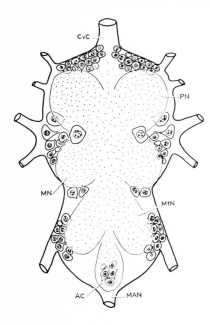

Figure 124. Diagram showing the thoraco-abdominal portion of the central nervous system in the fly Drosophila. The positions of the groups of large nerve cells are indicated. (From POWER, 1948.) AC: abdominal center; CvC: cervical connective; MAN: median abdominal nerve; MN: mesothoracic neural segment; MtN: metathoracic neural segment; PN: prothoracic neural segment.

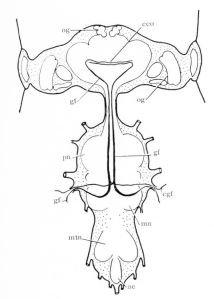

Figure 125. Diagram of entire central nervous system in Drosophila, displaying the giant fibers. (From POWER, 1948.) cco: central commissure; cgf: collateral from giant fiber; gf: giant fiber; og: optic neuropilemes; other designations as in Fig. 124. (The left upper og should read ag: antennal glomerulus; cf. fig. 126).

abdominal portion. The thoracic portion displays 14 pairs of peripheral nerves.

The nerve cells are arranged in an outer cellular layer, enclosing the neuropilemes, as is typical for arthropods. This layer is thin dorsally, and thicker laterally and ventrally. Among the ordinary cells, there are regularly arranged, symmetrical groups of much larger cells. This, of course, corresponds also to the findings made by ZAWARZIN (1924, 1925) in Aeschna. Thoraco-abdominal ganglion and brain are interrelated by a rather thin, unpaired median connective which contains four fiber tracts. A fibrous layer in the dorsal part of the thoraco-abdominal ganglion is designated as 'tectulum' by POWER, who describes longitudinal components regarded as continuous with the four fiber tracts of the cerebro-thoracic connective. In addition, this fiber mass is said to contain transverse 'decussations', 'chiasmata', and 'commissures'.

POWER (1948) describes in Drosophila a pair of giant fibers, extending from protocerebral levels in the brain into the thoracic centers, where they branch once, turn laterally, and leave the central nervous system to innervate certain of the great thoracic muscles (Fig. 125, 126). Their diameter measures from 4 to 6 μ. Although rather small, this size is considerable if compared to other nerve fibers in Drosophila.

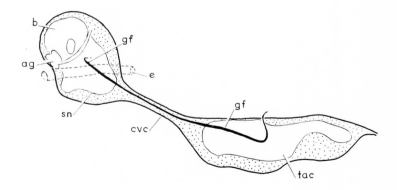

Figures 126. Diagram of entire central nervous system of Drosophila in lateral view. The course of a giant fiber is shown. (From POWER, 1948.) ag: antennal glomerulus; b: brain; e: esophagus; sn: subesophageal neuropileme; tac: thoraco-abdominal center; other designations as in Figs. 124 and 125.

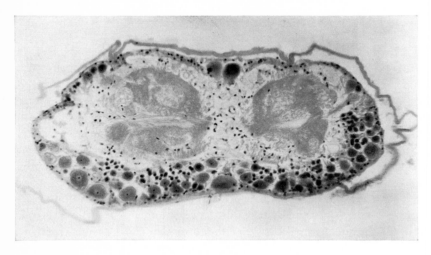

Figure 127. Cross section through a thoracic ganglion of the cockroach Periplaneta americana. (Original; × 250; red. $^2/_3$; hematoxylin-eosin.) The figure shows the peripheral, mostly ventral arrangement of nerve cell bodies, and two antimeric neuropilemes; most of the small nuclei pertain to the supporting elements; a few large nerve fibers can be seen, which, however, are of a lesser diameter than those in abdominal ganglia.

The exact location of the cell bodies from which the two fibers arise could not be ascertained by POWER in 1948.

In the cockroach Periplaneta (Orthoptera), three thoracic ganglia and six abdominal ganglia of the ventral nerve cord can be found. Figures 127 to 129 illustrate cross sections through a thoracic ganglion, an abdominal ganglion, and an abdominal connective. The abdominal portions of the ventral nerve cord are characterized by a number of giant fibers, some of which have a diameter in excess of 30 μ. Although giant fibers are somewhat less conspicuous in the thoracic portion of the ventral nerve cord, some large fibers can be traced through the thoracic ganglia into the brain without apparent interruptions. Various further details concerning cellular structure, general arrangement of tracts, and giant axons in the thoracic ganglia of Periplaneta have been reported by PIPA, COOK, and RICHARDS (1959). Another recent paper by HESS (1958) deals with observations on fine structure of neuronal and supporting elements.

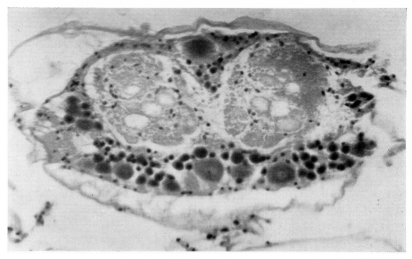

Figure 128. Cross section through an abdominal ganglion of the cockroach Periplaneta americana. (Original; × 280; red. $^2/_3$; hematoxylin-eosin.) In each antimere, at least four very large fibers are conspicuous.

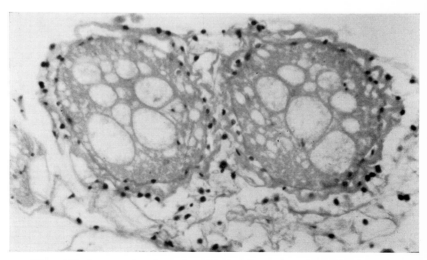

Figure 129. Cross section through a paired abdominal connective in the cockroach Periplaneta americana. (Original; × 375; red. $^2/_3$; hematoxylin-eosin.) The group of giant fibers is conspicuous.

In the cockroach, the giant fibers of the abdominal nerve cord mediate a startle response investigated by ROEDER (1963 and other publications). This reflex is triggered by the 'antenna-like' cerci at the tip of the abdomen (Fig. 130 A, B). Delicate sensilla on a cercus are stimulated by a gentle air current or by low pitched sounds. About 150 sense cell axons are connected by synapses with perhaps four of the ascending giant nerve fibers. The impulse is transmitted with considerable velocity to the metathoracic ganglion, and from there to the leg musculature. The conduction velocity in the giant fibers is here a 'rapid' one of 6 to 7 mps; and the impulse transmission over their full length requires about 2.8 msec. The conduction velocity in the smaller fibers is estimated to be somewhat less than one tenth of that in the giant fibers. The cited author, using the improved present-day technical methods, investigated a number of interesting synaptic and other functional properties displayed by this reflex, which is of the open, non-reset type, lacking feedback (cf. chapt. I, p. 8).

Turning from the central nervous system to the peripheral effector, motor mechanism, a typical insect muscle is said to be provided with two or three motor nerve fibers, each of which supplies from 30% to 100% of the muscle fibers (ROEDER, 1963). A 'fast nerve fiber' may initiate maximum contraction such as in jumps, and a 'slow nerve fiber'

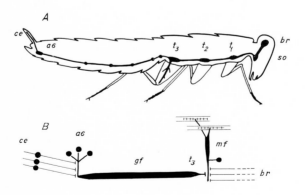

Figure 130. Diagrams illustrating the startle response in the cockroach, assumed to be mediated by abdominal giant fibers. (From ROEDER, 1963.) *A* Outline of central nervous system, indicating nerve supply of cercus (ce) and metathoracic (t_3) leg; br: brain; so: subesophageal ganglion. *B* Diagram of neuronal elements believed to be involved in the startle response. a6: last abdominal ganglion; gf: giant fibers of abdominal nerve cord; mf: motor neuron connected with leg muscles; other designations as in *A*.

may control gradual and 'tonic' contractions. Similar relationships seem to obtain in crustaceans, where 'inhibitory' fibers, perhaps likewise present in insects, have been demonstrated.

Experimental studies on the insect brain and central nervous system by means of various techniques, including the newer refined methods of stimulation and destruction, have yielded a number of further data related to behavioral activities.

Thus, in the mantis (Orthoptera), surgical removal of the brain causes the insect to walk continuously. Additional removal of the subesophageal ganglion (equivalent to decapitation) eliminates all spontaneous walking except for a continuous rotary movement seen only in mature males (ROEDER, 1963).

Removal of one half of the brain (right or left) causes the mantis to turn restlessly in a tight circle toward the intact side. A mere splitting of the brain in the midline seems to prevent the mantis from walking forward, even if prodded, although it may take a few steps backward. Otherwise, the split-brained mantis appears to behave in a completely normal manner, at least under some circumstances (ROEDER, 1963). The cited author assumes that in the split-brained mantis both right and left turning tendencies 'become enhanced to the point where they completely suppress the forward command generated in the subesophageal ganglion, and forward movement is blocked'.

By a combination of local stimulation and destruction, HUBER (1955, 1959, 1960) seems to have demonstrated that, in the cricket, the main source of inhibition to forward locomotion is actually located in the corpora pedunculata. These structures also appear to be a major control system for song production. The excitatory mechanisms in the behavior of crickets are believed to be provided by combined effects of central body and subesophageal ganglion, acting upon the locomotor loci of the thoracic nerve cord. The corpora pedunculata are assumed to exert an inhibitory regulating effect on these activities.

The experimental results of VOWLES (1955, 1961) in ants can be interpreted to show that disruption of the corpora pedunculata connections with optic centers interferes with learned patterns of maze running, without, however, eliminating all reactions to visual stimuli (ROEDER, 1963).

Another intricate behavioral mechanism, investigated by MITTELSTAEDT (1962), is involved in the prey capture by the mantis (Fig. 131). The image of the prey, e. g. a fly, in the binocular field of the compound eyes generates information controlling the neck muscles such that the

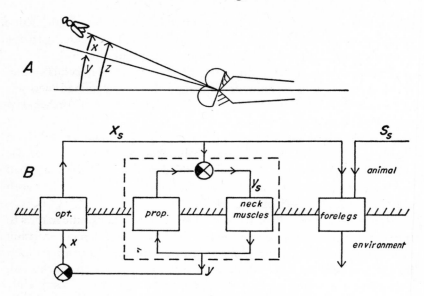

Figure 131. Diagram illustrating prey capture mechanism in the Mantis. (Modified after MITTELSTAEDT, 1957, from ROEDER, 1963.) *A* Head and prothorax of mantis 'fixating' on a fly; x: fixation deficit; y: deviation of head from body axis when prey is fixated; z: deviation of prey from body axis. *B* Block diagram of control mechanism concerned with prey localization and strike. The dashed box contains the proprioceptor loop included in the optic feedback loop. The optic output X_s transmits the correct aiming signal which takes effect upon transmission of the strike signal S_s. White segments in circles indicate addition, black segments subtraction.

asymmetry is reduced. A feedback of this type likewise obtains in vertebrates. The information includes prey-to-head angle, head-to-body angle, and measurement of striking distance. The preset contraction pattern is then released, presumably by a slight movement of the prey. The actual strike of the mantis is so rapid that it corresponds to a ballistic 'throw', and cannot be steered while in process of execution. At this stage, it is likewise (cf. above) an open cycle, non-reset reflex mechanism. MITTELSTAEDT studied strike performance and errors made by the mantis after various sorts of experimental interference with the proprioceptive system.

Another noteworthy aspect of control and computing mechanisms provided by the insect brain is the demonstrated capability of the brain, in the red forest-ant Formica rufa, to integrate light angles over time, and to take the time average of the result (JANDER, 1957, MITTELSTAEDT,

1962). This, of course, is perhaps much less startling than might appear to those unfamiliar with computing mechanisms, if the elementary principles concerning the arrangements of the circuits required for operations of that type in artificial computers are recalled (cf. e.g. BERKELEY, E.C.: 'Giant Brains or Machines that Think.' Wiley, New York 1949; BERKELEY, E.C., and WAINWRIGHT, L.: 'Computers. Their Operations and Applications.' Reinhold, New York 1962; STIBITZ, G.R., and LARRIVEE, J.A.: 'Mathematics and Computers.' McGraw-Hill, New York 1957).

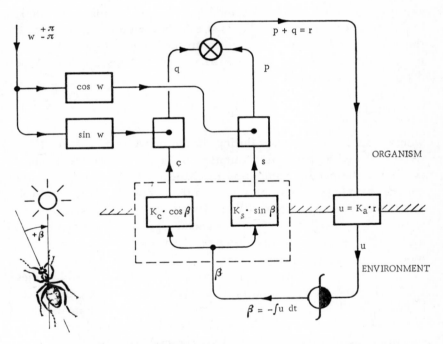

Figure 132. Block diagram showing the assumed control mechanism for insect orientation based on bicomponent modulation. (From MITTELSTAEDT, 1962.) β: light angle; w: course order; c, s: cosine and sine components of the light angle; p: product of cosine of course order and sine of light angle; q: product of sine of course order and cosine of light angle; the course order acts reciprocally on the two components of the light angle; r: turning tendency (sum of p and q); u: turning velocity of the insect relative to ground (+ : right turn); the half black circle indicates the physical relation between u and β (integration and reversal of sign); square boxes with central dot indicate multiplication of the input variable with the variable connected to the dot; K_a, K_c, K_s are coefficients related to several equations discussed by MITTELSTAEDT, 1962.

JANDER trained the red ant to run straight toward a black disk, while two light sources standing 135° left and right of the disk were switched on and off alternately, with a period of one cycle per min. After one hour, the black disk was removed, the alternating lights were replaced by one continuous light, and the directional tendency of the ants was tested with respect to that light source. If the two alternating lights had been on for equal amounts of time, the ants behaved, with respect to their orientation, as if there had been, during training time, a single continuous light source situated exactly between the two alternating ones. If the average time ratio at which the lights had been alternating was 3:1, however, the ants behaved as if a continuous light had been standing at a locus dividing the angle between the two alternating lights at exactly the same ratio 3:1, with the smaller angle toward the light with the longer on-period. Thus, in general, the resulting angle a_r to the continuous light could be expressed in the form

$$a_r = \frac{1}{T} \int_0^T a_i \, dt$$

where a_i are the light angles during the period when alternating lights were presented, and T the total duration of that period. Quite evidently, similar or comparable computing mechanisms, operating directly on angles, or on angle functions, obtain in the orientation of bees as well as of other insects (JANDER, 1960; MITTELSTAEDT, 1962). Figure 132 shows a diagram illustrating some general aspects of a course-control mechanism in an insect, operating on the principle of bicomponent modulation (MITTELSTAEDT, 1962).

Despite the rather numerous, often very detailed and careful studies concerning the insect central nervous system, particularly the insect brain (as well as some other arthropod and invertebrate brains), little is actually known about the more detailed or rigorously specifiable functional significance of tracts and 'centers'. Because of the very numerous collaterals, by means of small branches, and the multitudinous combinations and permutations provided by the neuropilemes, a 'complex system richly connected internally' (cf. p. 53, footnote 9) obtains, which is most difficult to interpret. In addition, the purely technical difficulties of such investigations are not inconsiderable. As regards the fibers in a tract, the position of their corresponding cell bodies and the direction of impulse conduction remain very often in doubt. Moreover, the differences in various orders and species as well as the differences in the terminology and in the descriptive procedures used by various authors, present, at this time, almost insuperable obstacles for an attempt at detailed systematization. Thus, only a very provisory and sketchy general outline can be given. Nevertheless, preliminary attempts to represent the functions of central nervous systems in engineering terms of 'blue-prints', circuit diagrams, and block diagrams (cf. e.g. GREGORY, 1961) may be regarded as fully justified.

HUBER (1963) brings a tabulation listing behavioral reactions upon local stimulation of brain centers in Orthoptera (on the basis of his studies) and in Hymenoptera (on the basis of the data obtained by VOWLES). Yet, these observed 'reactions' allow only very generalized and nondescript formulations, such, e.g., as the following, concerning 'Zellen und Becherregion der Pilzkörper' (HUBER, 1963).

Orthoptera: 'Hemmung der Atmung, der Lokomotion und Lauterzeugung; Suchbewegungen.'

Hymenoptera: 'Lageänderung, Laufen, Fliegen mit langen Nacheffekten, Drehbewegungen zur Reizseite.'

Concerning the lateral protocerebral neuropileme, the reactions are listed as follows (HUBER, 1963).

Orthoptera: 'Hemmung und Aktivierung von Atmung und Lokomotion je nach Elektrodenlage; Orientierungsbewegungen; Drehbewegungen nach beiden Seiten.'

Hymenoptera: 'Änderung der Körperhaltung, Lokomotion, Atmungssteigerung.'

As regards local lesions in the brain of Orthoptera and Hymenoptera, HUBER (1963) reaches the conclusion 'dass die Pilzkörper (a) Hemmungssysteme für die allgemeine Aktivität enthalten, (b) bei Hymenopteren und gewissen Orthopteren an der Kontrolle der Laufrichtung mitbeteiligt sind und (c) bei beiden Gruppen eine wichtige Stelle der Integration und Koordination für komplexes instinktives Verhalten und für Lernen sind.'

ROEDER (1963) believes that the complex behavioral mechanisms of insects 'are probably based upon a three-dimensional brain-wide network of connections that is somehow superimposed upon similar networks controlling other activities.' This, of course, corresponds exactly to my own views (K. 1927, p. 337) concerning the 'higher neural functions' of the vertebrate and human brain. Said functions were assumed to involve the activities of neuron groups arranged in intricate patterns, and distributed upon several separate regions, whereby the processes of such nerve cells 'sich netzartig über weite Abschnitte der Grosshirnrinde sowie des Hemisphärenmarks erstrecken'.

In summary, it might be said that corpora pedunculata, central body complex, and protocerebral bridge constitute perhaps the most important synaptic centers, whose function is related to behavior and 'instincts' of Hexapoda[35]. In view of the many and complex activities displayed by social insects such as bees and ants, including, e. g., the symbolic dance of bees (v. FRISCH, 1950) representing a language transmitting information, it is of some interest to ascertain the number of neuronal elements available in an insect brain.

In each half of an approximately 20 μ thick section of some insect brains at least between 400 to 600 neuronal elements can very easily be counted, amounting thus to a total of between 800 and more than 1200 nerve cells at such level. Taking into consideration various densities and distributions at different levels, this might perhaps be multiplied by a minimal factor of 10 to 20, so that one could, very roughly, estimate the total number of neural elements in some insect brains as between 10000 to 24000 and more, with perhaps 10^5 as an upper limit[36]. After obtaining myself this exceedingly crude first estimate, I had one of my students, Miss FARRELL, continue with a series of somewhat more systematic counts, samplings, and computations in my laboratory, and on the basis of our available, restricted insect material, merely prepared for purposes of general orientation and first-hand acquaintance with the subject matter.

Miss FARRELL's results, which we likewise consider to represent not more than a preliminary rough first approximation, are based on

---

[35] There is, in my opinion, no satisfactory definition for the ambiguous term 'instinct', which subsumes complex patterns of responses by organisms to various sorts of 'stimuli'. This behavior is supposed to attain 'adaptive ends', but without 'prevision or experience', in contradistinction to 'intelligence'. 'Instinctive' activities may proceed in regular, and almost 'automatic' chains of sequences. If 'instinctive' behavior is modified by experience and stored information, resulting in successful problem solving behavior under significantly different environmental circumstances, one might then perhaps consider such behavior a manifestation of 'intelligence'.

[36] In some small insect brains, such as that of Pulex irritans (Siphonaptera or Aphaniptera), or Pentatoma (Rhynchota, Hemiptera, 'true bugs' including the bed-bug), and others, a significantly lesser number of nerve cells seems to be present. In such forms, the corpora pedunculata are very rudimentary, and the protocerebral bridge may not be identifiable with reasonable certainty.

counts of nuclei, of which a substantial majority is assumed as pertaining to nerve cells. The obtained data can be summarized as follows:

In bee workers the ascertained body weight varied between 97 mg and 120 mg, the brain weight between 0.7 mg and 1.4 mg, and the brain volume between 0.68 and 1.35 mm³. The total number of cellular elements in the brain was found to be within the range of 3.2×10^5 to 3.6×10^5.

In the brain of the bumblebee (Bombus spec.), the number of cells was calculated as falling in the range from 3×10^5 to 3.4×10^5 (only fixed heads were available, and data on weight and volume were not ascertained).

In the horsefly (Tabanus spec.) the following figures were obtained. Body weight between 481 and 500 mg, brain weight about 3.45 mg, brain volume about 3.3 mm³, number of cellular elements in brain between 3.2×10^5 to 3.7×10^5.

In workers of the black ant (Monomerium spec.) the obtained data were as follows. Body weight between 5 mg and 7 mg, brain weight between 0.05 and 0.07 mg, brain volume between about roughly 0.05 and 0.07 mm³, number of cellular elements in brain between 1.6×10^5 and 3×10^5.

In comparison, the following figures were obtained with respect to a cockroach (Periplaneta spec.). Body weight 982 mg, brain weight 2.1 mg, brain volume 2.0 mm³, cellular elements in brain 1.2×10^6.

The figures calculated by Miss FARRELL, a capable and conscientious worker, seemed somewhat unexpectedly high to me, particularly in the case of the cockroach. Yet I was, so far, unable to detect any conspicuous flaw in her procedures and computations undertaken with my advice and under my general, if somewhat loose, supervision. Since, except for the partial figures published by GOOSSEN (1949–1951), we were unable to find comparable data in the literature available to us[37], and particularly since HUBER (1963) stated that 'bei den Insekten

---

[37] In the journalistic publication 'The Human Brain' by JOHN PFEIFFER, with the subtitle 'The wonderful story of the most complex and mysterious structure in the Universe' (Pyramid Books, New York 1962), we found the following information (p. 32, l. c.): 'The chances are exceedingly slim that we will freeze into the sort of system evolved by the so-called social insects. Ant brains have about 250 nerve cells, bee brains about 900. We have 13 000 000 000. Brave New World, 1984, and other novels that picture future races of semi-zombies make good reading; they are very poor science'.

The quoted gentleman, a well-publicized science writer, at times connected with Scientific American, and with 'Newsweek Magazine', introduces his book with a long list

fehlen solche Untersuchungen noch', our preliminary and tentative figures (which include the entire optic system exclusive of retinulae) are here presented for whatever they are worth.

In his detailed study on brain and body measurements concerning various Coleoptera and Hymenoptera, GOOSSEN (1949–1951) has included some cell counts, restricted to the globuli groups of corpora pedunculata ('Kernzahlen in der Globulizellgruppe der Corpora pedunculata'). His tabulation indicates 1176 cells (nuclei) in Melolontha (Coleoptera); 1009 cells in Vespa crabo, 889 cells in Apis mellifica, 811 cells in Bombus lapidarius, and 733 cells in Vespa vulgaris (the latter four species all Hymenoptera). Evidently, GOOSSEN's figures, although referring to only one set of brain structures, appear very low when compared with Miss FARRELL's total figures for apis or bombus, but could, perhaps, be considered barely approximately compatible with my own first rough total estimates as mentioned above.

As regards the perhaps questionable 10^6 range obtained by Miss FARRELL in a cockroach, it might be mentioned that in another, but much larger invertebrate pertaining to a different phylum, namely octopus, the number of nerve cells in the brain is supposed to be in the range of 100×10^6, that is 10^8 (YOUNG, quoted after HUBER, 1963; cf. also further below, section 11, p. 214). The various figures here under consideration, ranging from neighborhoods of 10^4 to perhaps at most 10^6 in insects and possibly to 10^8 in the octopus, compare with estimates of 1.2×10^{10} for the human brain, and perhaps 8×10^9 to 10^{10} for the human cerebral cortex.

It is thus quite evident that a vertebrate, mammalian brain, such as developed in man, provides an incomparably larger number of cellular elements for the combinations and permutations required by the mechanisms of a neuronal network.

---

of special acknowledgments to prominent and often vocal scientists who contributed to his (according to 'The New Yorker') 'impressive' story by conversations, interviews, and correspondence. This list includes, among others, W. McCulloch, K. S. Lashley, C. J. Herrick, E. C. Crosby, R.W. Sperry, Norbert Wiener, W. Grey Walter, and H.W. Magoun. One may wonder whether, with such truly formidable and awe-inspiring backing, the cited publication by 'Newsweek Magazine's' authority on the brain fulfils both the requirements of making good reading and being very good science. As regards the probability or improbability that humanity might evolve toward future races of 'semi-zombies', I do not claim to have the confident knowledge which Mr. Pfeiffer assumes, and I would merely remark, in the words of Aeschylus: 'ἀλλ' ἐκδιδάσκει πάνθ' ὁ γηράσκων χρόνος' (Προμηθεὺς δεσμώτης, 982).

Yet, there are here degrees of efficiency, and there can be little doubt that the type of organization manifested by the insect brain combines a high grade of efficaciousness with considerable compactness.

Even if we assume, on the basis of very elementary and oversimplified minimal premises, that no more than 2000 neuronal elements represent here the significant 'logical panel' or 'logical network' structures involved in complex 'instincts', including 'problem solving' behavior, and that these 'signal elements', with their on-off states, are all interconnected by means of the three centers mentioned above, we obtain a respectable number of different 'logical patterns', amounting to 2^{2000} or approximately 10^{600}. This is a far larger figure than the estimated number of elementary particles in the entire astronomically observable universe (about 10^{79} to 10^{80}).

In both vertebrates and invertebrates, the final 'motor' output seems to be characterized by a considerable degree of many-one convergence within the central nervous system, and a high degree of one-many spread from efferent nerve cell to muscle fibers. Thus, even in man, the motoneurons of the spinal cord remain within an order of magnitude of 10^5 for each side of the body. As regards arthropods, there may be, in Aeschna larvae, and according to estimates of ZAWARZIN (1924), about 80 nerve cells in an abdominal ganglion, and about 150 in a thoracic ganglion. The majority, but presumably not all of these cells can be regarded as motor elements.

Reverting to the problems of brain size discussed above in volume 1, page 267, it seems perhaps appropriate, in this connection, to quote some remarks from DARWIN's 'Descent of Man' (p. 436, 'Modern Library' edition as listed in bibliography to chapter II):

'No one, I presume, doubts that the large proportion which the size of man's brain bears to his body, compared to the same proportion in the gorilla or orang, is closely connected with his higher mental powers. We meet with closely analogous facts with insects, for in ants the cerebral ganglia are of extraordinary dimensions, and in all the Hymenoptera these ganglia are many times larger than in the less intelligent orders, such as beetles' (although some such differences in relative and absolute size doubtless obtain, I believe that DARWIN overplays here somewhat their significant magnitudes). 'On the other hand, no one supposes that the intellect of any two animals or of any two men can be accurately gauged by the cubic contents of their skulls. It is certain that there may be extraordinary mental activity with an extremely small absolute mass of nervous matter: thus the wonderfully diversified instincts, mental powers, and affections of ants are notorious, yet their cerebral ganglia are not so large as the quarter of a small pin's head. Under this point of view, the brain of an ant is one of the most marvellous atoms of matter in the world, perhaps more so than the brain of a man.'

Needless to say, my own evaluation is here somewhat more sober and sceptical. Extreme caution in using terms such as 'mental' and 'affections' seems indicated in dealing with the intricate problems of arthropod behavior. Yet, there is doubtless a modicum of justification for DARWIN'S comments and his enthusiastic appraisal of the insect brain.

While DARWIN, at the time, emphasized the ant's brain, the studies of v. FRISCH (1950, 1953 and many others) have revealed the complex-ities of the memory storage and symbolizing capabilities manifested by the brain of bees.

There is no doubt that these insects communicate with each other by means of a sign-language represented by a symbolic 'dance'. Returning to the hive from a foraging flight, a bee performs a series of motions closely watched by other members of the hive (Fig. 133). The round dance (Rundtanz) indicates the location of flowers or food near the hive (50 to 100 m), and the wagging dance (Schwänzeltanz) a location at a greater distance (100 m up to 6 km). The number of turns indicates here roughly the distance (from 9 to 10 complete cycles within 15 sec for about 100 m to only 2 cycles for about 6 km). Wind effect, i.e. 'airspeed' is included into the message carrying the relevant information. In addition, the orientation of the dance indicates the direction; this, of course, implies angle recognition. This latter is based

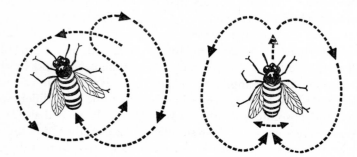

Figure 133. Diagram of bee dances as means of communication. (After VON FRISCH, 1950.) At left the round dance (Rundtanz), at right the wagging dance (Schwänzeltanz).

upon the position of the sun; the information provided by the polarization of light from the sky is here sufficient (cf. further below p. 265). Moreover, information as to the relative amount of forage is likewise given: the more food, the more vigorous are the dances of bees. The remarkable studies of v. FRISCH and his associates have established beyond doubt that the bees clearly 'understand' the information transmitted by the dances. When they fly out, they search only the neighborhood of the indicated range, ignoring food dishes experimentally set up closer or farther away. Also, the search proceeds only in the direction in which the original feeding dish is located. According to v. FRISCH, different populations of bees manifest slight differences of 'dialect', e.g. as regards the distances indicated by the symbolism, or as regards some minor variations of the pattern (e.g. 'sickle dance', i.e. a flattened figure eight bent into a semicircle, the concavity of the 'sickle' facing the source of food). Both odors and colors of flowers are attractive to the bees seeking new feeding places. The fragrance is carried by the 'scout' bee both externally and internally (in the so-called honey stomach). When bees have begun to visit a flower, they have the tendency to remain 'faithful' to this type.

Recent studies (H. ESCH, I. ESCH, and KERR, 1965) have indicated that stingless bees, of the genera Melipona and Trigona, which do not use 'dances' for communication, may use sound signals, perhaps combined with transmitted smells, to indicate the existence, and in some instances, the distance of a feeding place.

In this respect, it is also of interest that, more than 250 years ago, the well-known English writer and diarist JOHN EVELYN (1620–1706), a contemporary of SAMUEL PEPYS, reported some early observations on the 'dances' of bees. In a fragment dealing with apiaries, EVELYN remarked that bees appeared to communicate with each other 'by a kind of shivering motion'. This author also commented on peculiar sounds emitted by bees as signals related to preparations for their swarming. At present, such sounds are known as 'bee-piping'.

One might wonder whether this complex behavior of bees does or does not indicate the occurrence of consciousness, correlated with the neurologic circuit activities. The question is evidently undecidable, since consciousness, except as it pertains to the observer, is intrinsically unobservable. Personally, I am inclined to assume that bees are conscious, that is, not only register input and manifest output, but actually 'perceive', or, in other words, are aware of their surroundings and at least of some of their own activities.

A few details concerning the vision of bees will be discussed further below under heading 12, in connection with some general remarks on the structure of advanced invertebrate optic systems, as compared with vertebrate ones.

Concerning the chemoreceptor sense of bees, it seems experimentally established, according to v. FRISCH (1950 and others), that the outer 8 segments of the antenna in the worker is concerned with olfaction. Bees are said to distinguish about as many different qualities of odor as human beings whose sense of smell is fully developed. However, the olfactory apparatus of bees is presumably much more sensitive.

Bees are also provided with sense organs of taste located on the mouth parts, and examine food when it is taken up. If offered a solution containing 20% sucrose, bees ordinarily suck it up. If it contains 10%, there are individual differences: some bees drink, some hesitate, and others refuse it. If it contains 5%, they taste, but refuse it (v. FRISCH, 1950 and others). Bees distinguish, just as man, sweet, salty, sour, and bitter matter. They are, however, more sensitive to salty and sour substances, and much less to bitter ones. Thus, they will, to some extent, take up mixtures of sugar and quinine.

The brain of insects seems to provide, moreover, a 'computing mechanism' registering the 'flow of time' with respect to 'seasonal changes'. It appears possible that, as days become longer in the spring, the changes in the length of alternating periods of light and darkness may initiate, by means of the brain mechanism, arousal from 'winter sleep' as well as the onset of further growth and other activities.

Another difficult, and, for that matter, undecidable question is that of '*pain*' perception in arthropods. Thus, while a bee is engaged in sipping honey, its abdomen can be quickly severed from the thorax 'without disturbing it in the least'. Again, carnivorous caterpillars, according to v. BUDDENBROCK ('The Senses'. University of Michigan Press 1958, p. 53), may eat up 'sizable chunks of themselves'. If such caterpillar happens to touch with its mouth a bleeding wound on its own body, 'it will begin to feed on itself'. In one of his essays, J. HUXLEY reports that a worker wasp, attending its nest, and being without food for a hungry grub, may bite this latter's 'tail' off, and feed it to the mutilated grub's head.

One could thus infer that insects probably have no pain sense at all. Additional observations of this sort are briefly mentioned further below on page 188. Considering some further aspects of arthropod behavior as e. g. discussed on page 190, such lack of pain sense might appear highly appropriate, beneficial, or desirable. Moreover, there seems to be no evidence for the presence of peripheral nerve endings in insects directly comparable to those involved in 'pain' sensations of higher vertebrates. In many lower vertebrates, on the other hand, there are strong motor reactions to what one could consider 'painful' stimuli. Yet, this does, of course, not conclusively prove that 'pain' is actually experienced.

It is an evident truism that those neural activities of animals subsumed by the concepts 'sensory', 'receptory', 'afferent from periphery', etc., namely the neural inputs of variety, i.e. information, transduced by the neurosensory mechanisms, are, by a human observer, 'understood', 'described', 'defined', and 'gaged' ('gauged') primarily in terms of the available human sensory experience. *Per analogiam*, it seems not unreasonable to assume that in closely related animal forms, such as 'higher' mammals, comparable or similar experiences occur. Clearly, if said neural processes involve animal forms such as insects, which, in the aspect under consideration, might be regarded as entirely 'unrelated', inferences *per analogiam* will carry much less 'probability' or 'conviction'. A more abstract formulation, although less vivid, will then, because of the greater extension of its terms, seem preferable, at least for certain purposes[38].

In several previous publications, dealing with fundamental questions significant for neurologic theory (which means: for the formulation of neurologic theories, *für neurologische Theorienbildung*, not 'für eine Theorie der Neurologie' which I do not presume to proffer), I have outlined what I believe to be a suitable classification of the obtaining variety of events (Brain and Consciousness, 1957; SCHOPEN-HAUERS Bedeutung für die Neurologie. Der Nervenarzt *32*: 177–182,

---

[38] Since it is now customary that 'scientists', *per fas et nefas*, make headlines in the newspapers, with sensational announcements, the 'New York Times' of December 29, 1963, and the 'Philadelphia Inquirer' of the same date report from the Annual Meeting of the American Association for the Advancement of Science (Cleveland, Ohio, December 28, 1963) that, as tests by *'scientists'* indicate 'even the fly may love, hate, fear and suffer', and that 'tests on brains show insects have "moods"'. Frustrated cockroaches are, according to these reports, supposed to show changes in chemistry of their body fluids similar to those induced in higher animals by emotional stress. Depending, of course, on how 'emotion' and 'affectivity' is defined, we might, as I have discussed in 'Brain and Consciousness' (1957, p. 267/268 *et passim*) even observe emotional behavior in machines. Personally, however, I would favor a somewhat more sceptical and restrained attitude in extrapolating from insect behavior to behavior in mammals and man.

1961; Mind and Matter — an appraisal of their significance for neurologic theory, 1961). In a discussion of the senses of insects, the following summary may perhaps be appropriate.

Adapting and modifying some concepts of ZIEHEN, all physical events external to the nervous system represent one main class of variety designated as *R-events* ('reduced' events). These, again, *can* (but not *must*) be subsumed under three subclasses: mechanical, chemical, radiational. All those events within the physical nervous system which can be considered signals, that is, transduced or encoded R-events, represent another main class of variety, namely *N-events*. 'Code' is here merely the 'orderly' transform of one sort of variety into another sort of variety (by one-one, one-many, or many-one transformations), and 'signal' is no more than transmitted selected variety. Selected variety is information, and 'existing' but not selected, i.e. not 'determined' variety is 'probability' or 'uncertainty'.

A third main class of variety consists of all those events that occur in any given private field of awareness (or consciousness), or, in other words that are 'mental' or experienced. The word, 'experienced', is here used to denote an exclusively 'mental' or 'psychologic' referent. Because it may be postulated that such private, conscious events occur only in a causally unspecifiable, intrinsically inexplicable ('parallel') relation to certain sorts of N-events, all private conscious events are classified as *P (parallel)-events*.

Again, the terms non-parallel and parallel N-events may be used. The former term clearly indicates physical neural events of signal-significance. The term, parallel N-event, although permissible, is ambiguous, since it might refer to the physical neural component (in public physical space-time) of a mental event (in private perceptual space-time), or to its 'parallel' mental component alone, or to the 'correlation' of both. The somewhat involved epistemologic considerations justifying this trialistic formulation (variety of R-, N-, and P-events) are particularly elaborated in two of my cited publications (K., 1957; 1961).

While P-events are experienced by the observer and reasoner, all N- and R-events are inferred (and expressed in thought-symbols) on the basis of those P-events which represent behavioral manifestations of organisms or of 'objects'.

Since the observer experiences only the variety of his 'own' P-events within his given perceptual space-time system, the P-events in other such presumed systems can only be inferred. In human language, the variety of P-events is expressed by words denoting various sensory or perceptual modalities, such as sight, hearing, touch, taste, smell, pain, emotion, thought, etc.

Now, if we take, for instance, the phenomena designated as 'light' and 'color', these designations, quite evidently, primarily were coined as referring to a certain variety of consciousness modalities, namely of visual experiences or visual P-events. Yet, it is permissible to correlate these experiences with physiologic processes (N-events) in retina, neural optic channels, and brain. In turn, these N-events can be regarded, in terms of causal sequences, as effects of physical events (R-events), namely radiation, acting on the retina. Thus, 'light' and 'color' might be discussed in terms of either P-, N-, or R-events, or in terms of two or all three of said events.

Clearly, one runs then into considerable difficulties, if an attempt is made to correlate, say, chemical, radiational, or other physical events (R-events) acting on neurosensory transducers, and the resulting N-events, on one hand, with possibly occurring related P-events, on the other hand, in animal forms so different from man as, e. g., insects.

Thus, although one might speak, with reference to chemoreceptors and their activities, of 'smell' or 'taste' in arthropods or insects, it is obvious that, despite some similarities as regards the physical R- and N-events, said 'human' sensory terms should be used with the required cautious reservations. This, of course, applies here not only in general to all senses, but quite particularly to such terms denoting modalities of 'pain' or 'emotion'.

As regards numerical data on the sensory input of the insect brain, HANSTRÖM (1928) estimates the number of primary (sensory) cells in bees at several hundred thousand, perhaps even 10^6. In each antenna of a worker bee, there are at least, in addition to other sensory elements, 4000 presumably olfactory sensory plates, each comprising several sensory cells, while a drone possesses about 31 000 such structures (HANSTRÖM, 1928). Since the number of olfactory glomeruli does not exceed 900 to 1000 (e. g. in wasps), considerable 'concentration of the stimuli' (HANSTRÖM, 1928), that is, convergence of input, must here take place in the brain of insects.

Generally speaking, the *sensory system* of insects includes, in addition to the eyes, receptors for 'touch', chemoreceptors ('taste' and 'smell') and presumably proprioceptors. Muscular receptor organs similar to those found in the muscles of crustaceans have been identified by several observers in insects. Yet, in thoracic muscles concerned with flight, proprioceptive endings have not been demonstrated (at least until recently). Thus, PRINGLE (1957) remarks that, until thoracic muscle receptor organs have been shown to exist in a winged insect, it must be assumed that direct proprioceptive indication of flight movements is provided entirely by sense organs on the wings themselves. The wings of all insects so far examined receive a sensory nerve trunk with branches running in the main 'veins'. The complicated sense organs are bristles and hairs of different lenght, as well as so-called campaniform and chordotonal sensilla.

Bristles and hairs are presumed to be mainly tactile in function, but might also react to air flow over the moving wings. Campaniform receptors are believed to be mechanoceptors, reacting to strains in the exoskeletal sheet. Chordotonal sensilla may react to vibration, and particularly seem to register changes in length between their two points of attachment (PRINGLE, 1957). This system of sensilla can thus be regarded as proprioceptive. Another system of ampulla-like sensilla, found in antennae and genital organs of Hymenoptera, is known as *Forel's flasks*, and presumed to represent chemoreceptors.

An important role of the antenna in flight regulation has been assumed, through the registration of the air stream impinging on that structure, perhaps also through the mediation of chordotonal sensilla. Frontal hair plates may likewise register air flow. These structures are innervated by the nervus tegumentarius (dorso-tegumentary branch) of the tritocerebrum, mentioned further above.

Various methods of sound production ('sonification') are used (by means of wings, legs, as well as other body parts), and organs of sound detection are present, at least in a number of different insect forms. Sound receptors may be located on diverse portions of the body. Thinned parts of the body wall can represent a tympanum, and such tympana may be on the thorax, particularly metathorax, on the first abdominal segment, or on the 'tibiae' of the anterior legs. Antennae and 'hairs' of insects might likewise pick up sounds.

The simplicity of the chordotonal organs is combined with a considerable compactness and efficiency. Information is encoded in terms of change of frequency of discharge in single neurons. Various species such as those of crickets, locusts, cicadas and some others have their own songs, and different songs have different meanings (i.e. convey different sorts of significant information). Such insects respond selectively to different songs of their own species and ignore those of other species (PIERCE, 1949; JACOBS, 1953; VOWLES, 1961).

Chordotonal organs likewise detect direction of sound depending on the angle of sound incidence to tympanic membrane. The central nervous system may compute the average discharge frequency as the insect turns in relation to the source of sound, and presumably extrapolates a 'fix' for that source by comparing the pulse flow from the two sides of the body. In the tympanic organ of noctuid moths, only two 'A' cells and one 'B' cell represent the neurosensory elements. Here the direction of sound might be encoded by the relative latencies of the discharges from the antimeric organs.

The tympanic responses in noctuid moths have been particularly investigated by ROEDER (1963). These insects respond to the echolocating, high-frequency ('ultrasonic') sounds or 'chirps' emitted by the insectivorous Chiroptera (between 25000 to 100000 cps). The moth may detect bats at a distance of perhaps 100 ft or even more, and take evasive action.

By means of very ingenious technical methods, ROEDER (1963) has recorded flight tracks of bats and moths in the darkness. Depending on the distance at which the bat is detected, the moth will alter its flight path into a loop, or into tight 180 degree turns and similar evasive maneuvers, vertical or horizontal. The direction taken appears to be consistently influenced by the spatial relations of moth to bat. If below the bat, the moth mostly takes a descending flight course, if above, a climbing one, and if at the same level, a horizontal one. Moths reacting to detection of bats at short distance usually go into an abrupt dive with closed wings. The dive may also be interrupted by short bursts of wing action or may be a straight power dive into the ground.

This seems to indicate that high sound intensities produce non-directional responses, and low sound intensities directional ones (ROEDER, 1963). The evasive action displayed by simply 'dropping' to the ground can be interpreted as somewhat related to the 'death-feigning reflex briefly discussed further below (p. 190).

In addition to the flight tracks, this author obtained numerous oscillographic recordings of the moth's tympanic nerve responses to the high frequency 'sonar' pulses of bats, as well as to stimulation by artificial 'sounds' (ultrasonic pulses) simulating those of bats.

In some locusts, neither of the two sound receptive organs (tympanic organ and cercal hair sensilla) can perform frequency analysis. Yet, the central nervous system of that insect may probably be able to achieve this operation by matching the input from both organs, since these latter have different frequency ranges and are connected with different auditory large fiber tracts (SUGA and KATSUKI, 1961).

The use of sound waves for animal orientation by means of echo-location ('sonar') was first discovered in bats (DIJKGRAAF, 1946; GALAMBOS and GRIFFIN, 1940; GRIFFIN, 1944, 1958), and subsequently in porpoises (KELLOGG, 1953, and others). Among insects, the gyrinid water beetle ('whirligig beetle', 'Taumelkäfer') Gyrinus marinus and Gyrinus natator seems to present a case of such orientation. EGGERS (1926) investigated the behavior of this swimming insect, that skims the water surface, performing intricate gyrations. These animals were shown to avoid collision with the walls of a glass vessel even in total darkness, while unable to avoid obstacles after their antennae were amputated.

The gyrinid antennae are complex, club-shaped structures, whose second segment contains a peculiar sensory arrangement, known as *Johnston's organ*. In addition, it is provided with a fringe of stiff hairs floating on the surface film of water as the beetle skims about. EGGERS interpreted this apparatus as a pressoreceptor registering fluctuations of the water surface.

GRIFFIN (1953, 1958, 1959) has elaborated on EGGERS findings and assumes that surface waves generated by the beetle's motions are reflected from solid objects that interrupt the surface of the water. Such reflected waves are detected by the movements which they impart to the second segment of the antenna. Dust particles and the very thin surface film of oily substances often present on water seem to play an important role in this type of orientation, since the detection of obstacles was much less effective when the beetles were placed in pure distilled water. The mechanical coupling of the antennal hairs to the water surface may thereby be impaired.

The specialized antenna thus presumably provides an extension of touch over the water surface; the detection of reflected waves is apparently facilitated by repeated brief interruptions of the beetle's swimming movements. GRIFFIN (1958) states that the inclusion of this type of orientation within the category of echolocation is a matter of definition and semantics. Mechanical wave motion is clearly involved, but represented by surface waves, namely essentially vertical surface movements rather than compression waves like those of sound. Yet, in the cited author's opinion, there obtains an analogy in principle between the orientation of the whirligig beetles and the detection of flying insects by the bats.

As CARTHY (1956) justly pointed out with regard to animal navigation, it occurs quite often that a highly specialized mechanism which allows one animal to perform some particular part of its activities, is also found in other, quite unrelated animals.

It is, moreover, of interest that the orientation of animals by means of reflected wave motions initiated by the animal itself was properly understood only after this procedure (*echolocation, sonar, radar*) had been worked out as an artificial, technical mechanism. This circumstance illustrates an old remark by philosophical authors such as KAPP and others, 'dass wir oft die organischen Mechanismen erst dann richtig verstehen, wenn wir sie künstlich nacherfinden können'. Echolocation (sonar, radar) is, of course, in abstract principle, not different from the trivial method of finding one's way in the dark by using a flashlight, namely by scattering and reflection of emitted 'waves'. Yet, there are very numerous complex factors related to the peculiarities of the particular sorts of waves used in such procedures (velocity, frequency, scattering, reflection, relation of wavelength to minimal size of detectable objects, etc.). Other important factors concern the organic or artificial mechanisms of detection, particularly as regards not only direction, but distance. Surface waves on water, which may, as discussed above, play a rôle in echolocation by gyrinid beetles, travel much more slowly than sound waves, and, if within ordinary ranges of amplitude and frequency, can be directly observed by visual inspection. Such waves are occasionally used as 'slow-motion models' in the study of wave motion[38a]. Various aspects of echolocation are discussed in one of GRIFFIN's publications (1959), which provides an elementary yet thorough introduction to the relevant problems.

Concerning the problem 'how animals find their way about', that is, the problem of animal orientation and navigation, CARTHY (1956) has presented a generalized survey, and various aspects of this question are also dealt with in the treatise on instincts by TINBERGEN (1951). AUGUST FOREL (1910, 1920, 1921–1923) particularly emphasized the 'world of scent', and the thereto pertaining antennal chemoreceptors significant for ant behavior; he postulated spatially configured (i.e. 'shaped') odor perceptions in these insects. Such assumed 'shaped odors' would, as it were, parallel the perhaps spatially

---

[38a] Cf. e.g. BRAGG, W.: The Universe of Light (Dover, New York 1959).

configurated 'auditory perceptions' ('shaped sounds') of animals using 'sonar systems'.

As regards insects, it may perhaps be sufficient, in this context, to mention only a few *'navigational procedures'*, such as the scent trails of ants, the visual pattern orientation of wasps returning to their holes, and the orientation by the registration of polarized light patterns in the compound eyes of bees, ants, and possibly various other insects or arthropods. A few additional remarks on shape-recognition and on the ability to detect *polarized light* are included further below in a short discussion of invertebrate optic systems (section 12, page 265).

In many insects the dominance which the brain, perhaps because of its optic input, maintains over the total behavior, is quite conspicuous; yet the ganglia of the various segments can act independently. If silk-worm moths are decapitated, the headless moths live as long as normal ones (McCracken, 1907), and, according to Herrick (1924), 'do not seem to mind the operation very much'. In other moths, both head and thorax were snipped off before or after mating. Such females were incapable of mating and survival was shortened to about five days. The animals previously mated did not lay eggs spontaneously, but, by rubbing the abdomen, could be induced to deposit the eggs. This reflex apparently required the activity of the last abdominal ganglion. It was concluded that the mating and egg-laying reflexes can be initiated by stimuli received by the brain, and that they do not begin 'spontaneously' without the brain. Also, the selection of the proper kind of leaf on which to lay the eggs seems to require the action of cerebral mechanisms. The insect brain, in cases of this sort, has been assumed to play an essential role 'in setting off a complicated system of instinctive activities, involving some rather fine sensory discriminations'. 'When the activity of the body segments is once initiated it can be executed perfectly without the brain' (Herrick, 1924).

The sexual behavior of the praying mantis (Mantis religiosa, Hierodula, and others) demonstrates the possibilites of copulation by a headless insect. The male mantis, somewhat smaller than the female, approaches this latter very slowly, as if stalking a prey. When the partners are within a short distance, the male mounts the female by taking a flying leap. In numerous instances, the female may strike at the male and devour the partner's head as well as prothorax. This 'cannibalistic' response may take place during the male's approach, directly after mounting, or at the time of separation, but not during the actual copulatory event which starts after 5 to 30 min and continues for several hours.

Even if decapitation of the male occurs before actual copulation, mating will be accomplished. Decapitation 'is followed within a few minutes by intense and continuous sexual movements' of the headless male's abdomen (ROEDER, 1963). By a sufficiently strong motion, the male's body pulls itself out of reach of the female's mandibles, so that rarely more than a part of the decapitated thorax can be eaten. 'The sexual movements of the male abdomen continue with vigor, and coupling takes place shortly after mounting. Copulation continues for several hours and a normal spermatophore is formed' (ROEDER, 1963). I suggest that *Freudian* and similar psychoanalysts include this peculiar sexual behavior of the mantis in some of their elaborate as well as nightmarish speculations (if they have not already done so)[39].

ROEDER (1963) reports that experimental decapitation or 'transection of the nerve cord at any point' releases intense sexual behavior in males, even before maturity. This continues for several days, and the decapitated male clasps any object approximating the size of the female body 'and makes vigorous and prolonged attempts to copulate. Although a decapitated male cannot locate a female, he clasps her immediately if placed on her back, and normal copulation usually follows'.

ROEDER put this reaction to practical use in maintaining an inbred strain of mantis in which the intensity of courting by intact males was much reduced. 'A high percentage of fertilized eggs was realized by decapitating the males and placing them on the females' (ROEDER, 1963).

According to the cited author, most of the brain can be removed without subsequent change in sexual activity. It is only after elimination of the subesophageal ganglion that continuous sexual behavior and rotary locomotion is released. It appears that nerve impulses are continuously transmitted from said ganglion through the ventral nerve cord to local centers, where they inhibit the regional motor activities associated with mating. This inhibitory effect becomes,

---

[39] As regards the general biologic aspects of sexual behavior in the animal world, a very comprehensive study has been undertaken by J. MEISENHEIMER: 'Geschlecht und Geschlechter im Tierreiche' (Jena, G. Fischer, 1921). Discounting that author's evident precedence, one might jocularly designate MEISENHEIMER as the 'zoological KINSEY'.

in turn, inhibited or suppressed, when a male with undamaged central nervous system comes in actual contact with a female.

A 'cannibalistic' attitude of female to male is, of course, not exclusiveyly found in Hexapoda. Among other arthropods, the mating of many sorts of Araneae provides another such example. The female is usually larger than the male and devours any intruder of edible size. In some instances there is a pronounced sexual dimorphism, whereby the male has become so small as to be below the prey-size threshold of the female. The male then clambers undisturbed over the female body. BARNES (1963) cites, for the spider Mastophora bisaccata, an average length of 12 mm for the female, and somewhat less than 2 mm for the male.

As regards fixed types of behavior, the so-called 'death-feigning' reflex is of particular interest. Some insects 'disturbed' by 'unusual' situations 'freeze' into rigidly motionless attitudes, whereby, if 'protective' coloring is available, this coloration is displayed to 'advantage'. This sort of 'instinctive' biological reaction is considered 'phylogenetically old', and likewise plays a role in so-called 'animal hypnosis' among vertebrates. Some of these implications of the 'Totstellreflex' were emphasized by KRETSCHMER[40]. Explanations of such mechanisms on the basis of 'natural selection' beg the question, since not 'selection' but origin and working principles of the here involved processes represent the significant problems. There is, however, no valid reason to exclude the possibility that an 'explanation' of the involved parameters could be provided in purely 'mechanistic', non-teleologic terms.

A complex cycle of 'instinctive' reactions is manifested by some wasps, such as mason wasps or mud daubers (Sphecinae, Trypoxylon, Sceliphron). These insects construct or burrow mud cells, into which their eggs are to be deposited. Before sealing the porous chamber, spiders or small insects are captured and so stung as to paralyze these animals. An egg is laid on the crippled, but usually not killed victim, which is then, together with others, up to about twenty, entombed in the cell. The hatched larvae devour the paralyzed prey, and then dig their way out of the chamber. The mother wasp presumably never

---

[40] E. KRETSCHMER, 'Medizinische Psychologie' (Thieme, Leipzig 1926, 2nd ed.; many subsequent editions). The 'Totstellreflex' is likewise briefly considered, from a slightly different viewpoint, in the monograph 'Brain and Consciousness' (K., 1957, S. Karger, Basel/New York, p. 288).

sees her offspring. Other wasps like Pompilidae and Eumeninae (which paralyze caterpillars for use as larval food) have similar habits. In some instances the eggs are deposited within the body of the victim. Thus, the Ephialtes wasp injects her eggs into various insect larvae, particularly into caterpillars of the cabbage butterfly. Some species of Ephialtes select as victims larvae of the wood wasp, hidden within the bark of a coniferous tree. The Ephialtes wasp, exploring the surface of the bark by means of the olfactory receptors in its antennae, is able to locate the victim in its burrow. The predatory wasp's needle-like ovipositor then drills a hole through the bark and into the body of the ensconced larva, depositing the eggs.

In his interesting treatise 'Number: The Language of Science' (Macmillan, New York 1954), the mathematician Tobias Dantzig refers to the behavior of solitary wasps which lay their eggs in individual cells and provide each egg with a number of paralyzed caterpillars as food for the hatching larva. The number of victims per cell, e. g. 5, 12, or 24, is said to be remarkably constant for a given species. Again, in one species of the wasp Eumenes, in which the male is much smaller than the female, a parthenogenetic male egg is supplied with five, and a fertilized female egg with ten victims. Dantzig (1954) regards such behavior as instances of 'number sense' in animals. The quoted author distinguishes here 'number sense', registering the extension of a collection, from 'counting'. 'Direct number perception' may involve operations of one-to-one mapping comparing two collections without actual 'counting', and involves cardinal number. 'Counting' a collection, on the other hand, is supposed to assign, to every member of the collection, a term in the 'natural sequence' of ordered succession, resulting in an ordinal number corresponding to the last term. Be this as it may, there can be little doubt that the neural mechanisms of insects are capable of registering, and operating with, 'numerical aspects' of events. Mathematics and logic, as manifested in human conscious processes, can evidently be considered further developments of this intrinsic property inherent in the activities of neural networks. Hence, instead of stating that logic and mathematics may be expressed in terms of circuit algebra, artificial or neural, it seems justified to reverse the statement and say that logic and mathematics are an expression of neural circuit activities at a high level of brain organization (K., 1957, 1961). Yet, it seems rather incongruous to imply, as some authors do (e. g. Kalmus, in Nature 202: 1156, 1964), that insects or other animals, manifesting 'intelligent' behavior involving complex problem-solving mathematical operations of neural mechanisms, are thereby 'mathe-maticians'.

Among the social insects with elaborate community organizations there are various castes, such as queen, drones, and workers among bees[41], the drones being killed off by the workers at the end of the season. Among ants, there are females, males, workers and soldiers. Ant communities may cultivate the equivalent of agricultural crops, and manifest peculiar sorts of symbiosis, including guests, commensals, and captives; raiding ants, such as Formica sanguinea and others, may enslave other species of ants by robbing eggs or pupae, which are then reared as 'slave workers'. Termites (Isoptera) have likewise a highly developed caste polymorphism.

It is of interest to compare the brains of different insect castes belonging to one and the same species. Thus, in bees (Figs. 108, 109), it is evident that the optic 'centers' display the highest development in drones, who likewise possess highly differentiated olfactory 'centers'. In the queen, as a more 'passive' sexual individual, these just cited, and most other 'centers', are least developed. Workers manifest a fairly good overall differentiation, with olfactory neuropilemes and corpora pedunculata certainly not 'second' to those of drones. Generally speaking, Apis and Bombus are believed to possess the most highly developed corpora pedunculata of insects. Yet, ants also display

---

[41] The queen bee becomes impregnated by the drone only once in her life time, during the 'nuptial flight'. The spermatozoa, received by the queen's spermatotheca, may remain alive for several years. Fertilized eggs are diploid, and give origin to workers or queens, depending on the diet administered to the larvae, and possibly also on some other variables, including even perhaps the size of the 'cell' in which the larva is kept. Drones arise parthenogenetically from unfertilized eggs, and are haploid. In spermato-genesis, no reductional division (meiosis) occurs. In ants, workers and soldiers are likewise modified females. As in bees, the castes, apart from the sex differences, seem to be determined by the type of nourishment supplied to the larvae. In termites, the caste system is more complex and the mechanisms of its differentiation are not yet fully under-stood. The caste system differs somewhat in the diverse taxonomic groups of termites. Altogether, there are winged males and females, males and females in which the wing buds remain abortive, and sterile workers as well as soldiers of both sexes. The repro-ductive castes and the workers give off exudates containing inhibiting substances. These substances are passed to the larvae through the exchange of exudates (trophallaxis) within the colony. Soldiers tend to inhibit the development of other soldiers, males inhibit male development, and queens inhibit the development of other queens. Thus, the proportional representation of the castes in a population seems to be regulated by this hormone mechanism (EMERSON, A. E.: 'Populations of social insects'. Ecological Monographs 9: 287–300, 1939).

unusually well differentiated 'mushroom-bodies'. In ants, moreover (Figs. 113,114), conspicuous caste-differences in brain structure can be easily recognized. In Figure 113, the high differentiation of the female worker's brain is evident even in superficial inspection of the diagram.

PIETSCHKER (1911) has estimated the size relation of corpora pedunculata in workers, females, and males of some ants as corresponding to the ratio 8:4:1. Again, according to THOMPSON (1913) the corpora pedunculata of some ants can comprise slightly more than 40% of the brain, as compared with 10% or less in those forms of insects, arthropods or other invertebrates in which corpora pedunculata, although present, may be poorly developed. Yet, in the brain of the bee, with highly developed corpora pedunculata, the relative size of these structures remains within an order of magnitude of about 13.5% (worker), 9.2% (queen), and 5.6% (drone) according to figures given by BULLOCK and HORRIDGE (1965). The cited authors also tabulate the following additional figures concerning relative and absolute sizes of brain structures in bees: 'optic centers' 31.4%, 33.9% and 67.6% (again in worker, queen and drone, respectively); 'antennal glomeruli' 3.3%, 2.6%, 1.9%; absolute size of central body in mm^3: 0.37, 0.34, 0.16; absolute brain size in mm^3: 0.74; 0.71; 1.175 (cf. Miss FARRELL's figures for workers, within the range of 0.68 to 1.35, as cited above on page 175).

Some authors (e.g. GOOSSEN, 1951; ROEDER, 1958) have remarked that among Hymenoptera and Coleoptera larger species tend to have a smaller brain to body ratio than their smaller 'relatives'. Again, in larger species the corpora pedunculata are said to be larger in proportion to the overall brain size, and their structure is reported as being 'more complex'; also, the number of cells in the calyces seems to be greater (cf. e.g. ROEDER, 1958, in a review of pertinent insect literature).

The approximate figures obtained in our own incidental findings (cf. above p. 175) could be interpreted as very roughly agreeing with such generalized statements. Thus, we would have a brain-body weight ratio of about 1:100 in some ants, of between 1:85 to 1:120 in bees, of circa 1:143 in horseflies, and approximately 1:500 in a cockroach[42]. In the corpora pedunculata of this latter insect, we noticed

[42] J. RANKE ('Der Mensch.' Bibliograph. Inst., Leipzig 1923, Vol. I, p. 594f.) tabulates various figures on brain weight and its relationships (cf. also K., 1927, p. 86f.). The highest brain-body weight ratios are said to be found in some small song birds, namely of about 1:12; in pigeons, this ratio sinks to approximately 1:104. For mammals, the

indeed not only a relatively perhaps 'greater' number of globuli cells, but also a particularly dense crowding, almost comparable to the packing of red blood cells or of lymphocytes, elements which form some of the most compact cell aggregations in the mammalian body.

HANSTRÖM (1926), on the basis of careful investigations, reached the conclusion that the corpora pedunculata of decapod crustaceans are, in general, both relatively and absolutely larger than those of insects. He adds, however, the well-founded remark that quantitative expansion is not necessarily correlated with functional significance or efficiency. In view of some discrepancies obtaining in the available reports by different investigators, and because of various additional uncertainties, one may perhaps be justified to regard the entire set of questions dealing with absolute and relative size of corpora pedunculata as still rather unsettled and ambiguous, particularly with regard to an evaluation or 'grading' of the functional significance attributed to these structures.

RATZERDORFER (1952) has studied the degree of 'cerebralization' in various insects by means of volumetric studies, based on plani-metric reconstructions from serial sections, and referring to structures such as mushroom bodies, protocerebral bridge, central body, optic ganglia, and antennal glomeruli. In agreement with views expressed

---

following ratios are given: adult homo about 1:36; cat 1:82 to 1:156; gorilla (adult) 1:100; horse 1:400 to 1:700; ox 1:500 to 1:800. As regards man, the ratio sinks from about 1:8 at birth to 1:18 with 3 years, and 1:22 at 15 years. For other vertebrates, figures of this sort are given: frog 1:172; carp 1:248; turtle 1:2240; shark 1:2500; tuna-fish 1:37 440. In my opinion, it is not possible to draw any significant conclusions from such figures at the present time. At most, one could say (a) that body weight and volume may vary within a considerable range without being correlated with changes in brain size and weight of corresponding magnitudes. Also, (b) that wide variations in absolute brain weight do not necessarily correspond to comparable differences in 'in-telligence', whatever this term may mean. Evidently, if a more complete information concerning the significance of brain structures, the details of neural mechanisms, and the various factors of growth processes were available, meaningful parameters and variables could be defined which might be used for a suitable formulation of 'laws' expressing, in a generalized and intelligible form, the various relationships under consideration. As regards such relationships, it has been claimed that, in a series of related vertebrates, the mass or volume of the central nervous system shows the tendency to increase roughly in proportion to the body surface rather than to the body weight. Again, in certain instan-ces, e.g. in some snails, the 'brain weight' in a species of small size may represent a smaller percentage of the body weight than in another but similar species of larger size (cf. BUL-LOCK and HORRIDGE, 1965), thus manifesting a tendency opposite to that mentioned above in the text.

by PORTMANN, such biometric analysis is supposed to bring forward new evidence for the interpretation of evolutionary trends. Because the significance of most of the variables involved in the calculation of these 'volumetric indices' remains insufficiently clarified, the data obtained by this method are, in my opinion, still inconclusive.

With regard to the question of 'instinct' and of 'automatisms', it is of particular interest that observers such as TURNER (1907; also cited and discussed by HERRICK, 1924) and others have detected individual differences in what might be called the 'intelligent' behavior of ants and diverse other insects. Thus, in certain experiments, what appeared an 'insoluble' problem to ant *B* of a given species, was easily and rapidly solved by another individual, ant *A*. Two individuals of the same colony, at the same time, and under identical external conditions, were shown to respond to the same situation in different ways. Each had acquired a different procedure in 'solving a problem', and each had retained and utilized the information gained by experience.

Insect flight is likewise a behavioral manifestation of considerable biologic and general interest. Winged insects appear in the Upper Devonian or Lower Carboniferous (about 300 or 280 million years ago), at first with lateral expansions of the thoracic exoskeletal coverings or 'nota', perhaps merely used for gliding flight.[43]

In the majority of recent flying insects, lift *and* propulsion are produced by active movements of the wings, and the lift does not here merely depend upon the airflow resulting from the insect's forward motion. Although in many instances, forward motion of the body as a whole may be required for flight, the advanced insect fliers can hover or fly backwards and sideways. The analogy with a helicopter is, in this respect, closer than that with a conventional airplane. Yet, unlike a helicopter, the insect's wing motion is oscillatory rather than rotatory, but in both types of mechanism (helicopter and insect) changes in the angle of attack of the airfoils in different parts of the stroke are needed to produce lift, propulsion, and control.

The motions performed by the insect wing in flapping flight comprise thus rather complex combinations of elevation and depression, promotion and remotion (fore and aft movement), pronation and supination (twisting), and changes of shape by folding and

---

[43] The *modus operandi* of 'flight', in the widest sense, is manifested by various groups of organic systems, such as airborne pollen, airborne seeds (parachute-like, or statically winged) in plants, flight of insects, 'flight' of fishes, flight of sauropsida, and of mammals.

buckling. The problems here involved have been studied by MAGNAN (1934) as well as subsequent authors, and a critical summary of insect flight, based on original investigations, has been published by PRINGLE (1957)[44]. As regards the control of flight in the locust, WILSON (1961)

---

[44] PRINGLE (1957) reaches the conclusion that there is at present no generally valid simplified theory of insect flight. Yet, some concepts of classical aerodynamic theory can doubtless be used in order to obtain a significant appreciation of the problems involved. Many attempts to understand the nature of animal flight have been based on erroneous concepts about the principles of the subject, and on unreliable data. Thus, a clarification of the matter is perhaps appropriate. The aerodynamic 'forces' involved in the relative motions of airfoil and air are lift (L) and drag (D) which are proportional to the square of the airspeed. Flight of any organic or anorganic configurated system requires sufficient speed to generate a lift at least equal to the system's weight (W). Below a critical airspeed the airfoil, because of additional factors, may, in the manner of a step-function, *suddenly* lose most of its lift, and 'stall' (drop). The lift coefficient (C_L) depends on airfoil shape and angle of attack. Scale, that is order of magnitude, within certain critical ranges, greatly affects lift coefficient (C_L) and drag coefficient (C_D) because of the relationship of air density and viscosity on one hand, and dimensions of airfoil on the other hand. The scale effect is expressed by the *Reynolds number*

$$\mathrm{Re} = \frac{\varrho\,\mathrm{v}\,l}{\mathrm{u}}$$

where ϱ stands for density, v for velocity, l for units of linear dimension, and u for a coefficient of viscosity (cf. my previous discussion in 'Mind and Matter', Basel 1961, p. 361). Because of that scale effect, very significant differences between aerodynamic behaviors of insects, birds, small scale aircraft models, and large full-scale aircraft obtain. However, regardless of these differences due to scale effects, the required minimal airspeed (V_{min}) can be expressed by the formula

$$V_{min} = \sqrt{\frac{2W}{C_L\,\varrho\,S}}$$

where W/S is the wing loading (ratio of weight to surface area), and ϱ, again, air density. Although additional factors are introduced by aspect ratio (wing 'length' to 'breadth'), airfoil shape, slots, etc., a large wing requires less airspeed than a small one, and thus allows rather slow flight. For flapping flight, or flight by rotary motion (propeller, helicopter), involving angular momentum, the airfoil must be moved relatively fast, and small size is here an 'advantage', which particularly favors insects. On the other hand, sustained gliding and soaring flight at low airspeed is found mostly in large birds. As regards insects, we have here a 'favorable' wing loading in various butterflies.

It is perhaps pertinent to emphasize these matters, since J. B. S. HALDANE's publication 'Possible Worlds' (Harper, New York 1928), and D.W. THOMPSON's book 'On Growth and Form' (1942; chapter II: 'On Magnitude') contain the most astounding solecisms concerning these problems. Thus, HALDANE (1928) states that, because it is an elementary principle of aeronautics that the minimum speed, needed to keep an aircraft of a given

concludes that the 'basic coordination' of flight represents an 'inherent function' (whatever this may be) of the central nervous system, but that peripheral feedback loops influence the frequency of operation and the details of pattern. WATERMAN (1950) has elaborated on some

shape flying, varies as the square root of its length, an aircraft of four times a given dimension must fly twice as fast and requires a still very much larger multiple of the motive power. HALDANE entirely forgets here that, to a significant degree and within a significant range, increasingly favorable wing loadings may be combined with increasing dimensions. His additional remark that 'even soaring becomes more and more difficult with increasing size' is simply plain nonsense. Although there are, of course, parameters limiting size, HALDANE gives here an entirely misleading picture by ignoring elementary and significant aspects of aerodynamics.

THOMPSON (1942) is even worse: he tells us that the airspeed of a bird 'must increase as its size increases', and that 'the bird's necessary speed, such as enables it to maintain level flight, must be proportional to the square root of its linear dimensions'. Again: 'the heavy birds must fly quickly or not at all'. 'The bigger the bird becomes, the more swiftly must the air stream over the wing'... 'and the harder must it be to fly.' He then comments: 'The above considerations are of great practical importance in aeronautics, for they show how a provision of increasing speed must accompany every enlargement of our aeroplanes. Speaking generally, the necessary or minimal speed of an aeroplane varies as the square root of its linear dimensions.'

Now, when I was an enthusiastic private pilot, I flew once (in the late nineteen thirties) with CLARENCE CHAMBERLIN in what was at one time considered the world's largest airplane (carrying about forty or so passengers). This huge 'crate', an old-fashioned biplane, had a stalling and landing speed of little over forty miles, and this type aircraft was soon discarded as being far too slow. At the same period, I flew once in a very small size and much faster two-seater monoplane that had a stalling speed of about sixty miles, and, in order to be on the safe side, one had to make what was then regarded 'hot landings' with between 70 to 80 miles on the last approach.

I am pointing out the rather trivial solecisms of Messrs. HALDANE and THOMPSON merely to stress my sceptical attitude toward learned academic pundits who constantly preach about the accuracy based on mathematical method, and condescendingly look down on mere morphologists or on scientists not pertaining to their particular coteries. In §79 of 'Mind and Matter' (1961) I have elaborated on various such aspects. I am well aware that, in dealing with a large variety of subjects, I might myself, at times, despite my efforts to the contrary, commit some spectacular blunders, and I am quite willing to 'face the music'. But then, I do not claim to be a mathematician nor even an uncritical admirer of mathematics.

It reflects little credit on the editor of 'The World of Mathematics' (J. R. NEWMAN, ed., Simon and Schuster, New York 1956) to have incorporated HALDANE's and THOMPSON's misleading statements on flight, under the heading 'On Being the Right Size', and 'On Magnitude', respectively, in a collection of mathematical literature supposed to enlighten interested outsiders. As regards biologic implications of 'size' and 'magnitude' in general (disregarding the problems of flight), he would have done somewhat better by including J. HUXLEY's essay 'The size of living things' (in: Man stands alone. Harper, New York 1941).

analogies between aircraft flight instruments (air speed indicator and gyroscopic turn indicator) and insect sense organs (connected with antennae and with the dipteran halteres).

Wingbeat frequencies of 150 to 300 cps (cycles per second) are characteristic for many flies, bees and wasps. Much higher frequencies in short bursts of thoracic vibrations have been reported from a small

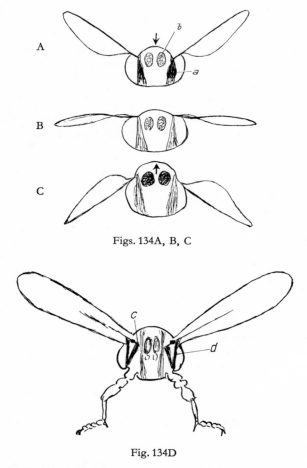

Figs. 134A, B, C

Fig. 134D

Figure 134. Diagrams showing, in transverse sections through the insect thorax, the mechanisms of indirect (*A, B, C*), and (*D*) direct flight muscles. (Adapted and modified after MAGNAN, 1934, and various other authors.) a: vertical (dorsoventral) muscles; b: (dorsal) longitudinal muscles; c: wing elevators; d: wing depressors; A: top of upstroke; C: bottom of downstroke. In *D*, the pivot or fulcrum of wing motion is indicated by a black dot.

midge after amputation of the wings. ROEDER (1958), in reviewing these data, remarks that nerve excitation in many of the insect muscles produces a tetanus at stimulus frequencies higher than 50 cps. Thus, the high wingbeat frequencies would make it evident that considerable discrepancies obtain between certain sorts of experimental neuro-physiological findings, and normal functions as actually observed. ROEDER (1958) opines that said high wingbeat frequencies 'suggest other factors in the excitation of indirect flight muscles'.

The power for the up- and downstrokes may be provided by direct muscles attached to processes of the wing base. These muscles are dominant in Blattoidea (cockroach-like insects), and remain im-portant in all Orthoptera (grasshoppers, etc.), Coleoptera (beetles), and Odonata (dragon flies). In most other flying insects, the main power for the stroke seems to be provided by indirect muscles (Fig. 134). The direct muscles become reduced in size, but seem always to remain of some importance for the control of the wing beat. The indirect muscles are longitudinal and oblique dorso-ventral. The complexities obtaining in the peripheral innervation of some muscles significant for flight mechanisms are indicated by Figure 135.

In concluding these various remarks on behavioral aspects of the biologically highly important group of organic forms represented by the Hexapoda or insects, some comments on *neurohumoral* and related activities seem pertinent.

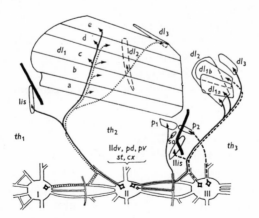

Figure 135. Innervation of certain flight muscles in meso- and metathorax of Telea polyphemus (Lepidoptera). (After NUESCH from PRINGLE, 1957.) cx: coxal; dl: dorsal longitudinal; dv: dorsoventral; is: intersegmental; p: pleural; pd: tergopleural; pv: pleurosternal; st: sternal; the thoracic segments are indicated by the subscript of th.

The initial stimulus in the moulting of insects has been shown to originate in the brain, which is presumably the source of a hormone, demonstrable in extracts of insect brains. Neurosecretory cells are found in several parts of the protocerebrum, particularly in the pars intercerebralis. Additional elements of that type may occur in other subdivisions of the brain and in the subesophageal ganglion. Axons from such cells in the pars intercerebralis form a neurosecretory pathway to the paired corpora allata, the corpora cardiaca, and perhaps a number of other endocrine glands with different names in different taxonomic forms, e. g. the pericardial gland, the prothoracic glands, and the peritracheal gland (HANSTRÖM, 1938).

The corpora allata were the first endocrine glands identified in insects. These glands arise by budding of ectodermal cells between the mandibular and maxillary segments, becoming separated from the epidermis, and, in some forms, fusing into a single median structure. The corpus cardiacum is closely associated with the corpora allata, but nervous in origin, and apparently arising, like the remainder of the stomatogastric nervous system, from an ingrowth of the dorsal wall of the stomodeum. One or two pairs of nerves from the brain innervate corpora allata and corpora cardiaca. The axons in the medial nerve cross in the midline.

The secretory material can be stained deep blue with chrome-hematoxylin after oxidation with permanganate (*Gomori* method), in the same manner as in vertebrates. By means of this method, it can be followed along the axons to the corpus cardiacum where it collects between the cells. The corpus cardiacum seems to serve as a storage organ for the secretion. If the nerve to the corpus cardiacum is cut on one side in the cockroach Leucophaea maderae (Fig. 136), there is a considerable accumulation of neurosecretory material above the cut, while a striking depletion occurs, distal to the cut, in the corpus cardiacum of that side (B. SCHARRER, 1952).

The analogies between the corpus cardiacum and corpus allatum system of insects and the pituitary system of vertebrates are of considerable interest and were pointed out by HANSTRÖM (1941) and WIGGLESWORTH (1954). In both instances there is an epithelial ectodermal component (corpus allatum and adenohypophysis) as well as a neuro-ectodermal component (corpus cardiacum and neurohypophysis) forming a secretory complex. Both neurohypophysis and corpus cardiacum are innervated in the same manner (HANSTRÖM, 1953) by neurosecretory pathways from neurosecretory cells (hypothalamus and pars intercerebralis). In both systems it is possible to trace the secretory material, by means of the *Gomori* technique, from nerve cell to endocrine structure.

From the corpora cardiaca, nerves have been traced to the digestive tract and some other organs. Although substances stored in the corpora cardiaca are generally believed to be released into the blood, there is evidence that some neurohormones may be distributed from said

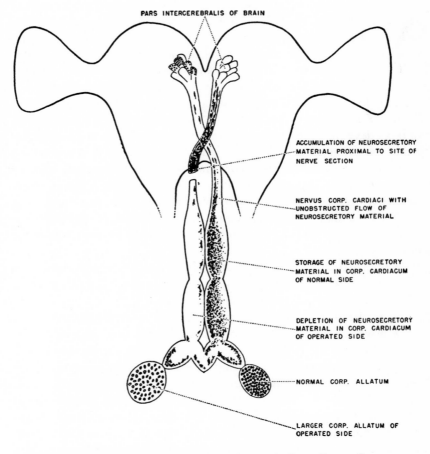

Figure 136. Diagram of the neurosecretory intercerebralis-cardiacum-allatum system of Leucophaea maderae in dorsal aspect. (From B. SCHARRER, 1952.)

On the left side the nervus corporis cardiaci is severed; neurosecretory material is increased proximal to, and depleted distal to, the cut; corpus allatum enlarged on operated side.

corpora to the effector or 'target' organs along nerve axons (JOHNSON and BOWERS, 1963).

In addition to the effects of this neurosecretory system upon pupal development and moulting, extracts of the corpora cardiaca affect water metabolism, activity of musculature and heart, as well as pigmentation. The corpora allata may influence fat metabolism and egg production.

B. SCHARRER (1953) summarized hormonal events in the course of insect development as follows: In response to a nonendocrine, such as a nervous stimulus, a hormone is released either from the neurosecretory cells of the brain which produce it, or from the corpus cardiacum which stores it. The hormone triggers prothoracic or comparable structures, which in turn give off the growth and differentiation hormone. This 'principle' acts on the effector organs which respond with changes leading to imaginal differentiation, unless an additional 'juvenile hormone' is present in the circulation at the same time. The interaction of both developmental hormones results in larval (or nymphal) molts, while the presence of the growth and differentiation hormone alone (e. g. in animals in which the corpora allata were extirpated) leads to metamorphosis. Periods of growth may thus occur without interference by precocious metamorphic changes. Once the insect has reached a certain size and stage, the completion of development presumably takes place in the absence of a sufficient amount of juvenile hormone.

The neurosecretory cells, in their 'dual capacity' as nerve cells and 'gland cells' are believed to act as 'mediators between the two systems of integration' (neural and hormonal).

In addition to growth and moulting, the swarming reactions of some insects, such, e. g. as locusts (Orthoptera), may involve neurohumoral processes. It is believed that male locusts secrete an exudate pertaining to the biochemical group of 'ectohormones' or pheromones (BUTENANDT, 1961; KARLSON and BUTENANDT, 1959). In locusts, this substance seems to stimulate the females, triggering neurohumoral brain centers. These latter, by way of the corpora allata, initiate, perhaps through some neural feedback-effect, a state of feverish excitement, crowding, and jostling, which finally results in the well-known mass migrations.

As regards the generalizing term 'neurohumoral processes', it should be kept in mind that, within such neurosecretory activities, various processes of different nature may be involved. Thus, CAZAL and BOGORAZE (1943a) justly remark: 'Ne pas confondre la neuricrinie, sécrétion d'hormones par des cellules d'origine nerveuse (neurosécrétion de SCHARRER), et la neurocrinie, transmission d'hormones le long de formations nerveuses.'

10. Mollusca

These soft-bodied and non-metameric, bilaterally symmetrical invertebrates are usually enclosed within a calcareous shell secreted by the animal. Besides the generally recognized five classes, namely, Amphineura (with the genus Chiton), Gastropoda, Pelecypoda, Scaphopoda, and Cephalopoda, another group was recently discovered. Some specimens of Neopilina, pertaining to a type previously only known in Cambrian fossils, were dredged from a deep ocean trench of the Pacific near the coast of Costa Rica in 1952. These animals externally resemble a combination of gastropod and chiton, but display an apparent metameric plan of organization, and develop from trochophore larvae. This has been interpreted as evidence for the annelid origin of mollusks. Yet, the metamerism might be a secondary acquisition and would thus not preclude the origin of mollusks from non-metameric forms similar to Turbellaria. In the opinion of BARNES (1963), at the present 'the older theory that assumes a common origin for both mollusks and annelids still seems to have the greatest weight of evidence'. The cited author also believes that the elevation of the group Monoplacophora (the fossil group into which Neopilina has been included) to that of a sixth 'class' of Mollusca (namely a class characterized by an independent tendency toward metamerism), is 'completely justified'.

As regards the nervous system, Chiton, representing the *Amphineura*, displays a general arrangement quite similar to that in Planaria, and suggesting, as PLATE (1922) emphasized, the possibility of a derivation of Mollusca from Turbellaria-like forms.

In Chiton (Fig. 137, 138), there is a pharyngeal ring, including a 'cerebral' medullary portion; this ring is connected with two paired medullary cords, a lateral (palliovisceral) and a basal (pedal) one. In addition there are small ganglia, such as a buccal, and a subradular ganglion. The paired cords are comparable to those of Turbellaria. Moreover, these cords are interconnected by an irregular network which has some similarities with a 'primitive' peripheral plexus.

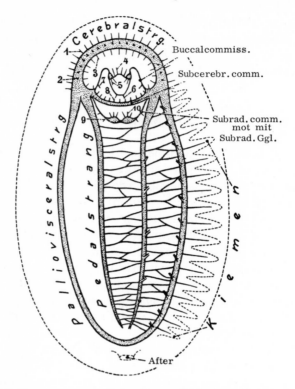

Figure 137. Nervous system of Amphineura (Chiton), as seen in dorsal aspect. (Simplified after PLATE and others by BÜTSCHLI, 1921, from HANSTRÖM, 1928.) 1: mantle nerves; 2–10: various peripheral nerves.

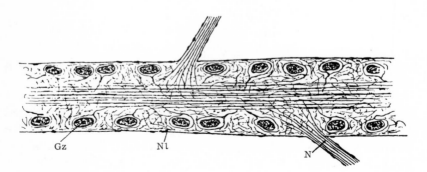

Figure 138. Medullary cord of Chiton, with (pseudo) unipolar nerve cells. (After PLATE, 1922.) Gz: nerve cell; N: peripheral nerve; Nl: sheath of medullary cord.

The nervous system of the other mollusk classes can be easily derived from the relatively simple arrangement obtaining in Chiton (Figs. 139, 140, 141). Concentration of nerve cells in various regions provides the cerebral, pedal, pleural, visceral, and other ganglia as indicated in Figure 142, which shows the configuration obtaining in a species of Aplacophora. These latter, worm-like mollusks, lacking a true shell, are considered to represent a small group of 'aberrant' Amphineura, comprising approximately hundred species.

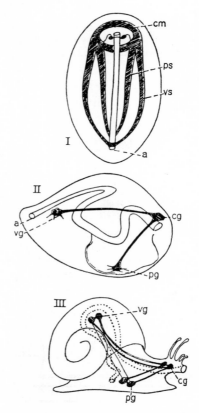

Figure 139. Very simplified diagrams showing general configuration of central nervous system in different groups of Mollusca. (From K., 1927.) I. Chiton, modified after PLATE (the small rostral ganglion near the oral end of the gut represents the buccal ganglion). II. Lamellibranch mollusk (e. g. clam). III. Gastropod (snail). a: anus; cg: cerebral ganglion cm: cerebral medullary ring; pg: pedal ganglion; ps: pedal cord or strand; vg: visceral ganglion; vs: pallivisceral cord or strand.

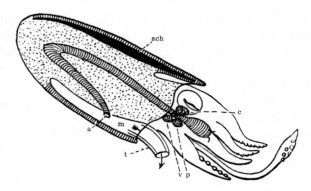

Figure 140. Simplified diagram showing general configuration of central nervous system in cephalopod Mollusca. (After R. HERTWIG, 1912.) a: anus; c: cerebral ganglion; m: mantle cavity; p: pedal ganglion; sch: shell; t: funnel; v: visceral ganglion.

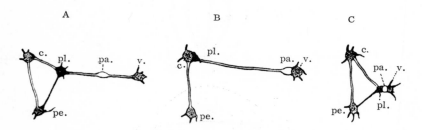

Figure 141. Different patterns of nervous system configuration in various Mollusca. (After R. HERTWIG, 1912.) *A* Majority of Cephalophora. *B* Lamellibranchia. *C* Cephalopoda and Pulmonata (Cephalophora). c: cerebral ganglion; pl: pleural ganglion; pa: parietal ganglion; pe: pedal ganglion; v: visceral ganglion.

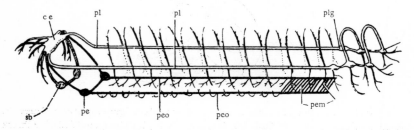

Figure 142. Diagram showing configuration of nervous system in the aplacophore mollusk Proneomenia sluiteri. (After LANG, from SELENKA-GOLDSCHMIDT, 1919.) ce: cerebral ganglion; pe: pedal ganglion; peo: pedal cord; pem: commissures of pedal cord; pl: pleurovisceral cord; plg: posterior pleurovisceral ganglion; sb: sublingual ganglion.

Diverse patterns of reduction by fusion, as well as increase in number by additional cell groupings are manifested in the different classes, orders, and genera of mollusks. Generally speaking, even in the most 'primitive' forms of this phylum, a more or less continuous outer layer of nerve cells, enclosing the inner neuropilemes, is displayed, in conformity with the structural pattern manifested by the larger nerve trunks, or the ganglionated masses, of other, relatively well differentiated invertebrates.

Concerning synaptic or asynaptic connections in mollusks, HERRICK (1924), on the basis of experiments by CROZIER and AREY (1919) and by MOORE (1917), reached the conclusion that in 'primitve' mollusks the body is pervaded with a non-synaptic nerve net from which, however, synaptic ganglia also have become differentiated. In higher mollusks (and for that matter, in other 'higher' animal forms) a progressively larger proportion of the entire nervous system is assumed to be transformed into the synaptic type, 'but usually with some remnants of the non-synaptic type remaining' (HERRICK, 1924). In this respect, MOORE (1917) had concluded that small doses of strychnine in a definite concentration disturb the functions of synaptic nervous systems without affecting non-synaptic nerve nets. The function of these latter, however, are said to be abolished by doses of magnesium sulfate in certain concentrations.

Pelecypoda (or Lamellibranchiata)[45] display at least a cerebropleural ganglion, a pedal ganglion, and a visceral ganglion. *Scaphopoda* (e.g. the 'toothshell' Dentalium) which some taxonomists still include with the Lamellibranchiata, display the same general arrangement; the pleural ganglion, however, may here be separate from the cerebral

---

[45] The class Pelecypoda, Lamellibranchia, or Lamellibranchiata (Acephala) was formerly conveniently subdivided into the two orders Protoconcha and Heteroconcha. Recent systems of classification are more complex, and include, roughly, the orders Protobranchia (e.g. Nucula), Filibranchia (e.g. the edible oyster Ostrea, the pearl oysters Pinctada and Meleagrina, the scallop Pecten), Eulamellibranchia (e.g. the clam Mercenaria, the giant clam Tridacna, the 'shipworm' Teredo), and Septibranchia which have lost the gills, respiration being performed by the mantle (the fold or envelope which, on its outside, produces the calcareous shell).

As regards sensory receptors, the mantle margin of Pelecypoda may bear sensory tentacles; a statocyst may be located near the pedal ganglion, and ocelli, some of which can be unusually well developed, as in Pecten, may be present along the mantle edge. A patch of sensory epithelium, the osphradium, is regarded as possibly representing a chemoreceptor organ.

ganglion, and some additional ganglia, such as a buccal ganglion, and a subradular ganglion, similar to those of Chiton, are present.

Gastropoda (Cephalophora)[46] display various complexities in the arrangement of their nervous system. A buccal ganglion is located rostrally to the cerebral ganglion, and innervates the muscles of the radula[47] and other structures. The paired visceral nerve cord contains additional (pleural and parietal) ganglia. The different ganglionic masses may display various degrees of displacement and concentration. If the connectives between ganglia are long, a characteristic asymmetry results from a torsion into a figure eight. This is called the chiastoneural condition (Fig.143, I), and is regarded as a 'primitive feature' of the gastropod nervous system, since torsion may have developed during the 'evolutionary history' of all gastropods. If the connections between ganglia are short because of concentration, their configuration is not influenced by torsion, and the so-called orthoneural condition obtains (Figs.143, II, 144). Thus, a tendency toward secondary bilateral symmetry becomes manifested. Reduction of the shell, concentration of the ganglia, and displacement of the organs of the mantle cavity are commonly regarded as important evolutionary changes in the phylogeny of opisthobranchiate gastropods.

The cerebral ganglion of the land snail Helix pomatia (Pulmonata) shows several distinct subdivisions such as procerebrum, mesocerebrum, commissura centralis, and postcerebrum (Fig.145). The mesocerebrum contains rather large nerve cells, and two giant cells, a superior and an inferior one, are found in the postcerebrum. The procerebrum is believed to be a characteristic structure of Pulmonata (HANSTRÖM, 1928). Some details concerning the pattern of fiber connections in the gastropod nervous system can be gathered from an inspection of Figures 146 to 148, which are based on HANSTRÖM'S

---

[46] The main subdivisions (orders or perhaps 'sub-classes') of Gastropods are, very roughly, Prosobranchia, Opistobranchia, Heteropoda, Pteropoda, and Pulmonata. This last named order is characterized by an air sac (lung), and includes some purely terrestrial forms such as the snail Helix and the slug Limax; a few Pulmonates have 'lungs' and gills. Most other Gastropods have gills. In the generally transparent, pelagic Pteropods or 'sea butterflies', the anterior part of the 'foot' is expanded to form swimming fins. Some Pteropods, devoid of gills, are skin breathers. The sense organs include ocelli, tentacles, statocysts, and osphradia. In Gastropods, the osphradium is believed to be a sense organ that may react to the sediment present in the water flowing over the gills. It is absent in some forms, particularly in those without gills.

[47] The molluscan radula is a belt-like or plate-like organ of the buccal cavity functioning as a scraper. This motile organ carries rows of chitinous teeth.

investigations. Figure 149 indicates the elementary structural features, which conform to the arrangement prevailing in most groups of invertebrates.

Reverting to molluscs in general, presumably 'genuine' neurosecretory elements were found in supraintestinal and pleural ganglia of some species of prosobranch gastropods. In various species of opistobranch gastropods evidence of neurosecretory activity was observed

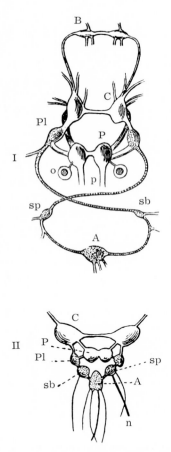

Figure 143. Chiastoneural and orthoneural pattern in Cephalophora. (After various authors from R. HERTWIG, 1912.) I. Chiastoneural pattern in Paludina. (After IHERING, in GEGENBAUR, 1898.) II. Orthoneural pattern in Limnaeus. (After LACAZE-DUTHIERS.)

A: visceral ganglion; B: buccal ganglion; C: cerebral ganglion; n: 'olfactory' nerve; o: statocyst; P: pedal ganglion; Pl: pleural ganglion; sb: subintestinal ganglion; sp: supraintestinal ganglion (parietal ganglion).

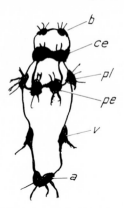

Figure 144. Simplified orthoneural pattern in opisthobranch Gastropods. (From SELENKA-GOLDSCHMIDT, 1919.) a: abdominal ganglion; b: buccal ganglion; ce: cerebral ganglion; pe: pedal ganglion; pl: pleural ganglion; v: visceral ganglion.

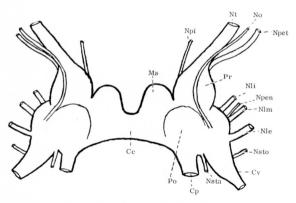

Figure 145. External aspect of brain in the land snail Helix pomatia. (After HANSTRÖM, 1928.) Cc: central commissure; cp: pedal connective; cv: visceral (pleural) connective; Ms: mesocerebrum; Nle, Nli, Nlm: labial nerves; No: optic nerve; Npen: penis nerve; npet, npi: peritentacular nerves; nsta: otocyst nerve; Nsto: cerebrobuccal connective (stomatogastric nerve; Nt: tentacular nerve; Po: postcerebrum; Pr: procerebrum.

in the cerebral ganglion. In both groups of gastropods, the seasonal variation in neurosecretory activity is reported as related to the maturation of gonadocytes. As regards pulmonates, a neuroendocrine system has been recently described by RÖHNISCH (1964); the secretion is apparently transmitted to the nervus labialis (NOLTE, 1964). This latter author also speaks of a 'Cerebraldrüse' in various species of

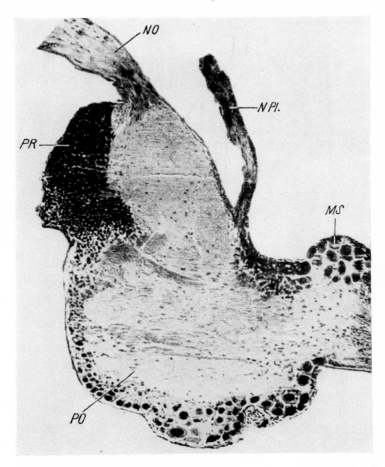

Figure 146. Horizontal section through left half of brain in Helix pomatia. (From HANSTRÖM, 1928.) MS: mesocerebrum; NO: tentacular nerve; Npl: internal peritentacular nerve; PO: postcerebrum; PR: procerebrum (cf. Fig. 145).

helicids.[47a] In pelecypods (Lamellibranchia, bivalves), cerebral and visceral ganglia are said to exhibit consistent neurosecretory activity, but not the pedal ganglia (ORTMANN, 1960).

[47a] Histologic and functional data on the cerebral gland in Gastropoda can be found in a recent publication by NOLTE and KUHLMANN (1964), and by RÖHNISCH (1964a).

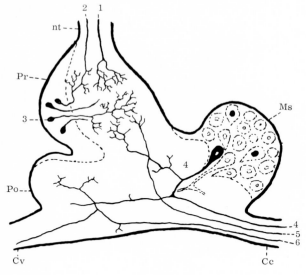

Fig. 147A

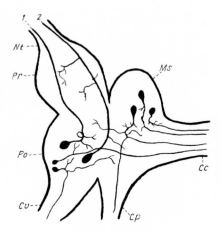

Fig. 147 B

Figures 147 A, B. Diagrams of horizontal sections through left half of brain in Helix pomatia. (From HANSTRÖM, 1928.)

A 1: afferent fiber from tentacle ganglion; 2: fine efferent fiber to tentacle ganglion; 3: internuncial neuron; 4: large nerve cell of mesocerebrum; 5, 6: commissural fibers.

B 1, 2: coarse motor fibers originating in postcerebrum and innervating retractor muscle of tentacle (cf. Fig. 148). Cc, Cp, Cv, Ms, Nt, Po, Pr as in Fig. 145.

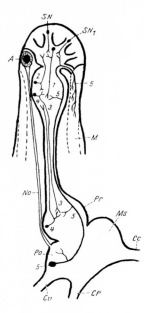

Figure 148. Connections between brain and tentacle in Helix. (From HANSTRÖM, 1928.) A: eye; M: retractor muscle of tentacle; SN, SN_1, 1–5: various neurons involved in the indicated system of pathways. Other abbreviations as in Fig. 145.

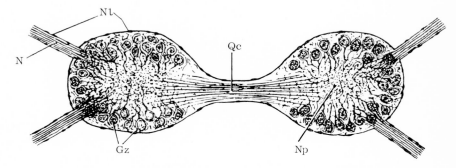

Figure 149. Simplified diagram of paired ganglion (e.g. pedal ganglion) in a snail. (From PLATE, 1922.) Gz: nerve cells; N: peripheral nerve; Nl: sheath of nervous system; Np: neuropileme; Qc: interganglionic commissure.

11. Mollusca:
Cephalopoda, Including Some Remarks
on a Few Relevant Behavioral Activities

The nervous system of *Cephalopoda* manifests a high degree of concentration (Fig. 140), whereby cerebral, pedal, and visceral ganglia may fuse into one almost continuous, single mass, which, however, still displays distinct subdivisions. To this mass, at least in Dibranchia, a brachial ganglion is added (Fig. 150). The cephalopod class as a whole includes the most specialized and most differentiated types of mollusks, and some of its representatives have attained the largest size among all generally known invertebrates.[48]

In conformity with this high level of development, the nervous system of cephalopods can be said to differ rather substantially, as regards both structure and function, from the nervous system in other groups of mollusks. Again, the high development of the central nervous system in Dibranchia is matched, among invertebrates, only by some insects and perhaps arachnids. One could be inclined to consider the dibranchiate 'brain' the most advanced invertebrate one. As regards the number of neuronal elements in the nervous system of octopus, YOUNG (1964) gave an estimate of about 5×10^8. Of this number, more than half, namely about 3×10^8 are believed to be located in the nerve centers of the arms. As regards the central nervous system proper, about 6 to 9×10^7 cells may be present in both optic lobes,

---

[48] The cephalopods can be roughly subdivided into the orders Tetrabranchiata, with the single recent genus Nautilus, and Dibranchiata, with the two sub-orders Decapoda (10 arms: Sepia, Loligo) and Octopoda (8 arms: Octopus, Argonauta). The fossil Ammonites were presumably Tetrabranchiates, and the fossil Belemnites probably decapod Dibranchiates.

The sense organs include eyes, statocysts, osphradia (only in Nautilus), and chemoreceptors. The eyes of Dibranchiata (e.g. the squid Loligo, and Octopus) are the most highly developed eyes of invertebrates and are closely analogous (but not homologous) to differentiated vertebrate eyes. In contradistinction to these latter, the photoreceptor elements of cephalopods are directed toward the light. An iris diaphragm is present, and accommodation is effected by forward or backward displacement of the lens (this method, however, also obtains in some vertebrates such as various fishes).

Copulation is particularly complex in Dibranchiates, where one of the male arms becomes modified as an intromittent organ or hectocotylus, which plucks the spermatophores from *Needham's* sac (which opens into the mantle cavity). In octopods, this arm may break off. It was once described as a distinct organism, namely a parasitic worm, although ARISTOTLE (more than 2000 years ago) had already recognized its significance (cf. chapt. II, p. 50, volume 1).

about 3.5×10^7 in the supraesophageal centers, and perhaps 3×10^6 in the subesophageal centers (cf. also YOUNG, 1960). Yet, taking into consideration the complex social behavior of bees and ants, as well as the intricate structure of the brain in these arthropods, one might, nevertheless, and despite the much larger number of neuronal elements

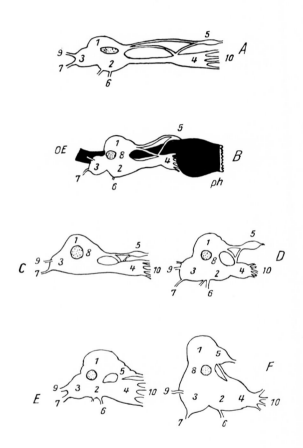

Figure 150. Outlines of central nervous system in diverse dibranchiate Cephalopods. (After PELSENEER from HANSTRÖM, 1928.)

A Ommastrephes; *B* Sepiola; *C* Loligo; *D* Sepia; *E* Octopus; *F* Argonauta. *A–D* Decapoda; *E*, *F* Octopoda; 1: cerebral ganglion; 2: pedal ganglion; 3: visceral ganglion; 4: brachial ganglion; 5: upper buccal ganglion; 6: infundibular nerve; 7: visceral nerve; 8: optic nerve (cut); 9: mantle nerve; 10: brachial nerves; in *B* oe: esophagus; ph: pharynx (indicated in black).

in cephalopods, possibly be justified in evaluating, alternatively, the dibranchiate 'brain' as second to that of said insects[49].

Biometric investigation on the central nervous system of cephalopods by means of planimetric reconstructions, from which 'volumetric indices' were derived, have been undertaken by WIRZ (1959). These data purport to indicate levels of 'cerebralization' and to provide evidence for phylogenetic speculations. As in the case of similar studies on the insect brain (cf. above, section 9, p. 194), I am inclined to regard the results of such procedures as rather inconclusive.

Generally speaking, the nervous system of cephalopods can be subdivided into two portions, namely 'brain' and peripheral ganglia. The brain-complex comprises cerebral, buccal, labial, pedal, brachial, and palliovisceral ganglia in addition to the large optic lobe. The peripheral ganglia include stellar (mantle) ganglion, branchial, cardiac, and visceral ganglia, in addition to peripheral arm (tentacular and sucker) ganglia.

The circulatory system in cephalopods is largely a closed one, and is more highly developed than that of any other group of mollusks. The well vascularized brain receives an ample blood supply (E. SCHARRER, 1944), and the brain vessels are said to be innervated (HUBER, 1963).

The coloration of the skin in most cephalopods is due to the presence of many chromatophores of rather complicated structure. Small muscles are attached to these elements. Upon muscular contraction, the chromatophore is stretched into a large flat plate with maximal pigment display; upon muscular relaxation, the elastic sac containing the pigment contracts, and the pigment, concentrated into one spot, becomes less apparent. Black, blue, purple, pink, brown, and

---

[49] PIÉRON (1911), however, who undertook pioneering studies on the memory functions of cephalopods (as regards these capacities cf. further below p. 238 f.) holds that these animals are more intelligent than some lower vertebrates. He comments (1911): 'Le niveau mental auquel arrivent les Céphalopodes est relativement très élevé, et le Poulpe *(Octopus vulgaris)*, en particulier, semble supérieur à un grand nombre de vertébrés, en particulier à des poissons ou des batraciens, et peut-être même des reptiles.

Une des méthodes d'études les plus utilisées consiste à faire acquérir une habitude à un animal donné, ce qui permet de se faire une idée précise de sa plasticité et de sa mémoire. C'est cette méthode que j'ai employée en juillet et août derniers au Laboratoire maritime de Tatihou, avec un Poulpe de moyenne taille conservé à l'aquarium depuis quelques semaines.'

yellow chromatophores may be arranged in groups. Each individual chromatophore with its muscles is innervated, and the animal may change its color with great rapidity. Optic input provides here an important component of this peculiar mechanism, whereby the animal can simulate background coloration to a most remarkable degree. Thus, a squid swimming first over light sand bottom and then over dark rock immediately changes from a pale color to a corresponding dark one. During states of excitation, waves of changing coloration may 'flow' over the body of an octopus.

As regards additional aspects of behavior, including locomotion, two interesting procedures or methods are manifested by cephalopods. In dibranchiates, a large ink sac is located near the intestine; an ink gland secretes fluid, with a high concentration of melanin, stored in the sac. When an octopus or squid is disturbed, the ink is ejected through the anus and produces a dark cloud of inky water behind which the animal can escape. In analogy to the 'chemical warfare' of Diplopoda (cf. p. 125), we have here the principle on which the 'smoke screens' employed in human warfare are based.

Again, all cephalopods swim by using the principle of recoil, reaction, or jet propulsion[50]. Water is rapidly expelled from the mantle cavity, whose volume is controlled by longitudinal and circular muscles in the mantle. Upon contraction of the circular muscles, water is forced out of a jet-engine-like ventral tubular funnel which can be moved in various directions, allowing thus forward or backward locomotion. In Nautilus, the funnel rather than the mantle is contracted. The speed of water expulsion can be finely controlled. The squids display the highest specialization for this type of locomotion, and are provided with a posterior pair of lateral stabilizer-fins.

Reverting to morphology and structure of the nervous system, significant differences in the degree of development can be noticed in comparing tetrabranchiates and dibranchiates.

The genus Nautilus is the only recent form pertaining to the more 'primitive' *Tetrabranchia*. The central nervous system consists here, in addition to the buccal ganglia, of three broad medullary cords, of which one lies dorsal, and the two others are located ventral to the pharynx

---

[50] This recoil, or jet-propulsion principle was known to, or perhaps even first discovered by, the Greek mathematician and philosopher HERO of Alexandria before or about the beginning of our Era, roughly 2000 years ago. However, the model steam engines constructed by HERO did not find a technological application.

(Fig. 151). The dorsal cord represents the cerebral ganglion, and the additional ones correspond to pedal and pleurovisceral connectives and ganglia of other mollusks. The cord-like arrangement exhibits certain similarities with the type of nervous system found in Chiton.

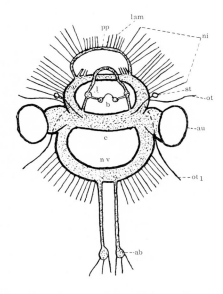

Figure 151. Nervous system of the tetrabranchiate cephalopod Nautilus pompilius. (Simplified after PLATE, 1922, from HANSTRÖM, 1928.) ab: abdominal ganglion; au: eye; b: buccal ganglion; c: cerebral ganglion; 1: labial ganglion; lam: nerves from prepedal ring; ni, ot: tentacular nerves; pp: prepedal ring; nv: pleurovisceral cord; st: statocyst.

The central nervous system of *Dibranchia*, such as Sepia and Loligo (Decapoda), as well as Octopus (Octopoda) is illustrated by Figures 152 to 165. In contradistinction to Nautilus, where only a ventral cartilage is present, the central nervous system of Dibranchia is almost entirely surrounded by a cartilaginous capsule, providing a sort of 'skull'.

Generally speaking, one might distinguish a 'cerebral mass', and a cerebral ganglion proper. The esophagus runs through the cerebral mass and subdivides this latter into a supraesophageal and an infraesophageal complex. The former, which includes the optic lobes located in the 'orbit', and separated from the cerebral ganglion *sensu strictiori* by a narrow isthmus representing the so-called 'optic nerve', corresponds to the cerebral ganglion of annelids and arthropods. It may be interpreted as kathomologous to the 'brain' of articulates. The infraesophageal mass, in toto, corresponds to the subesophageal ganglion of articulates and could be considered kathomologous to this latter structure.

The infraesophageal mass consists of three subdivisions; the anterior one is the brachial lobe or ganglion; the middle one represents the pedal ganglion (with anterior and posterior pedal lobe), and the posterior one or visceral ganglion is also designated as pallio-visceral lobe. Some authors use different terms and also distinguish additional subdivisions, such as 'lobus lateralis' for pedal ganglion and 'lobus infundibuli' (connected with pedal ganglion) or 'lobus accessorius' (connected with visceral lobe), in accordance, e. g., with THORE (1939). Again, in Sepia, YOUNG (1939) and BOYCOTT (1961) distinguish magnocellular lobes, of which the anterior (ventral) one might be included in the pedal ganglion of the simpler terminology I have here attempted to preserve, while the posterior and dorsal magnocellular lobe could be considered related to the pallio-visceral lobe.

As regards the supraesophageal complex, the cerebral ganglion *sensu strictiori* displays an external lobulation, to which distinctive internal neuropileme masses correspond (Fig. 158). This lobulation is suggested by shallow transverse or longitudinal furrows or both. The following lobes of the octopus cerebral ganglion can be enumerated in approximately anteroposterior sequence: buccal, anterior frontal, vertical, subvertical, posterior basal (with dorsal and medial part), and, more basally, anterior basal lobes (cf. Fig. 158).

In Sepia (Fig. 158 A), the buccal lobe is separated from the main cerebral mass, and becomes the ganglion buccale superius. While the nervus staticus seems to have a direct connection with the cerebral ganglion proper, it runs upward, along the pedal ganglion, into the brain in close connection with the subesophageal mass to which it appears also to contribute direct fibers. The somewhat dubious nervus olfactorius seems to join the cerebral ganglion in the isthmus region near the peduncular ganglion.

The median cerebral ganglion proper and the bilateral optic ganglia of the cephalopod central nervous system are, by topologic one to one mapping into (a) arthropod optic lobes and (b) the more medial parts of the arthropod brain, quite evidently homologous, in toto, to the brain of these latter forms. Moreover, peduncular ganglion, 'olfactory

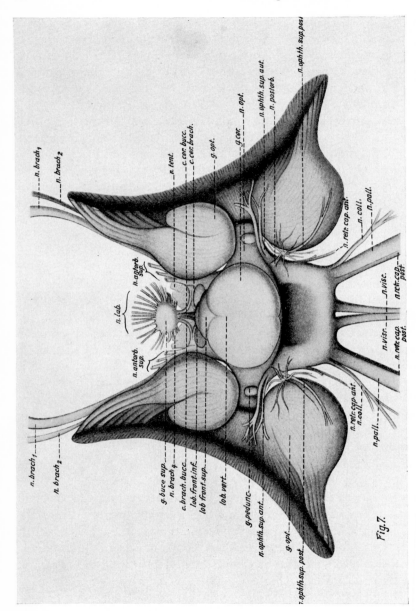

Figure 152. Dorsal aspect of cerebral complex in Sepia officinalis. (From Hɪʟʟɪɢ, 1912.) c: commissura (brachio-buccalis, cerebro-buccalis, etc.), g: ganglion (buccale superius, cerebrale, opticum, pedunculi); n: nervus, nervi (antorbitales, brachiales, collaris, labrales, oculomotorius, ophthalmicus, opticus, pallialis, retractor capitis, visceralis); lob: lobus (frontalis inf., sup., verticalis).

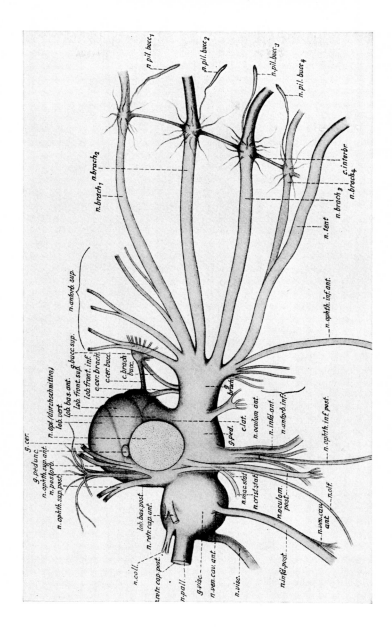

Figure 153. Lateral aspect of cerebral complex and nerves in Sepia officinalis. (From HILLIG, 1912.) g. brach: brachial ganglion; g. ped.: pedal ganglion; g. pedunc.: ganglion pedunculi; g. visc.: visceral ganglion; other abbreviations as in Fig. 152.

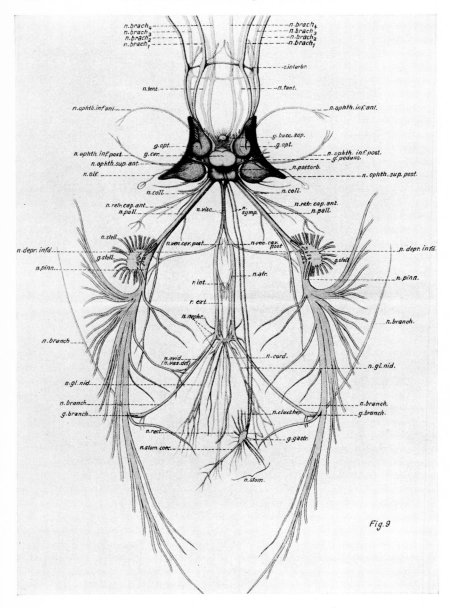

Fig. 9

Fig. 154 A

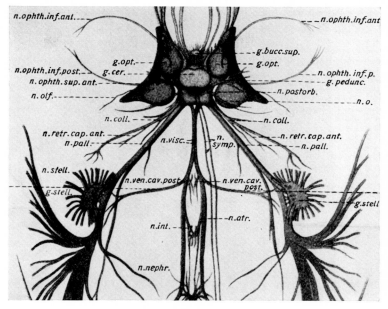

Fig. 154 B

Figure 154. A Total view (dorsal aspect) of nervous system in Sepia officinalis. (From HILLIG, 1912.) *B* Detail of Figure *A*. (From a slightly retouched reproduction of HILLIG's original figure in PLATE, 1922.) Ganglion stellatum (g. stell.); nervus palliallis (n. pall.), and nervus visceralis (n. visc.) should be particularly noted.

ganglion', and perhaps 'optic gland' may be considered 'stalked' structures representing specific form-elements in the region of the isthmus, lateral to 'cerebral ganglion' and medial to optic ganglion. It seems thus possible to regard said cephalopod structures as kathomologous to the corpora pedunculata of some platyhelminths (Notoplana), of annelids, and of arthropods. Yet, quite evidently, structure and functional significance of these cephalopod configurations differ substantially from the structural and functional relationships obtaining in flatworms and articulates.

The optic lobe is connected with the photoreceptor cells of the retina by a chiasma (Fig. 161) and contains the so-called retina profunda of CAJAL (Figs. 161 and 162), consisting of lamina granularis externa and interna, separated by a plexiform layer of synaptic structures (CAJAL, 1917). The ganglion opticum of CAJAL contains clusters of nerve cells of the fourth or perhaps also third serial order[51], and of various sizes, which transmit the optic input to other 'centers' of the cerebral mass.

The optic lobe of cephalopods is surrounded by a mass of lymphoid tissue designated as the 'white body' (Fig. 159). In addition to its well-known function concerned with the formation of white blood cells, a 'nephrocytic' function, concerned with the storage of purine compounds, has been suggested by CAZAL and BOGORAZE (1943a).

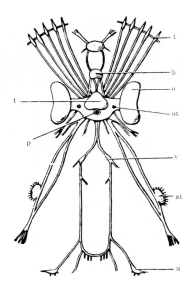

Figure 155. Simplified diagram of nervous system in Sepia. (After IHERING from SELENKA-GOLDSCHMIDT, 1919.) b: superior buccal ganglion; c: cerebral ganglion; o: ganglion opticum; ot: optic gland; p: pharynx; st: stellate ganglion; t: tentacle ganglia; v: visceral ganglion; u: branchial ganglion; the superior buccal ganglion is shown in its connection with a displaced inferior buccal ganglion (at middle top of figure); the diagram provides a good orientation sketch for the preceding detailed figures of HILLIG (the lower t should read c, for cerebral ggl.).

Near the connection of optic lobe with cerebral mass, there is, closely adjacent to the small prominence formed by the peduncular ganglion, an additional small swelling containing modified neuronal elements

---

[51] In this serial order, the sensory cells represent the first neuron, the small cells in lamina granularis externa the second, the bipolar cells in lamina granularis interna the third, and the cells of ganglion opticum the fourth neuron. The possibility that an impulse may be directly transmitted from sensory cell to cell of lamina interna cannot be entirely excluded.

(Figs. 159, 163). This structure was described as glande pédonculaire by CAZAL and BOGORAZE (1943b): 'La jonction entre le pédoncule et le lobe optique est marquée par un renflement dont la structure histologique a été étudiée par CAJAL et reconnue comme incontestablement nerveuse, c'est le ganglion pédonculaire. Sur le quadrant postéro-supérieur de ce ganglion s'insère une petite formation globuleuse, sessile, de teinte jaune orangé sur le vivant, ayant 0,5 à 1,5 mm de

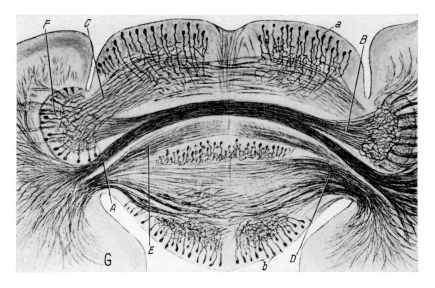

Figure 156. Horizontal section through the cerebral ganglion of Sepia officinalis at the level of commissura optica. (After CAJAL, 1917.) A: crossed optic pathway; B: end of crossed pathway in ganglion pedunculare (ganglion pedunculi); C: optic connections (so-called optic 'reflex pathway'); D: optic connections with anterior part of cerebral ganglion; E: middle optic pathway; F: ganglion pedunculare; G: ganglion opticum; a: posterior part of cerebral ganglion; b: anterior part of ganglion.

diamètre, que nous nommerons la glande pédonculaire'. The cited authors interpret this structure as a neurosecretory organ which will be briefly discussed further below at the end of this section.

BOYCOTT and YOUNG (1956), however, point out that the 'gland' in question, said to be distinct in all cephalopods so far studied, was already described as 'optic gland' in 1828 and 1841 by DELLE CHIAJE, in two Italian memoirs published at Naples. In addition, a corpus subpedunculatum, described by THORE (1939) is represented by

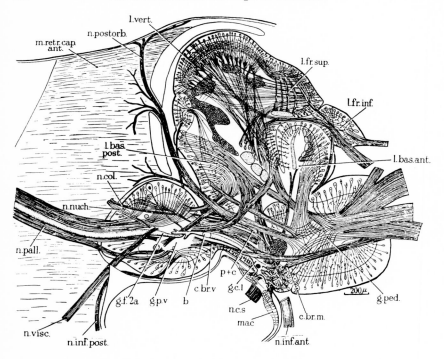

Figure 157. Semi-diagrammatic view of thick sagittal section through the lateral portion of the central nervous system in a young Loligo. Based on a combination of several sections processed with CAJAL's silver impregnation. (From YOUNG, 1939.) b: interaxonic bridge (anastomosis); c. br. m.: brachio-magnocellular connective; c. br. v.: brachio-palliovisceral connective; g. c. 1: giant cell (1st order); gf 2a: second order giant cell axon running to stellate ganglion (its cell body is easily identifiable); g. ped.: pedal ganglion; g. p. v.: pallovisceral ganglion; l. bas. ant.: lobus basalis anterior; l. bas. post.: lobus basalis posterior; l. fr. inf.: lobus frontalis inferior; l. fr. sup.: lobus frontalis superior; l. vert.: lobus verticalis; mac.: macula of statocyst; m. retr. cap.: retractor musculature of head; n. c. s.: nervus cristae staticae; n. col.: nervus collaris; n. inf. ant., post.: nervus infundibuli ant., post.; n. nuch.: part of n. collaris; n. pall.: nervus pallialis; n. postorb.: nervus postorbitalis; n. visc.: nervus visceralis.

Figure 158. Outline diagrams illustrating configurational aspects of the central nervous system in Cephalopoda. *A* Approximately midsagittal diagrammatic section through the central nervous system of a Decapod (combined and simplified after SCHKAFF from HANSTRÖM, 1928, and BOYCOTT, 1961). c: cranial cartilage; e: esophagus; o: otocyst; 1: gangl. buccale sup.; 2: gangl. bucc. inf.; 3: gangl. brachiale; 4: gangl. pedale; 5: gangl. viscerale; 6: lob. frontalis inf.; 7: lob. front. sup.; 8: lob. verticalis; 9: ant. basal lobe; 10: posterior basal lobes.

B Diagrammatic transverse section through the central nervous system of the Decapod Sepia (adapted and simplified after BOYCOTT, 1961). bd: part of posterior basal lobe (lob.

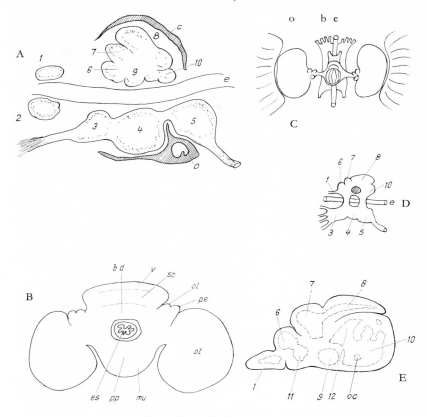

Figs. 158 A, B, C, D and E

basalis dorsalis); es: esophagus; mu: ventral magno-cellular lobe; ol: 'olfactory lobe'; ot: optic lobe; pe: peduncular ganglion; pp: posterior pedal lobe; so: subvertical lobe; v: vertical lobe.

C Dorsal aspect of central nervous system in Octopus (combined after WELLS, 1961, and original observations). b: brachial nerves emerging from brachial lobe; e: esophagus; o: optic lobe; the three rounded structures connected with the optic stalk are: peduncular ganglion anterolateral, 'olfactory lobe' anteromedial, optic gland posterior; the parallel longitudinal furrows of the cerebral ganglion indicate the vertical lobe.

D Lateral aspect of central nervous system in Octopus (modified after WELLS, 1961). e: esophagus; 1: buccal lobe; 3 to 10 as in Fig. 158 A; the cut optic stalk is indicated by hatching.

E Sagittal section showing lobulation of cerebral ganglion in Octopus (modified after WELLS, 1961). oc: optic commissure; 1: buccal lobe; 6–10 as in Fig. 158 A; 11: subfrontal lobe; 12: subvertical lobe; the lobular outlines vary according to the different sagittal planes (cf. Fig. 159 F–I).

Figs. 159 A, B, C

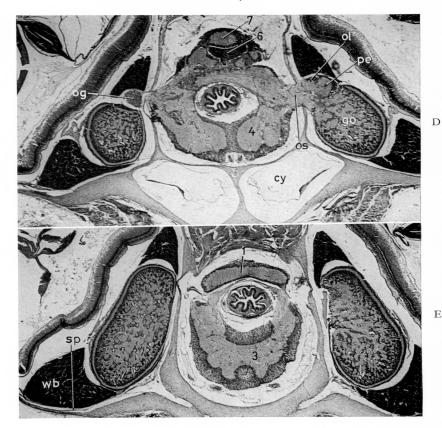

Figs. 159 D and E

Figure 159 A–E. Cross sections through the cerebral complex of a young Octopus. (Original; × 12; red. ³/₄; hematoxylin-eosin.) *A* Oblique section, dorsocaudal to rostroventral (from 50 μ celloidin-series). *B* to *E.* Transverse sections progressing from caudal to rostral level (from 20 μ paraffin series; section *C* accidentally turned over with respect to right and left). cy: otocyst; es: esophagus; go: ganglion opticum; le: lens; og: optic gland; ol: olfactory lobe; os: optic stalk; pe: peduncular ganglion; re: retina; sp: corpus subpedunculatum; wb: white body; 1, 3, 4, etc.: lobes as in Fig. 158.

strands of basophil cells running from the optic lobe to an 'anterior chamber organ' of the eye, described by Boycott and Young (1956), who also pointed out so-called 'paravertical bodies' associated with the 'subpeduncular tissue'. Again, medially or posteromedially to the peduncular ganglion (lobus pedunculi), there is a presumably olfactory ganglion (lobus olfactorius).

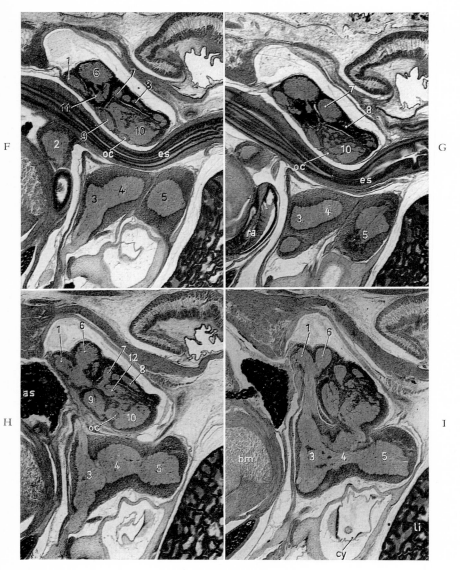

Figs. 159 F, G, H, I

Figure 159 F–I. Sagittal sections through the cerebral complex of a young Octopus. (Original; × 14; red. ²/₃; hematoxylin-eosin; sections 146, 153, 167, 173 of 50 μ celloidin series; midsagittal plane approximately between F: 146 and G: 153.) as: anterior salivary gland; bm: buccal (jaw) musculature; cy: otocyst; es esophagus; li: liver; oc: optic commissure; ra: radula; 1, 2, etc.: lobes and ganglia as in Fig. 158.

In octopods, a nervus subpedunculatus (THORE, 1939) is said to run from the neighborhood of the vertical lobe to the veins of the orbit (BOYCOTT and YOUNG, 1956). In decapods, vesicular structures of unknown significance have been described as located below the olfactory lobes. The cited authors use here the term 'parolfactory vesicles'. BOYCOTT and YOUNG (1956) comment on the complexity of the diverse structures found in the neighborhood of optic lobe and optic tract of cephalopods.

YOUNG (1960) and other authors have made further attempts at investigating the probable synaptic connections in the optic system of octopus (Fig. 163). Since it is very frequently not possible to distinguish clearly between 'dendrites' and 'axons', and because of many additional complications, it is most difficult to obtain, at this time, a sufficiently clear concept of the significant arrangements. According to YOUNG (1960) the outer granular layer of CAJAL would essentially consist of amacrine cells.

Another noteworthy feature is represented by various sorts of apparently efferent fibers from brain regions to optic lobe, and from optic lobe to retina proper, that is, to the neurosensory receptor cells. Arrangements of this sort may be interpreted in terms of feedback processes.

The output connections of ganglion opticum are not fully elucidated. The so-called ganglion pedunculare (Fig. 156) doubtless represents an important center for optic information, receiving massive crossed and uncrossed optic fiber systems. The anterior, the medial, and the posterior parts of the cerebral mass, in turn, receive fiber bundles originating in the ganglion pedunculare.

Various 'centers' for different activities have been tentatively outlined in the cephalopod brain (Fig. 164). Correlation of statocystic tactile and optic input, and control of jet propulsion, including motions for retreat and for attack, are performed by such centers. In addition, there seem to be 'centers' for eye movements, pupillary constriction, swimming, crawling, grasping, feeding, and respiratory movements. A central lobe, either necessary for the storage of memory, or at least for the proper use of stored memory, can be assumed. PIÉRON (1911) demonstrated that the octopus is capable of learning and of remembering specific situations. This was confirmed by the experiments of BOYCOTT and YOUNG (1956, 1957), who, by means of electric shocks, combined with the presentation of a white square and of a crab, obtained a 'conditioned' response in the octopus. The octopus then

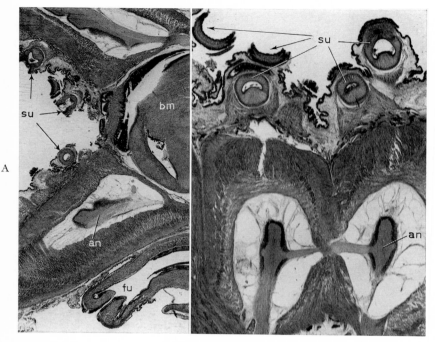

Figs. 160 A and B

Figure 160 A–C. Peripheral ganglia of nervous system in a young Octopus. (Original, hematoxylin-eosin; from 50 μ sagittal and transverse series.) *A* Sagittal section showing two arm nerves with peripheral ganglia (× 9; red. ²/₃). *B* Transverse section, showing arm nerves with ganglia and commissura interbrachialis, to be compared with Fig. 153. (× 14; red. ²/₃.) *C* Transverse section through body, showing stellate ganglion and nervus pallialis, cf. Fig. 154. (× 14; red. ³/₄.) an: arm nerve (with ganglion); bm: buccal (jaw) musculature; fu: funnel; gi: gills; gu: gut; li: liver; ma: mantle cavity; np: nervus pallialis; ps: posterior salivary gland; st: stellate ganglion; su: suction disks (suckers).

Figure 161. Semidiagrammatic drawing showing the retina profunda and the lobus opticus of Loligo. (After CAJAL, 1917.) A: eye; B: chiasma; C: lobus opticus; D: optic stalk (pedunculus lobi optici); a: neurosensory (visual) cells; b: so-called retina profunda of lobus opticus, the cell masses internally to retina profunda are customarily designated as ganglion opticum.

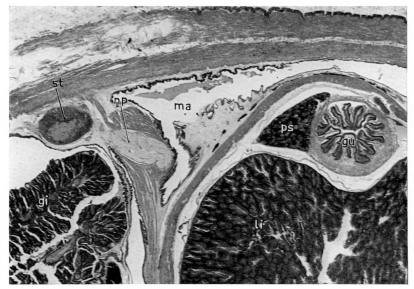

Fig. 160 C

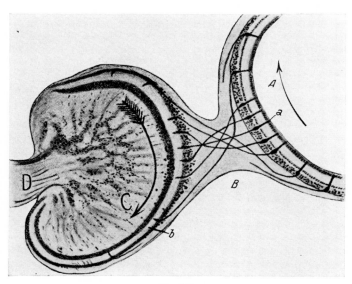

Fig. 161

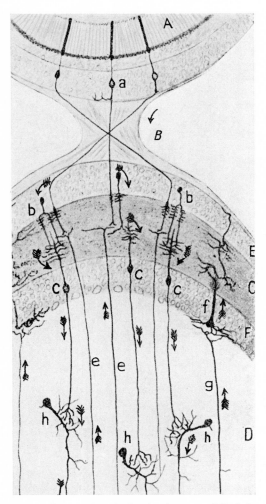

Figure 162. Diagram of connections in the visual centers of Cephalopods according to CAJAL's interpretation. (After CAJAL, 1917.) A: Receptor ending of neurosensory cells (layer of rods) in retina of eye; B: chiasma; C: retina profunda; D: ganglion opticum; E: lamina granularis externa; F: lamina granularis interna; a: body of visual cells; b: small unipolar cells; c: small bipolar cells; e: centrifugal fiber; f: large cell of lamina granularis interna; g: centrifugal fiber; h: cell of ganglion opticum with centripetal neurite.

Figure 163 A, B. Sections through the optic lobe of a young Octopus. (Original; A × 50; red. ³/₄; B × 40; red. ³/₄; hematoxylin-eosin.) *A* Transverse section. *B* Sagittal section, rostral side on right. a: retina with neurosensory (visual) cells; b: chiasma; c: retina profunda; d: ganglion pedunculare; e: perhaps portion of olfactory lobe; f: white body; g: optic stalk (optic tract); h: optic gland. (These two figures should be compared with Figs. 163 C, 158, 159, 161, and 162.)

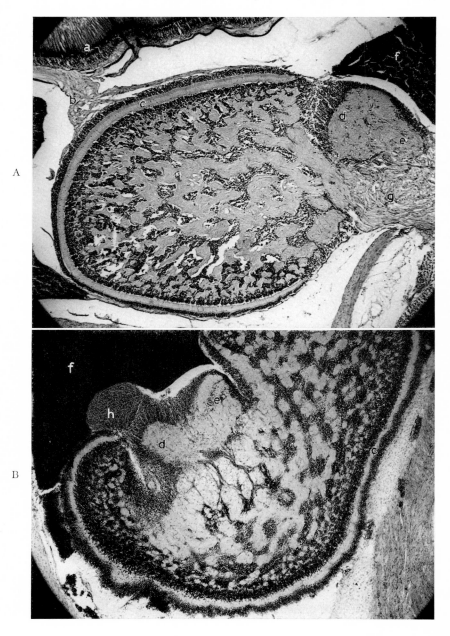

Figs. 163 A and B

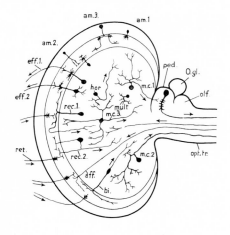

Fig. 163 C

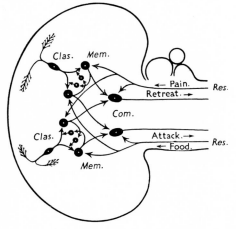

Fig. 163 D

Figure 163C. Diagram of pathways in optic lobe of Octopus according to YOUNG's interpretation. (From YOUNG, 1960.) aff.: Afferents from brain or contralateral optic lobe; am.: amacrine cells; bi.: bipolar cell; eff.: cells with efferent fibers to retina; hor.: horizontal cell; m.c., mult.: various cells of medulla; o.gl.: so-called optic gland; olf.: olfactory lobe; opt.tr.: so-called optic tract; ped.: ganglion pedunculare ('peduncle lobe'); rec.: cells with recurrent axons.

Figure 163 D. Diagram showing YOUNG's concept of encoding and storage mechanisms in the optic lobe of Octopus. Large classifying cells (Clas.) with spreading dendritic trees 'record the extent of horizontal and vertical contouring'. 'Memory storage cells' (Mem.) then connect with 'higher motor command cells' (Com.) 'producing either attack or retreat'. 'These pathways only operate if the 'results indicators' (Res.) are active. The operation of any one pathway closes the alternative, through the inhibitory collaterals and small cells' (from YOUNG, 1964, Fig. 47).

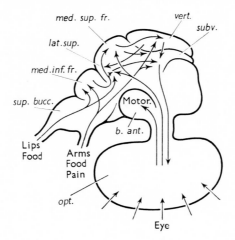

Fig. 163 E

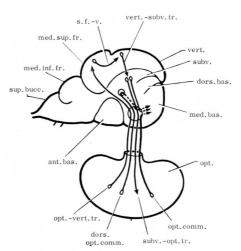

Fig. 163 F

Figure 163 E. Diagram of the connections of the optic lobe of Octopus with the higher centers of the supraesophageal lobes (from YOUNG, 1964, Fig. 67). b. ant.: anterior basal; lat. sup.: lateral superior frontal; med. inf. fr.: median inferior frontal; opt.: optic lobe; subv.: subvertical; sup. bucc.: superior buccal; v.: vertical.

Figure 163 F. Diagram of brain of Octopus showing additional connections of optic lobe. Supraesophageal lobes shown in midsagittal section (after MUNTZ, from YOUNG, 1964, Fig. 51). ant. bas.: anterior basal; dors. bas.: dorsal basal; dors. opt. comm.: dorsal optic commissure; med. bas.: median basal; med. inf. fr.: median inferior frontal; med. sup. front.: median superior frontal; opt.: optic lobe; opt. comm.: optic commissure; opt.-vert. tr.: tractus optico-verticalis; subv.: subvertical; subv.-opt. tr.: tractus subvertico-opticus; sup. bucc.: superior buccal; s. f.-v.: tractus fronto-verticalis superior; vert.: vertical; vert.-subv. tr.: tractus vertico-subverticalis.

refrained from attacking the crab when the white square was presented, but it continued to attack and eat crabs in the absence of such square. Removing the dorsal parts of the cerebral ganglion abolished the previously acquired response, as well as the capability to 'learn' from repeated additional experiences of that sort. Removing these brain portions did not seem to produce other defects, and, except for the 'memory defect', the behavior of the octopus appeared normal after the operation. Subsequently, YOUNG (1961) reached the conclusion that the process of 'memory storage', although not entirely abolished, is 'substantially less efficient' in octopuses deprived of the 'vertical lobe' (cf. Figs. 164 and 165).

WELLS (1961) assumes that the octopus has two 'learning systems', one in the inferior frontal and subfrontal lobes (cf. Fig. 158), dealing with tactile discrimination 'on a basis of the proportion of sense organ excited', the other in the optic lobes, handling visual discrimination 'on a basis of the pattern of sense organ excited'. The vertical lobe is believed to play a role in learning by either system; this lobe may represent a store for both tactile and visual engrams.

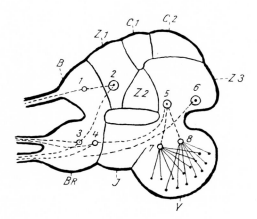

Figure 164. Assumed 'centers' in the brain complex of Cephalopods. (After UEXKÜLL and others from HANSTRÖM, 1928). B: buccal ganglion; Br: brachial ganglion; J: pedal ganglion; V: visceral ganglion; Z1, Z2, Z3, C1, C2: Lobus frontalis inferior, basalis anterior, basalis posterior, frontalis superior, verticalis; single figures indicate so-called 'centers' as follows; 1: closure of jaws; 2: eating; 3: attachment of suction cups; 4: release of suction cups; 5: swimming retreat; 6: crawling and climbing; 7, 8: inspiration and expiration.

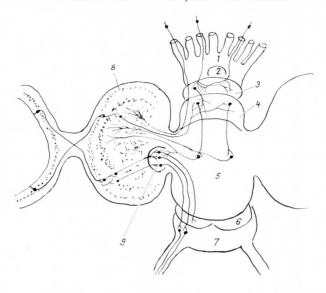

Figure 165. Diagram of diverse assumed pathways in the central nervous system of Octopus. (Adapted and combined after various authors.) 1: brachial lobe; 2: upper buccal lobe; 3: inferior frontal lobe; 4: superior frontal lobe; 5: vertical lobe; 6: posterior basal lobe; 7: visceral lobe with pallial nerve; 8: optic lobe; 9: peduncular nucleus.

As regards the memory mechanisms in octopus, YOUNG (1960/61) emphasizes that, in contradistinction to conditioning experiments as undertaken in mammals by PAVLOV and others, where repeated presentations were made use of, the experiments in octopus demonstrated changes (storage) after one presentation, and lasting for a duration of hours, but with gradual decay. Further presentations led to a stabilization of the new states (storage). According to the cited author, the decay accelerates, 'if the vertical lobes, with their vast number of small cells, are removed'. The question remains whether the lobes prevent the decay of stored information set up at the time of stimulation ('perhaps by re-excitation', YOUNG, 1960/61), or whether their effect is to increase the magnitude of the initial change. A convincing or conclusive answer to that problem cannot be given at this time. The vertical lobes may, however, be regarded as playing a significant role in allowing the animal to make the 'correct' classification of a pair of figures. This sets up 'representations ensuring correct response', and the neural mechanism hereby involved can be seriously impaired by the experimental procedures. YOUNG (1960/61) believes that the deficiency is perhaps 'essentially a shortage of neurons to make the connections that embody the representations'.

YOUNG's (1960/61) observations concerning subsequently decaying 'changes' after one presentation, are, of course, a confirmation of SEMON's (1904) fundamental theories, which were based on a wide range of data as well as personal observations by that distinguished biologist. According to SEMON's formulation, engrams may result immediately after the subsidence of the first excitation (cf. my introductory remarks in chapt. I, p. 27). Concerning decay, it seems not unlikely, as I have previously pointed out, in a general discussion of my views on memory mechanisms (K., 1957, p. 117), that said process takes place in accordance with the die-away curve, related to the die-away factor e^{-at} (i. e., the reciprocal of the growth factor e^{at}). I pointed out (K., 1957) that this decay curve can be regarded as significantly related to the autocatalytic nature of the biochemical processes, involved in memory mechanisms, according to the theories of T. B. ROBERTSON (1912, 1913, 1914, quoted in K., 1957).

BOYCOTT (1961) assumes an hierarchic grouping of neural centers or links in the functional systems of sepia. This author tabulates the responses obtained upon electrical stimulation of different cerebral lobes. Thus, stimulation of 'higher' centers led to coordinated generalized responses in extensive body regions. The responses did here not markedly differ upon stimulation of different regions of one and the same lobe.

YOUNG's recent treatise 'A Model of the Brain' (1964) is mainly based on the investigations of the cephalopod nervous system, particularly in octopus, but also in sepia, by this author and his collaborators, and contains numerous data concerning these forms.

As regards the peripheral connections and nerves in dibranchiates, particularly in the octopus, the cerebral ganglion is connected with the retina, the olfactory organ, the static organ, the eye bulb and some eye muscles. The visceral ganglion innervates an eye muscle, a large part of the mantle, parts of the funnel, and the various viscera, which, again, contain a plexus including peripheral nerve cells. The pedal ganglion also innervates some eye muscles, and parts of the funnel, as well as some mantle muscles.

The brachial ganglion innervates mostly the arms, and a strip of adjacent territory. The buccal ganglia (superior and inferior) innervate the 'mandibles', pharynx and salivary glands.

From the inferior buccal ganglion a paired 'sympathetic' nerve runs backward to a ganglion gastricum which innervates stomach and part of the rectum.

The large pair of mantle nerves, originating from the visceral ganglion, are each provided with a conspicuous stellar ganglion (Figs. 154, 160 C). The musculature of cephalopods, and of mollusks in general, appears to be of the 'smooth' variety. Although controlled by the central nervous system, the actual motor innervation, in some instances (mantle muscle), seems to be mediated by nerve cells in peripheral ganglia (stellar ganglion). Such motor fibers, from peripheral ganglion to effector, would thus be analogous to the postganglionic fibers in the autonomic nervous system of vertebrates. However, some muscles, as well as the chromatophores, are said to be directly innervated by fibers originating in the central nervous system (Fig. 166).

In the decapod Loligo, the rapid movements through the water are produced by impulses set up in a system of *giant fibers* (first, second, and third order) investigated by YOUNG (1936, 1938, 1939). The

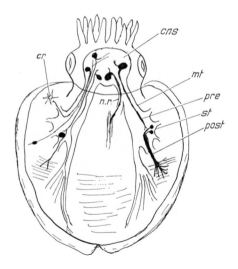

Figure 166. Diagram of the innervation of the mantle in Sepia officinalis. (Simplified and adapted after YOUNG, 1936/37.) The details of the connections of the giant fibers are still not completely elucidated. cns: central nervous system; cr: chromatophore; n.r.: nervus retractor capitis; mt: mantle connective (pallial nerve); post.: postganglionic fiber; pre: preganglionic fiber, arising in palliovisceral ganglion; st.: stellate ganglion.

giant fibers activate the rapid contractions of the mantle, and ink-sac, by means of which the animal shoots backwards behind a cloud of ink.

The impulse may be set up in either one of a single pair of first order giant nerve cells located in the central nervous system, namely in a special lobus magnocellularis ventral to the esophagus, and close to the fusion of cerebral, optic, pedal, and palliovisceral ganglia. This magnocellular lobe contains additional motor cells presumably concerned with arm and mantle movements.

The first order giant cells are activated by synapses providing optic, static, tactile and central impulses. Each giant cell has a single axon (first order giant fiber) which passes downward into the palliovisceral ganglion and there fuses, by means of a plasmodial junction (interaxonic bridge) with that of the opposite side (Fig. 167). Peripherally to that bridge, the first order giant fibers make synaptic contact with several second order giant fibers whose cell bodies lie in the palliovisceral ganglion. Some of the second order giant fibers run, through three different nerves, to funnel and retractor muscles of head. Other second order giant fibers, comparable to preganglionic fibers, reach, through

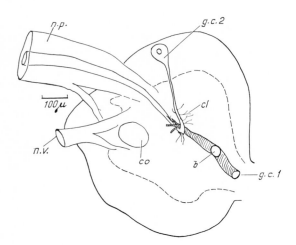

Figure 167. Diagram of synaps between first order and second order giant cell within the ganglion viscerale of Loligo, based on findings in thick sagittal sections. (Simplified and adapted after YOUNG, 1939.) g.c. 1, g.c. 2: first and second order giant neuron; n.p.: nervus pallii; n.v.: nervus visceralis. b: anastomosis between right and left g.c. 1; cl: short proximal axon collaterals of g.c. 2; co: commissure.

the nervous pallialis, the stellate ganglion, where they form synaptic junctions with giant fibers of the third order.

The giant fibers of the third order, which can be compared with, or evaluated as, postanglionic fibers, arise in the stellate ganglion, not from single giant cells, but according to YOUNG (1936), as syncytia, by the fusion of a large number of cells. In one species of Loligo, all the cells giving rise to the giant fibers of the stellate ganglion are connected together into a 'giant fiber lobe'. The giant fibers then reach the musculature through the stellar nerves. There are about ten giant fibers on each side (YOUNG, 1938), and, with respect to this sort of innervation, the mantle can be regarded as divided into 20 neuromotor units, each giant fiber innervating a very large number of muscle fibers. Threshold electrical stimulation at any point within the territory innervated by each single giant fiber sets up a contraction of the muscle fibers of all parts of the region 'with which the stimulated area is in connexion through the nerve' (YOUNG, 1938).

Experimental evidence indicates that stimulation of a stellar nerve produces a single impulse in the giant fiber, which is capable of exciting contraction in all the muscle fibers which it reaches: 'this confirms the conclusion reached on histological grounds that in spite of their syncytial nature each of the giant nerve fibers is a functional unit' (YOUNG, 1938).

Stimulation of the smaller fibers in a stellar nerve after destruction of the giant fiber also causes contraction of the circular mantle musculature. The amount of this contraction increases progressively with increased voltage, and the cited author assumes that this is due to the stimulation of more and more fibers. The maximum contraction developed in this way is said to be always very much less than that produced by stimulation of the giant fibers.

Thus, the mantle seems to be provided with a double mechanism of expiratory contraction, such that maximal and rapid contraction is produced by single impulses in the giant fibers, and graded, slower, as well as lesser contractions are obtained through the mediation of the smaller fibers of the nerve. In addition to the circular muscles, running through the thickness of the mantle, there are radial ones, whose contraction increases the volume of the cavity, thus providing an inspiratory effect.

In octopods, giant fibers have not been found, but YOUNG (1936) describes, in the location corresponding to the squid's giant fiber lobe, a small closed vesicle, with yellow pigmentation in some species, and designated as 'epistellar body'. In the walls of this body, neurosecretory cells were found, whose axons end within a homogeneous substance that fills the vesicle's cavity. These neurosecretory cells, in turn, are innervated by a small nerve which reaches them from the mantle nerve.

Removal of both epistellar bodies in an octopod species (Eledone) was followed, for several days, by 'general muscular weakness' in that animal (YOUNG, 1938). The cited author believes that the epistellar body 'has arisen from the giant fiber lobe', and that the neurosecretory cells produce a secretion which is 'poured into the blood-stream'.

The glandular structure connected with the optic stalk in octopus (CAZAL and BOGORAZE, 1943b; WELLS and WELLS, 1959) and presumably also in a number of other related cephalopods was mentioned above in discussing the optic lobe. Some authors believe that this so-called optic or peduncular gland (cf. Figs. 158C, 159, 163B–C) is functionally analogous to the anterior pituitary of vertebrates, and to the corpus allatum of insects. It is said to remain inactive in young animals 'because it is restrained by the nervous system, and it thus prevents the ovary from becoming mature' (SCHARRER and SCHARRER, 1963). Surgical isolation of the optic glands results in its activation. As a consequence, the ovary is said to enlarge 'tremendously' at a time when it would not do so normally (SCHARRER and SCHARRER, 1963). Concomitantly, the unrestrained optic gland displays structural signs of activation (WELLS and WELLS, 1959). According to other authors, however, the secretory phenomena manifested by the peduncular and epistellar glands of the cephalopods are 'not considered authentic neurosecretion' (ORTMANN, 1960).

12. General Remarks
on the Nervous Elements and Structures of Invertebrates with Respect to Vertebrate Analogies

Histologically, the conducting elements of the nervous system, representing communication channels, are nerve cells possessing elongated, fiber-like processes. The region of the cell comprising the nucleus and its neighborhood is usually designated as the cell body (or, more pompously, the perikaryon), in contradistinction to the various sorts of processes. These latter can be classified on the basis of structural and morphological criteria, or on the basis of functional criteria. All systems of classification remain arbitrary, and none is entirely satisfactory. It is semantically, or, for that matter, logically impossible to combine all these criteria, without resulting contradictions, into a consistent systematic grouping. Moreover, it is difficult to draw, in this respect, a logical boundary between the concept of a 'neurosensory cell', and of a 'true nerve cell' (cf. e. g. Figs. 16 and 168). Both can be included under the concept 'neuron' which will be more fully discussed in chapter V, dealing with the vertebrate nervous system. Thus, not only a neurosensory cell, but also the peripheral ending of a true nerve cell may respond to a mechanical stimulus, such, e. g., as stretching.

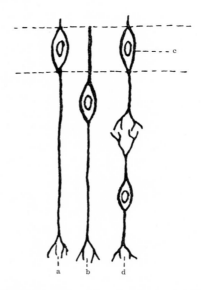

Figure 168. Neurosensory cells (a, b, c), and nerve cell of Actinia (coelenterate). This diagram refers to the hypotheses of the HERTWIGS *et al.* discussed in section 3 of this chapter. (From HANSTRÖM, 1928.)

It is customary to classify the fiber-like processes of nerve cells as dendrites and as neurites. In many instances, particularly among vertebrates, a nerve cell is described as having numerous dendrites, but only one neurite, which, however, may have abundant collaterals. For certain cell types, structural criteria for dendrites and neurites can be given, while these criteria do not hold for other cell types, including, e. g., 'amacrine' cells. The functional criterion of dynamic polarization, in its original formulation, assumed that dendrites conduct toward the cell body, and the neurite away from the cell body. This criterion, however, does not generally hold, since it conflicts with numerous 'facts' that can be either observed, or inferred with reasonable certainty. Further remarks on the classification of nerve cell processes will be included in chapter V, section 2 (vol. 3), of this series in a discussion of vertebrate nerve cells. In the present chapter, dealing with invertebrates, the traditional terms dendrite and neurite are tentatively used in accordance with a preliminary non-committal viewpoint based on the following argumentation.

Considered *in toto*, a nerve cell and its processes can be regarded as a communication channel provided with input and output connections. If said connections are permanently determined as distinct switches for either input or output, but not for both, at any given region of connection, that is as connections representing synapses, then we have polarized elements. If said connections, however, may, under variable conditions, transmit in opposite directions, that is, function as output switches at one time, and as input switches at another time, we have unpolarized or asynaptic elements.

If the neuron theory, as about simultaneously established by FOREL and HIS in 1886/87 (discounting the term 'neuron' subsequently coined in 1891 by WALDEYER), is interpreted to mean that the conducting elements of the nervous system represent (more or less) independent cellular units connected with each other by synaptic or asynaptic 'junctions', it appears convenient, in the first case (synaptic junctions) to classify the fibers on the basis of their impulse conduction from the 'receiving or affected side' of synaptic junctions, affecting the conducting element, to the 'transmitting or affecting side' of synaptic junctions by means of which said element transmits the impulse to other elements (K., 1927, 1957). The 'cell body' is often likewise directly connected, on the 'receiving side', with many synapses. If this cell body is 'intercalated' in the channel between receiving and transmitting synaptic junctions, then the functional definition of dendrites and neurite is easy. If, as is very common among invertebrates, and can also be the case among vertebrates, the cell body is not a part of the direct communication channel (cf. e. g. BETHE's experiment, discussed further below), some difficulties arise. One might then call any distinct trunk channel, which receives synaptic input by converging channels, and represents a diverging, or single channel toward synaptic output, as the neurite, and the branching fibers representing converging or direct channels toward the neurite, as dendrites. Yet, in some cases, semantic difficulties of classification will still remain. Thus, it is quite likely that some sorts of nerve cells may have more than one neurite.

Next, if a conducting element (nerve cell) displays asynaptic (i.e. unpolarized, amphidromic) connections of its fibers, then these fibers should be considered neither dendrites nor neurites, but undifferentiated or asynaptic fibers or processes (K., 1927). Evidently, there seems to be histologic evidence for direct fusion, namely cytoplasmic continuity (plasmodial, syncytial junction) between processes of some nerve cells in various invertebrate phyla, perhaps even, but apparently very rarely, if at all, in the vertebrate nervous system. All such connections are, most likely, asynaptic, and in some instances said connections, investigated with appropriate neurophysiological techniques, have been shown to be asynaptic.

Again, there are connections by close apposition, retaining the distinct surface membranes (or structurally limiting surface-films) of both separate cellular elements. Some such connections seem, likewise, to be permanently asynaptic, that is, unpolarized. Other connections, perhaps with some sort of further structural differentiation, may be partially or facultatively polarized, depending on a number of additional parameters. Connections of that sort might be designated, in contra-distinction to asynaptic and to true synaptic ones, as 'protosynaptic', and considered to represent a type of connection intermediate between asynaptic and synaptic ones.

In some of my previous publications, I have repeatedly discussed, with regard to the vertebrate nervous system, but also briefly referring, in 1927, to the invertebrate one, the questions pertaining to asynaptic neuronal elements (K., 1927, p. 5, 45, 56, 249, 314–315; K., 1954, p. 96; K., 1957, p. 112). If, by 'orthodox neuron theory' one refers to the interpretation forcefully propounded by Cajal (cf. K., 1927, p. 52 f.), then my own views concerning the neuron might be regarded as a 'liberal neuron theory', since I consider all nerve cells with their processes to be neurons, regardless of fusion or apposition, and regardless of asynaptic or synaptic connections.

The various types of invertebrate nerve cells, from some presumably asynaptic coelenterate elements to multipolar as well as 'unipolar' elements found in annelids, arthropods, and most other invertebrates, are illustrated in Figures 169 to 171. Additional details of the widespread 'unipolar' type are shown in Figure 172. Neurofibrillae and *Nissl* bodies (tigroid), to be further discussed in chapter V, are displayed by invertebrates as well as vertebrate nerve cells. It should, however, be mentioned that, despite the demonstration of neurofibrillae, by means of specific techniques, in the nerve cell bodies and nerve fibers of numerous invertebrates, these structures are only rarely recognizable in the living state (e. g. DeRenyi, 1929), and then mostly as no more than a rather faintly indicated striation. Even with the standard

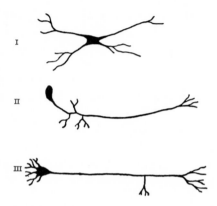

Figure 169. Three different types of nerve cells according to widely accepted inter-pretations. (Modified after Parker, 1919, from Hanström, 1928.) I: 'unpolarized neuron' of coelenterates; II: polarized unipolar invertebrate neuron; III: polarized multipolar vertebrate neuron.

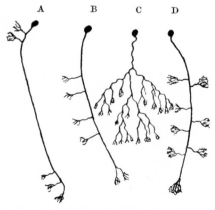

Figure 170. Unipolar globuli neurons of invertebrates, as seen in Golgi pictures. Attempts at definite functional interpretation of some of the terminal arborizations may meet with certain difficulties. (From Hanström, 1928.) *A* Periplaneta (cockroach, insect); *B* Pachygrapsus (crustacean); *C* Limulus (xiphosuran, arachnid in the wider sense); *D* Lithobius (myriapod). *A–C* after Hanström, *D* after Holmgren.

methods of impregnation, neurofibrils could not be demonstrated (as far as is generally known) in various giant axons of squids (Molluscs), of some Polychaetes, and some crustaceans (Arthropods). Thus, these fibrillar structures seem to display, as regards their occurrence in microscopic preparations, a certain 'randomness' which, at this time, cannot be satisfactorily 'explained'.

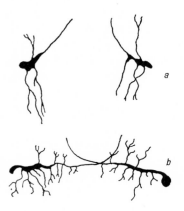

Figure 171. Multipolar nerve cells from the abdominal cord of polychaete Annelida. (After RETZIUS, 1892, from ZAWARZIN, 1925, and HANSTRÖM, 1928.)

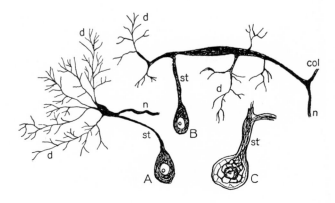

Figure 172. Manifestations of the invertebrate unipolar nerve cell type. (From K., 1927.) *A* Nerve cell of an Aeschna larva (insect; after ZAWARZIN); *B* nerve cell of a crayfish (crustacean); *C* nerve cell of the leech Hirudo (annelid), with neurofibrillar network; col.: collateral; d: 'dendrite'; n: 'neurite'; st: stem process.

Concerning true synaptic connections, the theories assuming transmitter substances provide a convenient 'explanation' for the phenomenon of polarization. If only certain regions or certain ends of a neuron are capable of producing the transmitter substance, and such ends are connected, by close apposition, to regions of a second neuron locally susceptible to the substance, but locally incapable of producing it, polarized conduction will evidently obtain. There are, of course, additional questions, e. g. whether a region producing transmitter substances can also, itself, be responsive to transmitter substances acting from the outside, or whether susceptibility to transmitter substances depends, itself, on regional structural differentiations or on fluctuating functional conditions. Despite considerable progress in the analysis of these problems, and despite an ever increasing amount of experimentally observed data, these various problems still remain at a rather unclarified stage.

The term neuropil or neuropileme (neuropilemes), which refers to a network formed by terminal arborizations of nerve fibers, can also be considered to denote 'synaptic fields', although various sorts of non-polarized or facultatively polarized connections might be included in such networks.

The term is, on the whole, more frequently used with reference to the invertebrate rather than the vertebrate central nervous system. Nevertheless, some regions of terminal arborizations in the vertebrate neuraxis have also been designated as neuropil. In many invertebrates

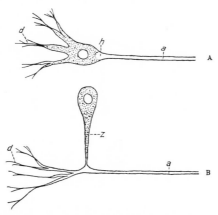

Figure 173. Distribution of tigroid *(Nissl)* substance in multipolar nerve cells of vertebrates *(A)* and in unipolar nerve cells of 'higher' invertebrates *(B)*. (From HANSTRÖM 1928.) a: axon; d: dendrites; h: axon hillock; z: cell process.

the areas of neuropil may consist exclusively of fibers and be devoid of nucleated structures ('cells'), but such 'lack of cells' is by no means an obligatory characteristic of neuropilemes.

The well-known different patterns manifested by neuropil-formations were recently reviewed by MAYNARD (1962) with special emphasis on invertebrates. The preliminary classification proposed by this author subdivides all neuropilemes into four types on the basis of their fiber arrangement: (1) unstructured plexiform; (2) unstructured diffuse; (3) structured glomerular; and (4) structured stratified. The cited author expresses the belief that specific forms of neuropil may have 'their own unique functional characteristics'.

Differences in the distribution of *Nissl* substance with regard to the dendrites of typical vertebrate multipolar nerve cells and those of the 'unipolar' nerve cells of 'higher' invertebrates are illustrated by Figure 173 in accordance with the views of HANSTRÖM (1928). Vertebrate 'unipolar' nerve cells of spinal and cranial ganglia (e. g. in mammals) manifest a certain similarity with 'unipolar' invertebrate nerve cells, but as a rule, display a very definite 'axon hillock', free of *Nissl*-material, at the origin of the one nerve fiber of the cell body.

The well-known fact that the position of the 'cell-body' (or perikaryon) is quite irrelevant as far as the signal-transmitting functions of the nerve cell are concerned, was elegantly demonstrated by a once much discussed experiment of BETHE (1897) in the crustacean Carcinus maenas. The cited author undertook his experiment in order to demolish the neuron theory, and interpreted his results according to his preconceived opinion. Yet, as I elaborated many years ago (K., 1927), BETHE's experiment actually supports rather than contradicts the neuron concept. BETHE isolated, by appropriate incisions, the neuropileme in the tritocerebrum of Carcinus from all motor cell bodies as well as from all connections with the rest of the central nervous system (Fig. 174). The reflex center for the second antenna, because of its peripheral location, was thus left in connection with the antenna, but had become entirely devoid of any nerve cell bodies.

Following the operation, the antenna maintained its normal reflex activity with normal movements, which, however, became weaker on the second day, and were then followed by complete paralysis. Since the synaptic connections were not disturbed by the operation, it is not surprising that reflectory activity was not immediately suppressed. On the other hand, the subsequent disappearance of that activity seems to demonstrate the 'trophic' function of cell body and nucleus, in full

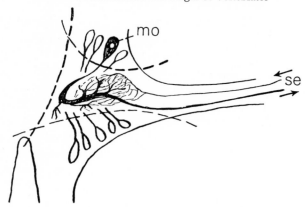

Figure 174. Sketch illustrating BETHE's experiment. The nerve cell groups of the crustacean tritocerebrum are removed, the tritocerebrum is completely isolated from the rest of the central nervous system. Only the central neuropil of tritocerebrum remains, with which the afferent fiber se is connected; mo: severed perikaryon of a motor neuron. (From K., 1927.)

agreement with the neuron concept. About 40 years later, BETHE's experiment was repeated by YOUNG on a ganglion of the squid (i.e. in a mollusc), with essentially identical results.

If the functional concept of a 'center' is used as referring to an assemblage of 'switches', it could be said that in the nervous system of invertebrates the cell bodies lie outside the assemblage, while in the vertebrate neuraxis the cell bodies lie usually inside the assemblage, and are, in fact, structural components of the switching device.

Because of this difference, with respect to location, in the arrangement of terminal arborizations and distribution of switching (synaptic) structures, one might also, generally, and perhaps somewhat loosely speaking, make the following distinction concerning so-called functional 'centers'. In the nervous system of invertebrates, the structural unit for such 'centers' is a neuropileme; in the vertebrate neuraxis, on the other hand, that structural unit is a 'nucleus' or a *'griseum'*, containing nerve cell bodies, neuropil-like terminal arborizations, and synapses (the possible significance of glial elements is here ignored).

VOWLES (1961) refers to what he calls a naive, but unstated belief that the invertebrate central nervous system 'is really just a simpler version of the vertebrate type'. This belief is said to be based on the assumption that, although the general anatomy of the invertebrate nervous system 'differs from that of the vertebrate, the properties of their individual neurons and their functional organization are the

same'. VOWLES' highly sophisticated argumentation is quite meaningless, since it amounts to an arbitrary and pedantic quibbling about
what should, or should not be considered 'the same', or, in other words,
which ones of the many obtaining invariants should be regarded
significant.

VOWLES (1961) makes a strenuous effort to stress, and even to
exaggerate the indeed obtaining not negligible differences. Thus, the
small nerve cell body of the insect brain, almost entirely filled with
nucleus, is pointed out. Now, in the vertebrate, including the human
brain, there are many types of granule (nerve) cells (cerebellar, olfactory,
etc.) whose body, in this respect, resembles a small lymphocyte. Again,
the peripheral location of invertebrate nerve cell bodies with respect
to the connecting structures (neuropilemes) is not unlike that of spinal
and cranial nerve ganglion cells in vertebrates, including the intracerebral cells of the mesencephalic root of the fifth.

Although synaptic connections can reasonably be inferred as
certain on the basis of very substantial circumstantial evidence, functional as well as histologic, including electron microscopic observations (WIGGLESWORTH, 1959), VOWLES (e.g. particularly 1955)
insists on the 'lack of evidence' for 'polarized' insect synapses, although
indirect evidence is here no more lacking than in numerous other
rather satisfactorily established and accepted theoretical concepts.

VOWLES (1961) emphasizes, in connection with the peripheral
location of cell bodies, the lack of synaptic endings on such bodies;
again, in comparison with vertebrates, a much smaller receptive
'dendritic surface area' is stressed, correlated with fewer, and shorter
dendritic ramifications. Moreover, the much slower impulse conduction velocity is adduced, which, even at its maximum in the giant
fibers, may be about ten times slower than in the fast vertebrate axons.
In the cited author's view, the insect nerve cells 'are potentially less
efficient as integrating units than are vertebrate neurons'. It is claimed
that these 'deficiencies cannot wholly be remedied by increasing the
number of neurons in the nervous system as a whole'.

Now, what should be regarded as 'efficient' or 'not efficient' is
quite evidently an undecidable question, based on arbitrary postulates
concerning a given goal or 'purpose' which must be defined by the
interpreting reasoner evaluating the system. It would therefore be
quite useless and even foolish to argue that point.

Strangely enough, VOWLES (1961) considers insects as 'probably
the most successful group of animals'. How, then, could a nervous

system, thus shown to be evidently 'adapted' to such 'success', not be 'efficient'?

It has been maintained, by very numerous observers, that the invertebrate, arthropod, and insect nervous system quite clearly shows less plasticity, and less diversity of behavior than that of the 'higher' groups among the vertebrates. This evaluation is anything but new. Yet, I believe that it can be regarded as essentially accurate, despite the important new data on remarkable insect performances such as e. g. reported in the ingenious investigations by v. FRISCH and his associates.

One may, of course, agree with VOWLES' (1961) remark that the properties of the insect neuron and the small size of the insect nervous system render necessary a rather 'simple functional organization of behavior', that is, in my opinion, an organization combining, as it were, a minimum of available means or resources with (at least in many instances) a maximum of variety, and with 'adapted' or 'appropriate' results. In several of its manifested forms, the insect and, more generally, the invertebrate nervous system can, I believe, be evaluated as highly 'efficient' and 'successful' either 'despite' or 'because of' its relative simplicity, smallness, and compactness.

The concentration of presumably synaptic structures into the compact neuropilemes (for which some distant analogies obtain in the vertebrate central nervous system) could be considered a significant factor of this efficiency. As regards insects, the cell bodies of the predominantly unipolar neurons are mostly very small (2 to 10 μ in diameter), and without synaptic or other junctional structures on their surface. The primary cell process ('axon') displays tufts or branches of short secondary processes ('dendrites'), while the cell body itself lacks any sort of 'dendrite'-like processes. The 'main' process (or 'axon') ends with numerous short ramifications within the neuropilemes of the ganglia or on the effector structures. Now, while some of the various proximal or distal (with respect to the cell body) ramifications might indeed be asynaptic (unpolarized) or protosynaptic (temporarily polarized), I am rather inclined to assume that true synapses can also be found in the insect central nervous system.

Thus, the powerful neurotoxic action of nicotine on insects clearly suggests that a true synaptic transmission of cholinergic type might perhaps obtain in insects. Various authors have, beyond doubt, identified acetycholine as well as cholinesterase in the central nervous system of Hexapoda. Yet, numerous additional factors intrinsic to said arthropod nervous system may be correlated with diverse aspects of neural activities that remain, so far, not sufficiently well elucidated. As regards other invertebrates, the recent work, by various authors, particularly J. Z. YOUNG, on the cephalopod central nervous system, can be evaluated as providing rather convincing evidence for the occurrence of true synaptic connections in these mollusks.

Thus, there is, in my opinion, little basis for the assumption that true, permanently polarized synapses might occur only in vertebrates and represent, as it were, a functional characteristic for the central nervous system of that phylum.

Following these remarks concerning the neuron theory and its validity for the invertebrate nervous system, a few comments on invertebrate nerve fibers are perhaps appropriate.

Generally speaking, the sort of myelin sheath, which is characteristic for many nerve fibers of most vertebrates, is very rare in the nervous system of invertebrates. Yet, the cephalochordate Amphioxus, and the cyclostomes, which latter are classified as true vertebrates, likewise lack 'genuine' myelin sheaths.

Nevertheless, the giant fibers or neurochords in some invertebrate groups, particularly in crustaceans and cephalopods, may be surrounded by a fatty sheath as shown by RETZIUS (1890) and other authors. This fatty layer is apparently located within a cellular sheath outside the axon. In some instances, even if no fatty sheath is detected by routine histologic methods, the use of the polarization microscope may disclose a layer of oriented fatty molecules in the sheath around some of the larger nerve fibers (YOUNG, 1937, and others). Electron microscopy appears particularly suitable for the demonstration of such myelin structures. On the basis of recent data it can be said that a 'loosely' organized myelin sheath may be present in certain nerve fibers of various invertebrates (e. g. annelids, arthropods, and molluscs; cf. also p. 80). Thus, the perhaps generally valid statement that myelinated fibers are not commonly found in the nervous system of invertebrates must not be taken too literally.

Again, constrictions of the sheath have been described. Some of these constrictions are presumably not directly comparable to those found in the vertebrate nervous system, while at least in one instance, *'nodes of Ranvier'* and compact, densely wound, or 'tightly spiraled', 'true myelin sheaths' with *'Schwann cells'* and *'Schmidt-Lantermann incisures'* have been described in an arthropod, namely in the central nervous system of a crab (MCALEAR, 1958). On the other hand, naked axons, devoid of glial sheath, seem to be characteristic for coelenterates, where elements comparable to glia cells, if at all present, are presumably very rare. 'Naked axons', however, may also occur, to a lesser extent, or as 'exceptions', in the nervous system of other metazoan forms.

The diameters of invertebrate axons may vary from less than 1 μ in small fibers to between 200 and 1000 μ in the giant axons of some cephalopods (YOUNG, 1937). The term, giant fiber, is, of course, a relative one, since in a very small insect, such as drosophila, fibers of a diameter from 4 to 6 μ could, not without justification, be classified as giant fibers (POWER, 1948).

Concerning the central nervous system as a whole, many of the available data on the vertebrate neuraxis seem to indicate that numerous significant linkages are here arranged in series[52] and proceed from 'lower' to 'higher' levels of integration. On the other hand, WIERSMA (1962) states that invertebrates such as arthropods appear to possess a central nervous system which is, to a great extent, linked in parallel at all levels.

'Fixed, interconnected reflex pathways provide for sterotyped motor patterns which, however, may be influenced by sensory input, and are under the control of higher order fibers. The complexity of the organization of the system is indicated by the wide spread of sensory information which is channeled simultaneously to the highest integrating levels and to efferent pathways at various levels' (WIERSMA, 1962).

In contradistinction to the views of VOWLES cited above (cf. p. 252), WIERSMA believes that all nervous systems will be found to function in a manner similar to that of arthropods. Thus, the latter author also assumes that the conception of a stepwise analyzing system with main linkages in series, and with a gradually proceeding integration from lower to higher levels is 'both inaccurate and inadequate'.

According to WIERSMA (1962), the arthropod nervous system can manage with relatively few 'command interneurons', partly because these animals have developed a rigid system of movement, which involves only a few motor fibers, and partly because the number of input channels is more limited. Many of the interneurons in the arthropods are said to have a widespread input and output, running

---

[52] With regard to the vertebrate neuraxis it should here be emphasized that a significant linkage in series is by no means incompatible with a considerable amount of linkage in parallel (cf. the remarks on redundancy in Vol. 1., chapt. I, sect. 4).

for considerable distances through the system. This feature, according to WIERSMA (1962) might help to account for the fact that the arthropod nervous system is smaller in terms of number of units than vertebrate nervous systems with comparable capabilities.

My own opinion in this matter could perhaps be summarized as follows. In comparing highly differentiated invertebrate nervous systems with vertebrate ones, we can only look for analogies, parallelisms and relevant invariants, but not for homologies in the morphologic sense, nor for very close similarities in the functional sense. The truism that the invertebrate or insect brain is not a vertebrate nor a human brain, should not, but apparently at times does, require affirmation.

As regards the neurosecretory cells repeatedly mentioned in the preceding discussions, HANSTRÖM (1954) points out, with respect to phylogenetic interpretations, that no sign of neurosecretory activity has as yet been found in the 'primitive' nerve net of coelenterates, nor (at least not as a well-established and widespread phenomenon) in plathelminthous worms. The cited author stresses that the neurosecretory hormones in crustaceans and insects, whose action has been relatively well studied, are often closely related to the specific mode of development and growth in these arthropods. Such hormones can therefore not be directly compared with 'universal stimulants' such as adrenaline and noradrenaline, 'whose activity may be applied to members of the whole animal kingdom'. The generalization that neurosecretion constitutes an 'old and fundamental form of endocrine activity' should therefore be evaluated with caution. Figure 175 shows HANSTRÖM'S concepts concerning the presumed transformation of 'ordinary nerve cells' into neurosecretory ones in both invertebrates and vertebrates. Although, to some extent, one might construe a 'similarity' between transmitter substances and 'neurosecretion', there are valid reasons for not applying the term neurosecretion to the 'humoral' transmission of the nervous impulse.

Again, generally speaking, some organs of internal secretion may be controlled by others (so-called 'master glands'), which latter, in turn, can be controlled by neurosecretory processes originating in the central nervous system. Such neurosecretory pathways have been interpreted as a final common path of complex neural circuits. Relationships of this type have been particularly studied in the Vertebrata with respect to the role of the hypophysis as a 'master gland', but a comparable arrangement seems to be displayed by vertebrates and invertebrates alike (cf. the review by SCHARRER and SCHARRER, 1963). Figure 176 demonstrates a comparison, according to the just quoted authors, between a series of such correlated events, interpreted as pertaining to the category of pheromones, in mammals and insects.

The *supporting cells* of the invertebrate nervous system consist, as in vertebrates, of ectodermal and mesodermal elements. HANSTRÖM (1928) distinguishes the following types of ectodermal elements: (a) epithelial cells on the surface of the central nervous system, and also in many instances, at the boundary between cellular layers and neuropilemes;

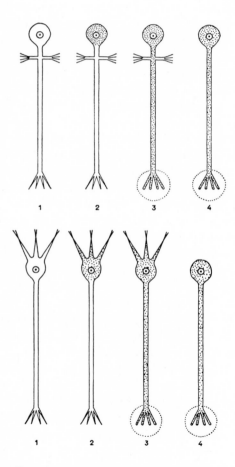

Figure 175. Transformation of ordinary nerve cell into neurosecretory nerve cell according to HANSTRÖM, 1954. 1–4 above: in nervous system of invertebrates; 1–4 below: in the vertebrate nervous system.

(b) 'neuroglia cells' in the stricter sense, again subdivided into (1) capsule or satellite cells for the body of the larger 'plasmatic' nerve cells; (2) supporting cells within the neuropilemes.

The mesodermal supporting elements, according to the cited author, occur (a) as covering or investing structures for the central nervous system and the larger peripheral nerves, and (b) as scattered connective tissue elements derived from or accompanying the tracheae, or the vessels, reaching the interior of the central nervous system.

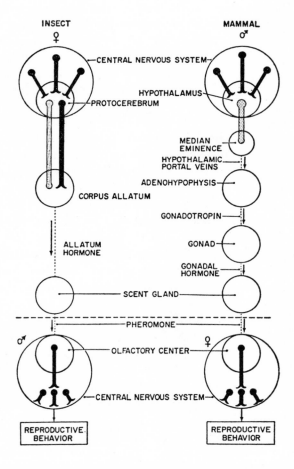

Figure 176. Diagram indicating some functional relationships involving nervous system, neurosecretion, and pheromones with respect to reproductive behavior of insects and mammals. (From SCHARRER and SCHARRER, 1963.)

According to B. SCHARRER (1939) the non-nervous constituents in the ganglia of insects, and as particularly studied in the cockroach, are represented by the following two sorts of structures, namely neuroglia, and connective tissue sheaths.

(1) The neuroglia is a supporting tissue within the central nervous system, and consists of elements that may display several cell processes, glia fibrils, and 'gliosomes'. Trypan blue is not stored by these cells.

(2) The connective tissue sheaths (perilemma), consisting of peri-neurium and 'neural lamella' cover, but do not enter the central nervous system. The perilemma structures stain with the *Mallory*-azan or with the *van Gieson* methods in a manner characteristic for connective tissue. Trypan blue is stored by the perineurium cells. Thus, this method of vital 'staining' is believed useful in distinguishing neuroglia proper from connective tissue elements.

It appears possible as well as not improbable that the supporting elements, particularly the neuroglia, have, in addition, a secretory and nutritive function; this however, is apparently not yet demonstrated by sufficiently conclusive evidence as far as invertebrates are concerned, and if the specific 'neurosecretory' or 'incretory' structures and organs studied by HANSTRÖM (1937, 1940) and by others are not considered typical 'supporting elements'. Concerning vertebrates, and, in particular, the peculiar paraependymal and paraventricular structures, further comments on this problem shall be included in chapter V, volume 3 of this series.

In addition, some sort of glial participation in neural 'transmission-processes' might perhaps, at least in some instances, be suspected (cf., however, the findings of KUFFLER and POTTER cited further below).

Following the descriptions of WIGGLESWORTH (1959, 1960) and other recent authors, the *outer sheath* of insect ganglia is said to include an inner cell layer, the perilemma proper, and an outer, non-cellular layer, designated as neural lamella or 'neurilemma'. It seems here preferable, however, to avoid the term 'neurilemma', which refers to the rather specific neuroectodermal covering elements of vertebrate peripheral nerve fibers ('neurilemma' is here also occasionally spelled 'neurolemma'). The *deeper glia cells* of invertebrates seem to include a number of diverse types, which, at present, are not yet classified in an appropriate, generally recognized fashion. In some instances, glia cytoplasm seems to be protruding into channel-like invaginations of the surface membrane of nerve cells. This structural arrangement is designated as a '*trophospongium*'. This latter term, however, referred originally to clear channels described in various vertebrate nerve cells by HOLMGREN. Further comments dealing with the questions related to HOLMGREN's 'trophospongium' will be included in chapter V, volume 3, of this series. Although the data concerning ontogenetic derivation of invertebrate glial elements are fragmentary, an overall ectodermal or neuroectodermal origin, in accordance with HANSTRÖM's views, can be considered fairly well established. The lack, or at least scarcity of 'glial' elements in coelenterates (and perhaps some other 'lower' forms) was mentioned above in connection with so-called 'naked axons'.

In a study of physiological properties of the glia in the central nervous system of the leech Hirudo (annelid), KUFFLER and POTTER (1964) found that glial elements did not give impulse-like responses even to large changes of their membrane potential. The quoted authors state that these glial cells do not seem to participate directly in the electrical signalling processes of the nervous system. It was possible to remove the glial cells without interfering, for a significant period of time, with the impulse activities of nerve cells. According to the cited findings, glia cells do not appear to be directly concerned with the action potential of nerve cells.

With few exceptions (such, e. g., as cephalopods) *blood vessels* do not enter the central nervous system of invertebrates. This non-vascularized status, of course, greatly differs from the conditions prevailing in most representatives of the vertebrate phylum. On the other hand, in tracheate invertebrates such as, e. g., insects, an adequate amount of oxygen is provided by a rich supply of tracheae passing through the central nervous tissue (B. SCHARRER, 1939).

The questions related to the aging of cellular elements represent still another set of problems concerning the nervous tissue of invertebrates. A few authors, notably SCHULTZE-RÖBBECKE (1951), WEYER (1931), SCHMIDT (1923), and others, have dealt with this matter, particularly with respect to arthropods. The actual data are difficult to evaluate, and the resulting inferences can be regarded as still inconclusive. In connection with the discussion of the vertebrate nervous tissue, this general problem will be briefly considered in the next volume (chapt. V, vol. 3).

Within the context of these generalized remarks on some features of the non-chordate invertebrate central nervous system, five additional topics of significance for a comparison with features obtaining in

vertebrates may appropriately require a brief discussion, namely
(a) olfactory connections; (b) optic connections; (c) various topographic
displacements of cell groups or centers in a taxonomic or morphologic
series, conforming to an orderliness designated as neurobiotaxis by
Ariëns Kappers; (d) certain fundamental topologic relationships;
and finally (e) the problem posed by the widespread decussation of
fiber systems, or contralateral connections, crossing the promorphologic midline.

(a) The olfactory neuropilemes in arthropods contain synaptic
structures which manifest a striking resemblance with the olfactory
glomeruli of vertebrates. This likeness prompted Bellonci (1883) to
introduce the designation antennal glomeruli for the structures under
consideration. The difference between the arthropod and the vertebrate arrangement can here be regarded as merely due to a different
position and shape of the secondary olfactory neuron (Figs. 177, 178,
179). Introducing the concept of self-reexciting circuits (K., 1927),
I had pointed out, as an example, certain connections in the olfactory
bulb of vertebrates. Hanström (1928), referring to my concept

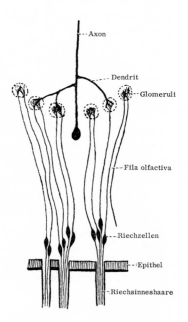

Figure 177. Diagram of olfactory connections in the deutocerebrum of arthropods.
(After Hanström, 1928.)

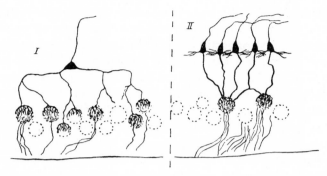

Figure 178. Diagram of olfactory connections in microsmatic (I, bird), and macrosmatic (II, dog) vertebrates. (Simplified after VAN GEHUCHTEN, from K., 1927.)

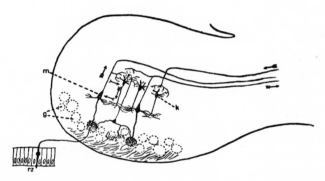

Figure 179. Diagram of self-reexciting or closed circuits in the olfactory bulb of a mammal. (After K., 1927.)

(which I had originally designated as 'generator principle' or 'Dynamoprinzip'), expresses the opinion that self-reexciting circuits of that type might likewise be present in the olfactory lobe of arthropods. It should, however, be pointed out, as I had already intimated in 1927, that the true closed loop circuits here under consideration, although suggesting self-reexcitation (positive feedback, e.g. 'reinforcement' by frequency increase, or 'holding', i.e. short-time storage), could also, depending on the parameters involved, act as self-inhibiting mechanisms (negative feedback).

(b) The considerable structural similarities manifested by the optic connections and 'centers' of arthropods, cephalopods, and vertebrates were pointed out by a number of authors (RÁDL, 1912; ZAWARZIN, 1914,

1925; CAJAL, 1915, 1918). Using the criteria discussed in the preceding chapter, these similarities represent morphologic analogies. Yet, taking the optic connections as arbitrarily disjoint, independent systems, manifesting a fundamental pattern, topologic one-one correspondences obtain that could here be designated as true homologies. The establishment of 'homologies' would then depend upon the 'elements', accepted as 'irreducible', in terms of which the structural pattern is described. Nevertheless, because arthropods, cephalopods and vertebrates do not display a common morphologic pattern (Bauplan) of the brain, we cannot, under the previously adopted premises, evaluate these similarities as 'morphologic homologies'.

The compound eyes of arthropods such as crustaceans and insects differ greatly, with regard to structural aspects, from the lateral vertebrate eyes, while, on the other hand, the eyes of cephalopods and even certain polychaete annelids, discounting the reversed (direct) disposition of the neurosensory elements, are much more similar to the vertebrate eyes.

It seems evident, as various authors have repeatedly pointed out, that apparently only in three of the major animal phyla, 'large, image resolving eyes' (WALD, 1963) have developed, namely in arthropods, in molluscs, and in vertebrates. In the quaint formulation of the just cited *Harvard* Professor, 'each of these eyes is a separate invention', (*sic;* who is the inventor?) 'anatomically, embryologically and phylogenetically unconnected with the others'.

'All these eyes, however, share the same fundamental biochemistry' (WALD, 1963).

Yes, indeed. But do not all terrestrial (i.e. 'planetary') living organisms share the same fundamental biochemistry with respect to the composition and activities of protoplasmatic systems in general? This 'unity in diversity' was already particularly stressed and elucidated in L. PLATE's introductory lectures on general zoology, which I heard, long ago, at the very beginning of my medical studies in Jena upon my return from four and a half years of military service in World War I.

A single ommatidium (cf. p. 144) from the compound eye of a bee is shown in Figure 180. Eight visual cells are attached to the inner end of the crystalline cone, and in cross section show a radial arrangement. Their inner parts, indicated as darker structures in the diagram, represent the presumably photoreceptive rhabdome, the segments of which may be considered as forming parts of the respective retinular cells. These latter, through their neurites, transmit the optic signals to the external optic neuropileme (external 'glomerulus'). According to Autrum and Stumpf (1950) as well as v. Frisch (1950), these radially arranged visual elements could analyze light in different planes, in conformity with their position. Thus, even a single ommatidium could, in theory, register the plane of vibration of the polarized light from any portion of the sky. Using polaroid material, v. Frisch (1950) has constructed a model of the bee's eye reproducing the polarizing effect (Fig. 181). The experiments performed by this author and his associates seem to prove quite conclusively that bees can orient themselves by means of the information which the polarization of the sky light provides, even if they can see only a small area of blue

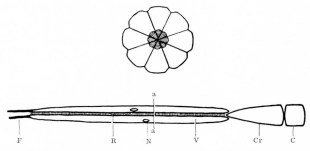

Figure 180. Simplified diagram of a single insect ommatidium. (After von Frisch, 1950). C: cornea; Cr: crystalline cone; V: visual cell; N: nucleus of visual cell; R: rhabdome; F: nerve fiber. At the top, enlarged cross section in plane a–a.

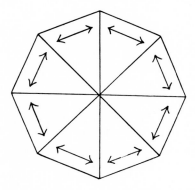

Figure 181. Model of polarizing arrangement in the bee's eye, constructed from eight triangles of polaroid material. Double arrows indicate vibration plane of transmitted light. (After von Frisch, 1950.)

sky, while the sun itself may be hidden behind clouds. Moreover, enough ultraviolet radiation usually penetrates the overcast and enables the bee eye to detect directly the position of the sun behind a cloud layer. Additional observations likewise proved that at least some ants orient themselves by means of polarized light. Furthermore, analysis of polarized light also seems to occur within the eyes of cephalopods. Moody (1962) has reported rather convincing evidence for the intraocular discrimination of vertically and horizontally polarized light by Octopus.

In the compound eyes of arthropods, only rays at an approximately right angle to the surface of the 'cornea' (cf. Fig. 180) are believed to reach the retinulae according to Exner (1891). Thus, as it were, a 'point to point' (or 'spot to spot') projection of 'external world' to compound eye, resulting in an upright (i. e. non-inverted) 'musivic' or 'mosaic' picture, has been assumed (Exner, 1891; Johannes Müller, 1826). There are, however, two in a certain degree different types of compound eyes, namely apposition eyes with short 'optic cylinders', predominant in diurnal insects, and superposition eyes, with elongated ommatidia, predominant in nocturnal forms (cf. e. g. Snodgrass, 1935). In the ommatidia of the superposition eye, the principal focus is said to be at a point roughly corresponding to half the length of the 'optic cylinder', and light beams with relatively small angle of incidence may reach the receptors. Yet, generally speaking, each ommatidium of a compound eye selects only that portion of the visual field which is 'circumscribed by its own projection' (v. Frisch, 1953). Visual acuity, on the whole, is comparatively low.

Various details concerning 'ultrastructure' of the light receptors in the compound eyes of insects, as displayed by electron-microscopy, have been described by Fernández-Morán (1958), but need not be discussed in this context.

As regards the color sense of bees, v. Frisch (1950) found that the 'visible' spectrum for bees seems to be shortened in the red, but extends into the ultraviolet, or, in other words, that the 'visible' region is merely shifted to higher frequencies (or shorter wavelengths)[53]. How-

---

[53] The visible spectrum for the human eye extends roughly from 0.8 μ (red) to 0.4 μ (violet) or, more accurately, from about 3900 to 7700 Å (390 to 770 mμ), while the visible spectrum for bees seems to extend from 0.65 μ (650 mμ; 6500 Å; orange for man), that is from 'yellow', to 0.3 μ (300 mμ; 3000 Å), into the ultraviolet.

ever, while the human eye can distinguish about sixty or more different colorations in the visible spectrum, bees apparently only discriminate four different color qualities: yellow, blue-green, blue, and ultraviolet. Butterflies (Lepidoptera), on the other hand, are presumably not red blind.

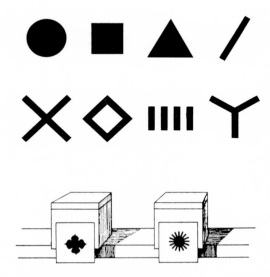

Figure 182. Shapes that are apparently recognized or not recognized by bees. (After VON FRISCH, 1950.) Bees do not learn to distinguish between the shapes in the upper row nor between those in the middle row. But for the optic pattern registration of the bee, each shape in the upper row is distinctly different from every shape in the middle row. The lower row shows two different shapes that bees can easily distinguish from each other.

Another problem concerns optic shape 'perception' or perhaps better shape registration. It is generally believed that most invertebrates equipped with eyes have a very poorly developed faculty for the registration of visual shapes, and this belief is at least partly supported by fairly convincing experiments. On the other hand, most vertebrate eyes, including those of fishes, seem to record shapes in a fairly efficient manner. Yet, cephalopods with well differentiated eyes, and even some spiders (particularly 'jumping spiders') appear to manifest some significant degree of visual shape registration. Among insects, bees are able to detect visual shapes and patterns according to a criterion of 'brokenness' (v. FRISCH, 1950). Shape registration depends here on the difference between a broken and a compact pattern. Since a bee's compound eye is rigidly fixed on its head, a broken pattern may result in a 'flickering effect' as the bee flies past the object. Figure 182 shows the types of shapes which, according to the studies of v. FRISCH and his associates, bees can and cannot distinguish.

In addition to light and dark, color, and shape registration, as well as directional orientation and phototaxis, the registration of motion, regardless of distinctive shape or configuration, plays likewise an important role as one of the sorts of information transmitted by the optic system.

Concerning the structural details, the central fibers of the neuro-sensory photoreceptor cells of arthropods (cf. p. 144) form peculiar synapses, known as 'optic cartridges' or neurommatidia (Figs. 183, 184), located in the external glomerulus. The primary optic input fibers transmit here their signals to the processes of cellular elements pertaining to the associated lamina ganglionaris (external optic neuropileme). This arrangement corresponds to the so-called retina profunda of cephalopods, and to the outer plexiform layer of the vertebrate retina,

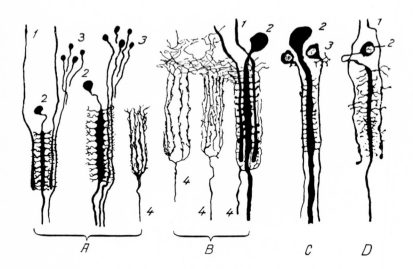

Figure 183. Neurommatidia or 'optic cartridges' in the external glomerulus (lamina ganglionaris) of arthropods. (From BECCARI, 1947.) *A* In the decapod crustacean Spiratocaris polaris (after HANSTRÖM). *B*, *C* In the dipteran fly Calliphora vomitoria. *D* In the lepidopteran Sphinx. (*B* to *D* after CAJAL and SANCHEZ, 1915.) 1: central fiber of visual neurosensory cell; 2: optic neuron of second order; 3: smaller accessory neurons; 4: fibers from optic lobe, ending with calyx-, or basket-like arborizations.

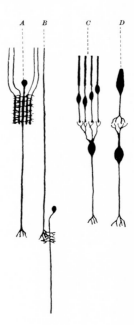

Figure 184. Diagram showing long and short visual cell neurites of arthropods, compared with rods and cones of vertebrates. (From HANSTRÖM, 1928.) A: large second order optic neuron of an arthropod, connected, in a neurommatidium, with the terminal arborizations of four 'short' visual cells. B: 'long' fiber of insect visual cell, connected with a nerve cell in the medulla externa (middle optic neuropileme). C, D: rods and cones of vertebrate retina connected with bipolar cells (of lamina granularis interna).

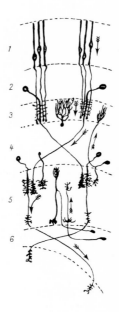

Figure 185. Simplified diagram of optic lobe connections in an insect. (After CAJAL from BECCARI, 1947.) 1: visual cells of retinulae; 2: layer of cell bodies pertaining to neurons of lamina ganglionaris; 3: layer of neurommatidia (external optic glomerulus); 4: external chiasma; 5: medulla externa (middle optic glomerulus); 6: internal chiasma (sometimes also referred to as 'middle chiasma'); medulla interna (internal optic glomerulus) not numbered, below layer 6.

including its correlated layer of bipolar neuronal elements. The
medulla externa (middle optic glomerulus) of arthropods with its
associated cells, and the ganglion opticum of cephalopods are then
analogous to the inner plexiform layer and the layer of optic ganglion
cells of the vertebrate retina. The medulla interna (inner optic glomerulus) of arthropods can thus be considered analogous to more central
structures of the cephalopod brain, and to grisea of tectum mesencephali
and diencephalon (lateral geniculate body) of vertebrates. Figures 184
to 192 illustrate these relationships and include, in Figure 186, CAJAL's
interpretation of the obtaining analogies. The role of nerve cells with
short processes located in synaptic regions of the invertebrate and
vertebrate optic input system, and known as amacrine cells, is poorly
understood. Such amacrines, which increase the complexity of con-

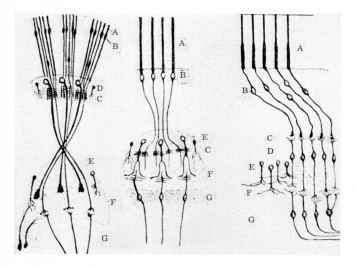

Figure 186. Diagram comparing analogous elements in the optic system of insects
(left), cephalopods (center) and mammals (right). (From CAJAL, Recuerdos de mi vida,
1923, plate CVI.) A: neurosensory visual cells and their nucleated portion (B); C: synaps
between first order and second order optic neuron (D); E: amakrine cells; G: third order
optic neuron; F: synaps between second and third order optic neuron; there are some
ambiguities in the diagram: D is not indicated, although self-evident in center picture,
next to amakrine cell E; again, in left picture, D stands next to what looks like a small
amakrine cell. In addition, it should be remembered that, in the two left diagrams, the
direction of the light is from the top, while in the right diagram, the light comes from
the bottom, and has to traverse the various layers before reaching the neurosensory cells,
which are directed away from the light (inverted type of retina). Cf. also Fig. 187.

nections, are shown in Figure 186. Some of the amacrines and some additional cells of the medulla externa are assumed to convey centrifugal impulses toward the neurommatidia and thus, perhaps, to affect the fibers of retinal cells. On the other hand, the conduction in these 'celulas centrifugas' might be amphidromic, e.g. interconnecting neurommatidia. Hence, one could either assume some

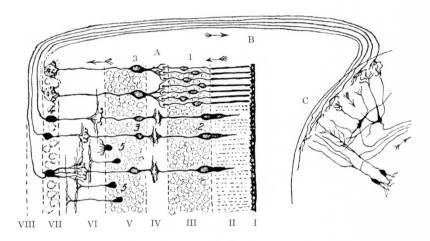

Figure 187. Neuronal diagram of optic pathway in a vertebrate (bird). (Adapted from drawings by CAJAL, after BECCARI, 1947.) A: retina; I: layer of pigment epithelium; II: layer of rods and cones; III: outer granular layer (1, 2: nuclei of rods and cones); IV: outer plexiform layer; V: inner granular layer (3: bipolar neurons); VI: inner plexiform layer; VII: ganglion cell layer (4: neurons of nervus opticus); VIII: layer of optic nerve fibers; B: optic nerve; C: tectum opticum (tectum mesencephali); 5: amakrine cells.

'feedback' or centrifugal 'adjusting' effect, or some correlation, coordination, and integration of neurommatidia activities. Various details concerning amacrine cells can be found in POLYAK's encyclopedic work on the vertebrate visual system (1957).

As regards the optic system of cephalopods, various sorts of centrifugal 'efferents', as assumed by YOUNG (1960), are shown in Figure 163C. In addition, YOUNG (1964) describes large 'classifying cells' (cf. Fig. 163 D) with spreading dendrite trees, presumed to 'record the extent of vertical and horizontal contouring'. The cited author also postulates storage mechanisms, related to 'memory storage cells' in the optic lobe of octopus (cf. Fig. 163 D). Thus, YOUNG's (1964) concept, if, e.g., compared with CAJAL's interpretation, involves numerous further complications which are, at present, difficult to evaluate in terms of relevant analogies.

On page 144, in discussing the general structural arrangement of the insect brain, brief reference was made to the so-called local chias-

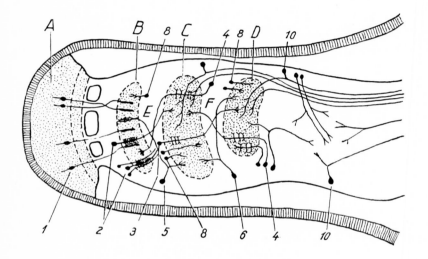

Figure 188. Details of optic lobe in a decapod crustacean with normally developed eyes. The neuronal arrangement is shown on the basis of GOLGI pictures according to a diagram by HANSTRÖM. (From BECCARI, 1947.)

This figure shows one example of so-called local chiasma between layer A and B. According to present interpretations, these local chiasmata may play a role in the flip-flop mechanism shown below in Fig. 193. The slightly rectangular spaces (lacunae) between layers A and B are tracheae. A: retinulae (retina externa); B: lamina ganglionaris (external optic neuropileme, op 1 in Fig. 85; also occasionally designated as retina intermedia; C: Medulla interna (middle optic neuropileme, op 2 in Fig. 85; also called retina interna); D: medulla interna (internal optic neuropileme, op 3 in Fig. 85; also called lobulus opticus); E: external chiasma; F: internal chiasma (also called middle chiasma, fibers crossing near neuron 10 being then called inner chiasma); 1: visual cells; 2: optic neurons of second order (unfortunately also sometimes called optic neurons of first order); 3: optic neurons of third order (unfortunately also at times designated as of second order; 4: neurons with peripherally directed (retrograde) neurite; 5, 6: various internuncials; 8: amacrine cells; 10: efferents of optic system.

mata of ommatidia, which provide connections with several 'optic cartridges' or neurommatidia. These chiasmata seem to form part of a circuit mechanism required for a processing of the information related to the peculiar flicker-pattern vision apparently obtaining in insects. The output from adjacent pairs or triplets of ommatidia must be operated upon in a manner such that the sequences of successive pulses will properly encode the significant features of the stroboscopic movement. HASSENSTEIN (1951) and REICHARDT (1962) have studied the problems involved in this type of vision, and REICHARDT (1962) has suggested some neural network models in terms of communication

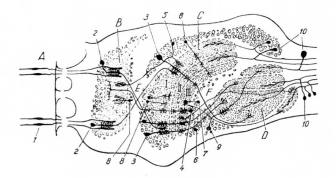

Figure 189. Details of optic lobe in an insect (Aeschna larva), combined after ZAWARZIN and CAJAL and SANCHEZ. (After BECCARI, 1947.) To be compared with preceding Fig. 188, abbreviations identical. Two 'optic cartridges' or neurommatidia are shown in layer B. (7, 9: internuncials of unknown significance.)

channels (Fig. 193). Periodicity, direction of movement, and velocity could be recorded by the functional structures suggested, which provide, by stimulating or inhibiting pulses, a computation of correlated ordered pairs. The inputs consist of alternating plus-minus, or minus-plus sequences, and the arrangement of the channels closely corresponds to that of a so-called flip-flop circuit element in communication engineering. The similarity of the circuit pattern, elaborated by REICHARDT (1962), to the theoretical neural model of a flip-flop mechanism as suggested in my monograph on brain and consciousness (K., 1975) is quite obvious. It should, however, be stressed, as REICHARDT justly remarks with respect to his solution, that these networks represent postulated communication channels, and not the actual nerve

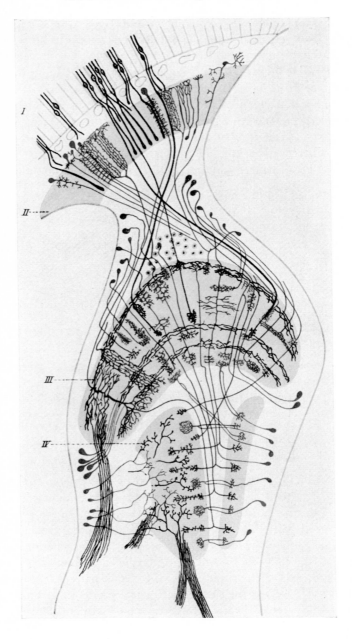

Fig. 190

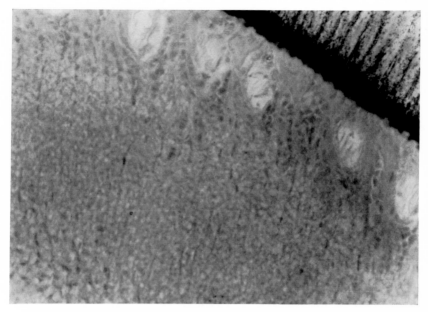

Figure 191. Details of optic lobe in worker bee as seen in a routine hematoxylin-eosin preparation. (Original; × 500; red. $^3/_4$.) At right top retinulae and heavy pigment accumulation; below this, a row of large tracheae, and a layer of optic neurons of the second order; the following wide, striated layer is the external optic neuropileme (lamina ganglionaris), containing the neurommatidia; at left bottom some nerve cell bodies pertaining and external to medulla externa (middle optic neuropileme, not shown).

fiber connections; with regard to my neural flip-flop models of 1957, I need hardly reiterate that their highly theoretical and artificial nature was duly pointed out. Nevertheless, it would seem reasonable to assume actual neural mechanisms working in accordance with the indicated logical and mathematical principles.

In addition to the decussation provided by the local chiasmata, the two sorts of connection furnished by the long and by the short neurites

Figure 190. Details of structures and connections in the optic lobe of flies. (Modified after CAJAL and SANCHEZ, 1915, from HANSTRÖM, 1928.) I: retinulae; II: lamina ganglionaris (external optic neuropileme; op 1 in Fig. 85); the lacunae between I and II represent large tracheae; likewise, three local chiasmata (cf. Fig. 188) are shown; III: medulla externa (middle optic neuropileme; op 2 in Fig. 85); IV: medulla interna (inner or internal optic neuropileme; op 3 in Fig. 85); this figure should be compared with Figs. 188 and 189. Components of some neurommatidia are shown in layer II.

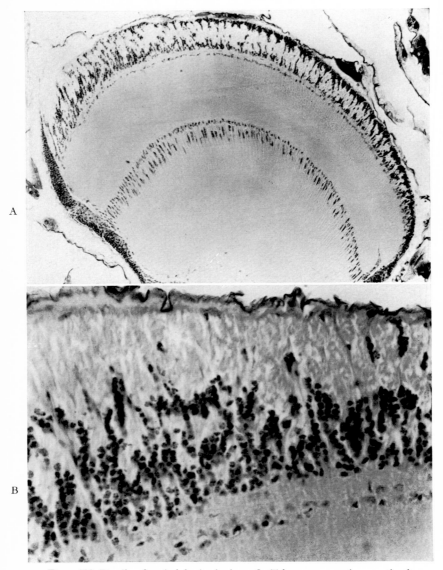

Figure 192. Details of optic lobe in the horsefly Tabanus as seen in a routine hematoxylin-eosin preparation (Original). *A* Medulla externa (middle optic neuropileme)
on top, and medulla interna (inner optic neuropileme) at bottom. Both layers show stri-
ations and are capped, on their external (lateral) border, by cell layers. (×150; red. $^2/_3$.)
B Cell layers of medulla externa. Above the wider one of the two cell layers, the inner
portion of the neurommatidial layer ('lamina'), is seen, as cut at an oblique angle (×450;
red. $^2/_3$). Figs. 191 and 192 A, B should be compared with the preceding Figs. 188 to 190.

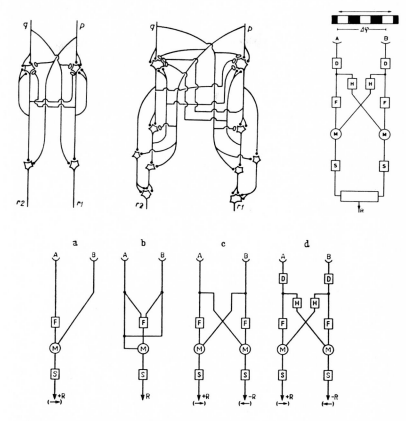

Figure 193. Diagrams illustrating REICHARDT's network model of communication channels in the optic system of insects. The two first diagrams in the upper row, left, represent neuronal models of flip-flop mechanisms suggested in my monograph of 1957. The other five figures (from REICHARDT, 1962) show the communication channels in the optic system of insects as suggested by this author. The local chiasmata, shown in the preceding Figs. 188 and 190 can be interpreted in accordance with the sorts of theories considered in the text.

of visual cells (cf. Figs. 184, 190) are likewise suggestive of a signal transmission in accordance with the aforementioned network models.

In a brief and summarizing formulation of the topic one might say that the spatial resolving power of the insect compound eye is of relatively low order, but that, because of the very effective neural mechanisms, said eye nevertheless displays rather good functional capabilities. The low degree of resolution in the individual ommatidium is compensated by a neuronal arrangement whereby frequencies of stimulation changes, and interrelations between stimulus-displacements allow, in rapidly flying insects, registration of some significant contour characteristics as well as of other configurational invariants.

In the neural mechanisms of a flying insect, the configurational orderliness of spatial neighborhood-relations ('räumliches Nebeneinander') is transformed into an orderliness of temporal sequences ('zeitliches Nacheinander'). Or, in other words, a high degree of temporal resolving power compensates for a low degree of spatial resolving power. This, of course, requires that object and eye must, in respect to each other, be in a state of motion. HERTZ (1933, 1934), in discussing these matters, remarks that the vertebrate eye and its mechanisms are 'spatial eyes', suited for the registration of the shape of objects, while the arthropod compound eyes are 'temporal eyes', best suited for the registration of changes displayed by objects ('Veränderungen an den Objekten'), that is, for the registration of objects as changing events. The adequate stimulus for the compound eyes is said to be flicker ('Flimmerlicht') in contradistinction to constant illumination assumed to obtain for the vertebrate eye. While these remarks of HERTZ (1933, 1934) are doubtless quite justified, it should, however, not be forgotten that the human, and presumably also many other vertebrate eyes and their neural mechanisms make use of temporal sequences by constant small movements of the extrinsic eye muscles, whereby the shifts of the retinal picture across the macula lutea represent a scanning procedure. The translation of temporal sequences into spatial distributions, and vice-versa, is a well-known and widely used sort of transformation in artificial as well as in neural control and communication mechanisms (cf. K., 1957, p. 252).

Concerning the general significance of the various chiasmata in the optic system of invertebrates, as here briefly discussed, an important difference with respect to the optic chiasma of vertebrates should be kept in mind. The vertebrate optic chiasma involves a crossing of the promorphologic midline by optic fibers, that is, a crossing from right side to left side, or vice versa. The chiasmata in the optic lobe of invertebrates, however, remain within right or left body half, respectively. Disregarding the above-mentioned special significance of the local chiasmata, there may be a crossing of fibers from upper and lower retinal halves of one and the same eye, as in cephalopods and, *mutatis mutandis* (retinulae) in at least some insects, as well as, in various insect forms, an additional chiasmatic crossing of fibers related to impulses from anterior and posterior retinular regions. It goes without saying that additional commissures, as e. g. mentioned above on page 145 in the discussion of the insect brain, interconnect optic 'centers' of right and left side, without representing 'chiasmata' in the strict sense.

Among cephalopods, Nautilus is provided with an eye of rather primitive structure if compared with that of e. g. Octopus. The eye of Nautilus is an open cup lacking cornea as well as lens, and thus resembles a simple 'pin-hole camera'. In this cephalopod, the optic nerve fibers, connecting eye cup retina and optic lobe, do not form a chiasma (according to the available reports).

While some data, allowing a number of inferences, are available about the compound eyes of insects, very little is known concerning the functional significance of the insect or arthropod *ocelli*. The ascertained structural arrangements and connections seem to preclude the possibility of shape 'discrimination' or registration. Its photoreceptors, however, appear to be quite sensitive. RUCK (1957) recorded potentials from the ocelli of cockroaches and grasshoppers. This author found that stimulation of the photoreceptor cells by light inhibits intrinsic activity originating in the peripheral end of the ocellar nerve fibers (i. e. in the neuron of the second order). There is considerable convergence, since the number of photoreceptor neurosensory cells, in the forms investigated, is much larger than the number of secondary fibers (perhaps only four or five) connecting with the brain. As far as can be inferred from the available data, the ocellus provides information about light intensity. It might seem surprising, as some authors concerned with these problems have pointed out, that this seemingly simple matter of changes in light intensity should be dealt with by a relatively very complex signaling mechanism. According to YOUNG (1964), adjustment of the animal's activities to the level of light intensity might e. g. mean that the function of the median eyes of insects 'is to stimulate flight, but not to guide it'.

(c) C. U. ARIËNS KAPPERS[54] elaborated, on the basis of his very extensive comparative observations of vertebrate brain morphology,

---

[54] Cf. bibliography to chapter V (KAPPERS, 1908, 1920, 1927 and many other publications), in volume 3.

the *theory of neurobiotaxis* which will be critically evaluated in the next chapter (chapter V). Discounting the particular causal explanation propounded by KAPPERS, the actual data subsumed under the concept of neurobiotaxis clearly disclose a correlation between the position of circumscribed cell groups (cell populations) as well as of neuropilemes, that is, of grisea, on one hand, and on the other hand the location of fiber systems which carry the principal afferent impulses (the input) to these grisea.

HANSTRÖM (1928) confirmed the validity of the neurobiotaxis concept with regard to invertebrates. If the morphologic findings are arranged in a topologic series, it can be seen that the corpora pedunculata, located near the centers for the palps in the polychaete brain,

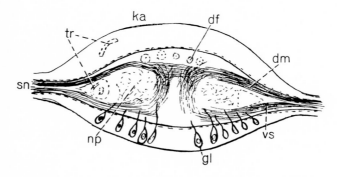

Figure 194. Ventral cord ganglion of an insect larva (Aeschna), showing dorsal and ventral root fiber bundles. (Adapted and simplified after ZAWARZIN, 1925, from K., 1927.) df: thick dorsal fibers (neurochords); dm: dorsal, efferent root; gl: nerve cells; ka: sheath of ganglion; np: neuropileme; sn: lateral nerve; tr: tracheae; vs: ventral afferent root.

'migrate' into the protocerebrum of arthropods, and even into the eye stalks of 'higher' crustaceans with particularly well differentiated compound eyes (cf. Fig. 85). If, however, the eyes of crustaceans are poorly developed, and, correspondingly, the significance of optic input decreases, while that of olfactory input increases, and is correlated with a conspicuous differentiation of olfactory centers, the corpora pedunculata are located in the protocerebrum. It is not unreasonable to assume, as HANSTRÖM (1928) does, that 'der Einfluss der von den Riechzentren nach den Corpora pedunculata strömenden Reize wird

mächtiger und die Corpora pedunculata wandern bei solchen Crustaceen sekundär ins Protocerebrum zurück'. Although I believe that a
'causal' explanation for changes of position must be postulated, and
do not doubt that, on the basis of more detailed knowledge, it might
become feasible to give such explanation, I am now inclined to consider
all the presently available causal 'explanations' premature. It is likewise difficult, although, of course possible, to justify evaluation of
various patterns in terms of 'primary' and 'secondary' phylogenetic
states or conditions.

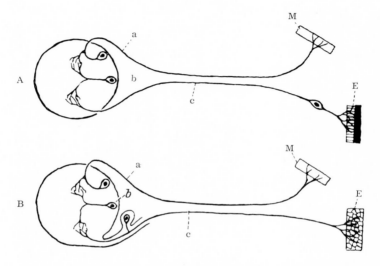

Figure 195. Diagram of simplified reflex mechanism in the ventral medulla of arthropods (A) and in the spinal cord of vertebrates (B). (From HANSTRÖM, 1928.)
   In arthropods the sensory roots are ventral, the motor ones dorsal; for the sake of
comparison, the spinal cord (B) is drawn with dorsal side at bottom. a: motor neuron;
b: internuncial neuron; c: sensory neuron (cell body in the vertebrate spinal ganglion,
and near the integument in anthropods); E: epithelium; M: muscle.

   Again, mollusks with poorly developed eyes have long optic
nerves, formed by the processes of the primary neurosensory cells,
while in mollusks with highly developed eyes the optic centers (Figs.
161, 162) have 'migrated' toward the periphery and are at only a short
distance from the retina proper. Similar 'displacements' can be noticed
in arthropods such a Myriapoda and Arachnida. HANSTRÖM (1928)
cites additional instances of neurobiotaxis concerning displacements

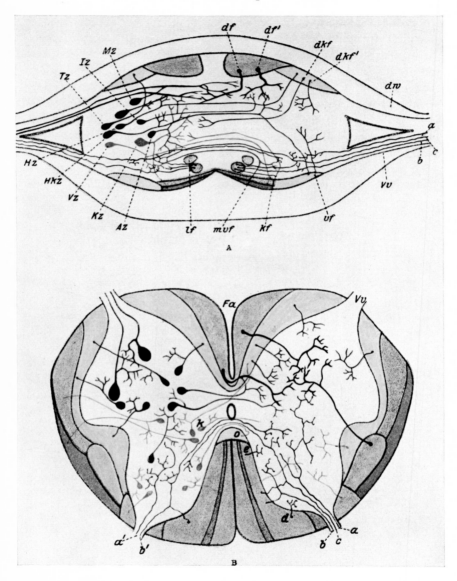

Figure 196. Cross sections through ventral medulla of Aeschna (A) and spinal cord of man (B). The spinal cord is shown with ventral side on top, while the ganglion of Aeschna medulla is drawn in the conventional orientation with ventral side at bottom. (After a color plate by ZAWARZIN, 1925.) a, b, c, d, e: sensory fibers; dw, vw: dorsal and ventral roots; Fa: fissura mediana anterior; Mz: motor neurones; Az, df, dkf, Iz, Hz, Hkz, K, kf, Kz, mvf, o, vf: diverse internuncial neurons; Fa: fissura mediana ant.

of the dendritic ramifications in various ganglia of Gastropoda (snails).

(d) As regards fundamental topologic relationships, the parallelism stressed by ZAWARZIN (1924, 1925) is in full agreement with an old concept expressed about 1822 by GEOFFROY (DE) ST. HILAIRE, namely that an arthropod could, to some extent, be 'converted' into a vertebrate by reversing dorsal and ventral sides. This interesting viewpoint will again be considered further below (p. 319) in the final subdivision of this chapter.

ZAWARZIN (1924, 1925) pointed out that the segmental peripheral nerves originating from the ventral medullary cord of insects are formed by a dorsal and ventral root, of which the former is essentially efferent (motor) and the latter afferent (sensory). The synaptic arrangements within the medullary cord are likewise, in many respects, similar to those in the spinal cord of vertebrates (Figs. 194, 195, 196). HANSTRÖM (1928) comments on the inverted functional relationship of dorsal and ventral roots in arthropods and vertebrates by pointing out that the sensory roots are significantly concerned with the innervation of the integument which is connected to the central nervous system by the shortest path. Thus, the sensory roots reach the dorsal side of the vertebrate spinal cord, and the ventral aspect of the insect medullary cord. We have, as it were, here a manifestation of the well known principle of least action, or least effort. Moreover, as HANSTRÖM justly remarks, the structural similarities studied and discussed by ZAWARZIN are by no means merely trivial or superficial. These analogies can be interpreted as demonstrating that functionally identical nerve centers display, or may 'acquire', fundamentally identical types of structure even in widely different animal groups which do not seem to be directly related.

Seen from another viewpoint, the 'reversal' of dorsal and ventral connections is evidently associated with the ontogenetic derivation of the central nervous system from the ectoderm. In various forms such, e. g., as the nematomorph worm Nectonema (Fig. 27), and the marine polychaete annelid Sigalion (Fig. 48), the central nervous system does not become entirely separated from its origin and remains in close connection with the ventral ectodermal body surface.

(e) *Contralateral fiber connections* represent a very generalized occurrence in the central nervous system of bilaterally symmetric metazoa. The 'explanation' for this widespead manifestation of decussations crossing the promorphologic midline or midsagittal plane has posed a complex and difficult problem.

Some authors, such as Cajal (1911, 1955), Spitzer (1910), and Jacobsohn-Lask (1924, 1928) have critically reviewed various hypotheses, and expressed their own opinions. Cajal (1911, 1955) has particularly stressed the significance of decussations ('théorie des entrecroisements') with respect to the optic system. His 'explanation' must, in my opinion, be regarded as unsatisfactory, because he introduces not only what amounts to 'teleologic' postulates, but, in addition, 'mental' concepts[55]. In accordance with my own viewpoint, mentalistic terms (or aspects of consciousness) must be entirely avoided, as far as relevant 'explanations' are concerned, in the notations pertaining to natural sciences *sensu strictiori* (physics, biophysics, chemistry, biochemistry, physiology, anatomy, comparative anatomy, evolution), and their introduction becomes here illegitimate.

Spitzer (1910) emphasizes 'Condensation des functionell Zusammenwirkenden'. Although his conclusions are unduly vague and are combined with rather unconvincing phylogenetic and morphogenetic speculations, I believe that this formulation, in a most generalized way, probably subsumes a justifiable concept. Jacobsohn-Lask (1924, 1928) does not provide a precise genetic explanation, but attempts to derive the decussations from primarily given architectural configurations. Although his detailed elaborations differ in many respects from those of Spitzer, the viewpoints stressed by both authors can be regarded as not mutually exclusive. If a phylogenetic derivation of the centralized nervous system in bilateral symmetric metazoa from the diffuse network

---

[55] Cajal (1911) states: 'L'entre-croisement des nerfs optiques, inauguré probablement chez les poissons et les céphalopodes en même temps que la vision au travers d'un cristallin, n'est qu'un moyen organique de correction ou de compensation de la vision; son but est de rendre continue et conforme à la réalité l'image mentale formée dans chacun des deux yeux.

Ce principe suppose comme postulatum que la perception mentale correcte de l'espace visuel ne peut se faire sans l'existence dans le cerveau d'un centre percepteur bilatéral dont chaque moitié agit de concert avec l'autre, de façon à rendre continues et de même sens les deux images que les rétines droite et gauche y projettent.

L'entre-croisement optique entraîne, pour des raisons économiques, celui des voies motrices d'origine cérébrale et cérébelleuse; il en résulte que le côté du corps atteint par l'excitation périphérique est celui-là même qui réagira de préférence. On en peut dire autant des voies centrales du toucher, de l'audition et du sens musculaire; elles s'entre-croisent pour que les foyers centraux, auxquels elles aboutissent et qui représentent une même moitié de l'espace, correspondent aux centres visuels affectés à cette moitié.' It should here be added that Cajal's very ingenious diagrams, based on the then available data concerning the optic system, do not, in some significant respects, conform to what is now known about the actual configurational arrangements.

in coelenterates is assumed, numerous connections across the pro-morphologic midline can evidently be considered primarily given. It is reasonable to presume that such fiber crossings were maintained, condensed, and even further developed in the course of phylogeny and in accordance with functional as well as topological orderliness. Unknown causal factors akin to those obtaining in neurobiotaxis may be postulated. This, of course, amounts to a rather unsatisfactory statement[56]. Yet, all elaborate attempts at explanation on the basis of available data can be regarded not only as unconvincing, but as still more unsatisfactory than the just given generalized and unbiassed statement.

The phylogenetically primarily given transverse connections as provided by the orthogon pattern (cf. p. 34), which will again be discussed further below in connection with the origin of verte-brates (p. 337), might perhaps provide a satisfactory clue for future studies of the problem, based on further progress in neurobiologic science.

---

[56] Miskolczy (1926) brings a short review of the problem under the heading 'Warum kreuzen sich die zentralen Bahnen des Nervensystems'; he justly recognized, in agreement with some of his predecessors, that phylogenetic origin of central nervous system from a diffuse nerve-net, intrinsic neuromuscular correlations, and development of bilateral symmetry are important factors involved in that problem.

His specific attempt at 'explanation' is cryptoteleological, and, moreover, implicitly calls for the hereditary transmission of acquired characteristics; it fails to carry any conviction ('wir geben es gerne zu, dass dieser Lösungsversuch mit jenem Prinzip der Evolution steht oder fällt, wonach die Funktion die Organe umzuformen vermag.' Miskolczy, 1926). At most, the perhaps valid or credible aspects of his argumentation might be reworded and expressed as follows. If a bilaterally symmetric animal sees either a prey or a dangerous enemy on its right side, then either attack or flight movements require the immediate and even primary action of at least some muscle groups of the opposite side (i. e. here left). Alternating as well as synchronous homo- and contralateral innervation can be regarded as mandatory for such type of motor behavior. Evidently, if a bilaterally symmetric animal of a certain kind would lack that sort of decussating, or 'crossed' neural connections, it might not survive and procreate in various types of surroundings. In contradistinction, comparable animals, possessors of such decussating connection, might survive various situations, procreate, vary (e.g. 'mutate') and evolve to greater glory. Does this word picture really 'explain', or indicate, in any strict sense, a 'cause', for the arrangements and the peculiar varieties of decussations and commissures? As regards their 'origin', the problem, of course, may be dismissed by stating that the 'origin' of commissures and decussations is implicit in any diffuse nerve net occurring in a bilaterally symmetric organism. But then, 'why' and 'how' did the nerve net originate, or, still more naively, in deference to some among my neo-primitive friends, what was its 'cause'?

13. Transition to the Vertebrate Pattern; the 'Minor' Chordata: Hemichorda and Urochorda

Depending upon taxonomic criteria and attitudes, Hemichorda and Urochorda can be regarded as subphyla of the phylum Chordata, which, in addition, would include the subphyla Cephalochorda (Leptocardii: Amphioxus) and Craniota (Vertebrata). Or, because of some significant differences, the *Hemichorda* might be considered a separate phylum comprising two classes, Enteropneusta and Pterobranchia.

Enteropneusta are burrowing worm-like marine animals with three main body divisions, proboscis, collar, and trunk. Pharyngeal gill slits and enteric celomic pouches are present. Although rather few different species are living, these animals, as represented by the acorn worms

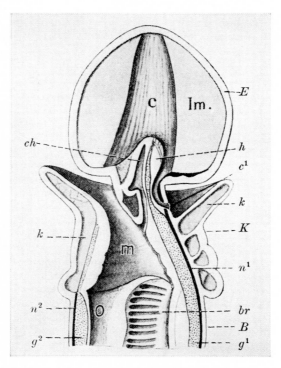

Figure 197. Sagittal section through the rostral end of Glossobalanus minutus. (Simplified after Spengel, from R. Hertwig, 1912.) B: branchial region; C: glans celom; E: glans; K: collar; O: esophagus; C^1: opening of glans celom; ch: chorda; g: vessels; h: so-called heart; k: collar celom; m: oral cavity; n^1: dorsal nerve strand; n^2: ventral nerve strand (br: region of branchial clefts; lm.: longit. musculature).

Balanoglossus and Saccoglossus, are fairly common. The inclusion of Enteropneusta among Chordata rests mainly on the evaluation of a diverticulum, extending into the proboscis or glans, and formed by the roof of the fore-gut (Figs. 197, 198). This diverticulum can be regarded as kathomologous to the chorda dorsalis or notochord. A number of competent zoologists (e. g. R. HERTWIG, 1912, 1931) refuse to accept this interpretation and speak of a 'so-called' chorda or buccal diverticulum. Yet, considering the ontogenetic origin of the notochord in Amphioxus (Fig. 209), there can be little doubt that we have, at a certain ontogenetic stage, a one-one topologic correspondence between the notochord anlage in this latter form, and a dorsal diverticulum of the gut as, e. g., in Balanoglossus. I am therefore inclined to regard said diverticulum as a morphologically 'true' notochord kathomologon.

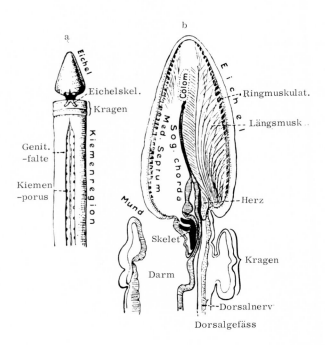

Figure 198. Diagrammatic views of rostral end in Schizocardium brasiliense. (Modified after SPENGEL by BÜTSCHLI, 1921, from HANSTRÖM, 1928.) a: dorsal view; b: sagittal section.

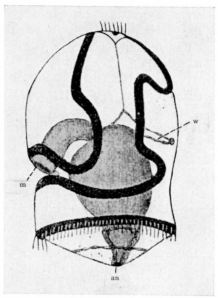

Figure 199. Tornaria larva of Balanoglossus. (After METSCHNIKOFF from R. HERTWIG, 1912.) an: anus; m: mouth; w: primordium of glans cavity.

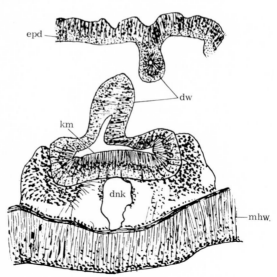

Figure 200. Cross section through dorsal part of collar in enteropneust Ptychodera bahamensis. (After VAN DER HORST from HANSTRÖM, 1928.) dnk: dorsal vessel; dw: dorsal stem of collar medulla; epd: epidermis; km: collar medulla (neural tube); mhv: lining of oral cavity.

The pharyngeal gill slits of Balanoglossus appear to me likewise as representing 'truly' homologous 'chordate' configurations. A number of additional interesting implications are evident. Thus, the Tornaria larva of Balanoglossus (Fig. 199) manifests a rather close resemblance

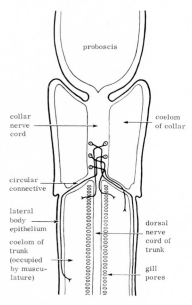

proboscis

collar
nerve
cord

coelom
of collar

circular
connective

lateral
body
epithelium

dorsal
nerve
cord of
trunk

coelom of
trunk
(occupied
by muscu-
lature)

gill
pores

Figure 201. Diagrammatic frontal section of a balanoglossid showing the giant fiber system. (From BULLOCK, 1944.)

to echinoderm larvae. Moreover, on the basis of their ontogenetic development, the Hemichorda, the taxonomically and morphologically still poorly understood Pogonophora[57], the Chaetognatha (p. 60), Urochorda, Cephalochordata, and Vertebrata, must be regarded, together with the Echinodermata, as representing the group of

---

[57] Pogonophora were completely unknown until a specimen was dredged from Indonesian waters in 1900. By 1963, about 22 species had been described, mostly obtained from the Northwest Pacific (BARNES, 1963). The wormlike body may reach a length of 35 cm. Tentacles of variable number (up to 200) are connected with the glans-like anterior lobe. While a celom is present, a digestive tract is completely missing. The animals live in secreted chitinous tubes. Although closely related to the hemichordates, these still poorly 'understood' animals have been classified as an independent small 'phylum'. The nervous system is (intra) epithelial; a rostral and dorsal 'brain' swelling, a dorsal nerve cord, and two nerve rings have been described (cf. e. g. IVANOV, 1958). A mouth is formed in the course of development but later disappears.

Deuterostomia (cf. p. 14, 305). Moreover, the gonads of Balanoglossus closely resemble those of Platyhelminthes, and, together with
certain characteristics of the nervous system, we have here a possible
clue pointing to further, more distant relationships.

The nervous system of Enteropneusta is very simple, and displays
features comparable to those obtaining in Platyhelminthes and Echino-

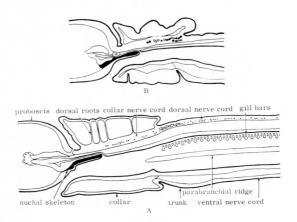

Figure 202. Diagrams showing distribution of giant cells in Balanoglossus and
Saccoglossus. (From Bullock, 1944.) *A* Balanoglossus, paramedian section; all the giant
cells of one side (shown as dots) are projected upon section plane; *B* Saccoglossus, median
sagittal section; all giant cells are shown in projection, right ones as dots, left ones as
circles; this species has fewer giant cells, which are confined to collar.

dermata. In addition to a diffuse epidermal or subepidermal nerve
plexus, Balanoglossus has two nerve cords, a dorsal and a ventral one,
containing some fairly large nerve cells (cf. further below). A true
'brain' is lacking, but, in the collar region, a 'pharyngeal ring' is formed
by a connection between dorsal and ventral nerve cord. Still more
interesting is the fact that in some species (Ptychodera flava, Glossobalanus sarniensis) a central canal is present in the collar nerve strand
(Fig. 200), and opens with an anterior and a posterior external 'neuro-
pore' (Hanström, 1928). A species of Balanoglossus displays transitory
manifestations of a central canal.

Bullock (1944) has described a system of giant cells and giant
fibers in the collar nerve cord of Balanoglossids (Figs. 201, 202). The
number of these large cells is said to vary from about a dozen or less
to 150 and more, depending on the species. The elements in question

are probably exclusively unipolar, the cell bodies being, with few exceptions, confined to the posterior half of the collar nerve cord. Generally speaking, the number of giant cells depends on the size of the animal, such that these cells are more numerous in larger species than in smaller ones.

Each giant fiber presumably represents the process of a single cell. The fibers cross to the contralateral side, run posteriorly, and reach the dorsal cord of the trunk. The fibers then leave this cord to enter the general nerve plexus. BULLOCK (1944) regards the balanoglossid nervous system as very 'primitive', and the giant fiber system therein contained as 'probably the most primitive example of a giant system known, as well as the lowest case of decussation'.

Pterobranchia are bottom-dwelling marine animals, living in secreted tubes (except for the genus Atubaria). The genus Rhabdopleura has two arms, and the genus Cephalodiscus is provided with five to nine pairs of arms. The arms, similar to lophophores, bear numerous small tentacles. Gill clefts are not developed (Figs. 203, 204).

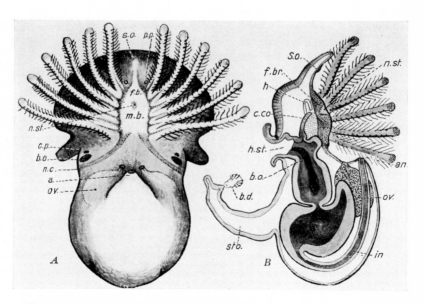

Figure 203. Diagram of Cephalodiscus. (From PATTEN, 1912.) A: neura surface; B: sagittal section; a: anus; bd: 'bud'; bo: 'branchial opening'; cco: 'cephalic caecum' (chorda); fb, fbr: 'forebrain'; h: hypodermis; hst: mouth; mb: 'midbrain'; nc: nerve cord; nst: 'neurostoma'; ov: ovary; so: sense organ; other abbr. not relevant.

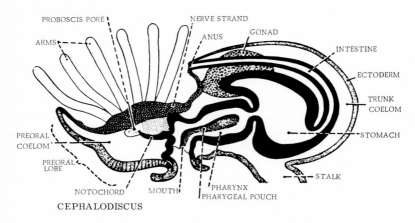

CEPHALODISCUS

Figure 204. Diagram of Cephalodiscus in median section, somewhat modified after PATTEN's diagram. (From NEAL and RAND, 1936.)

The nervous system consists of a pharyngeal ring in the collar segment, and a ventral, median longitudinal connective or nerve cord. Cephalodiscus possesses a brain-like enlargement of the pharyngeal ring. Two fairly large nerves are connected with this 'brain' on each side and divide into further branches innervating the tentacles. Two additional nerves, on each side, connect the brain with neighboring regions.

HANSTRÖM (1928) emphasizes that, seen from the histologic aspect, the nerve cells and their processes as differentiated and arranged in Enteropneusta and Pterobranchia display a striking resemblance with the nervous elements of Echinodermata, particularly Asteroidea. The cited author also finds here some relevant similarities with the nervous system of Nematoda and Gordiidae (Gordioidea, hairworms, Nematomorpha, cf. p. 54, vol. 1; 51, 66, vol. 2).

Urochorda (Urochordata) or *Tunicata*, also known as sea-squirts, are fairly common marine animals, mostly barrel-shaped, and attached with one end to a substratum such as rocks or wooden pilings, or stuck to the sand of the sea-floor. The larval stages display, loosely speaking, the general shape of an amphibian tadpole, and are provided with a tail containing a typical notochord, which is not present in the sessile adult. The designation Urochordata refers to the fact that the chorda dorsalis is limited to the tail. The pharynx displays gill slits, the number of which differs according to the species.

Three classes can be distinguished, namely Ascidiacea, Appendicularia (Larvacea), and Thaliacea (Salpaeformes). The body of Ascidians and Salpaeformes is invested with a tunic or mantle containing cellulose[58].

The Larvacea (Appendicularia or Copelata) are neotenic, that is, retain some larval features, particularly the motile tail with its notochord. The designation Larvacea refers to this neotenic condition. As regards Ascidians, some forms like Clavelina and Ciona are solitary, while other groups are colonial.

Pyrosoma, formerly included among the Ascidians, but now considered a Thaliacean, is a brilliantly luminescent[59] colonial organism. Salpa and Doliolum are solitary pelagic forms. The life cycle of the Thaliacea involves an alternating cycle of asexual budding and of sexually reproducing stages[60].

[58] The carbohydrate tunicine, representing a type of cellulose, composes about 50% of the tunic. In addition, the mantle contains proteins and inorganic compounds, such as spicules of calcium salts. Ameboid cells, and (e. g. in Ciona) blood vessels may penetrate the tunic. This latter may be soft or hard, cartilage- or glass-like. It may also be translucent or colored. In the 'sea-pork' Amaroucium stellatum (Ascidian) it has the texture and appearance of salted pork. Tunicates seem to be the only Metazoa producing cellulose (cf. chapt. II, p. 42). However, among Protozoa, some dinoflagellates are provided with cellulose plates presumably formed by these organisms.

[59] Luminescence or bioluminescence, namely emission of light without significant heat production ('cold light') is manifested by many organisms pertaining to a large variety of groups (bacteria, fungi, protozoa, coelenterates, echinoderms, worms, mollusks, arthropods, hemichordates, urochordates, and vertebrates). In metazoa, light may be emitted by specialized cellular elements containing an enzyme luciferase, or by symbiosis with luminous bacteria located in the cells of light producing organs.

[60] The solitary salpae produce chains of daughter-animals by budding. The colonial forms reproduce sexually. This alternation of generations was discovered by the Franco-German naturalist and poet A. VON CHAMISSO (1781–1837, of *Peter Schlemihl* fame, and known as editor of the 'Musenalmanach') who accompanied the Russian navigator Captain VON KOTZEBUE on a discovery voyage around the world (ADALBERT DE CHAMISSO: *De animalibus quibusdam e classe vermium Linneana in circumnavigatione terras auspicante comite N. Romanzoff duce Ottone de Kotzebue annis 1815, 1816, 1817, 1818 peracta. Fasc. I. De salpa. Berolini 1819*). Some twenty years later, alternation of generations (Generationswechsel) was rediscovered, as a more generalized phenomenon, by STEENSTRUP (JOH. J. S. STEENSTRUP: «Über den Generationswechsel» usw., übersetzt von C. H. LORENZEN, Kopenhagen 1842. Quoted after K. GROBBEN, 1905).

Some biologists regard this cycle as metagenesis, while others do not. Still others distinguish between metagenesis and heterogony. In this latter, parthenogenesis (as distinct from budding) occurs in the non-zygotic generation. In botany, the term alternation of generations or metagenesis usually implies a haploid gametophyte generation, reproducing sexually, and a diploid sporophyte generation, reproducing asexually by spores.

The chordate characteristics of tunicates are most evident during larval and some earlier ontogenetic stages. From this viewpoint it can be justly stated that the adult Ascidians and Thaliacea are 'less advanced in evolutionary development' than their larvae. Figure 205 indicates the typically chordate morphologic pattern of an Ascidian larva.

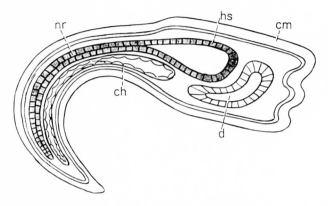

Figure 205. Diagram of dorsal neuraxis in an Ascidian larva. (Simplified after Kowalensky and others, from K., 1927.) ch: notochord; cm: cellulose mantle; d: gut; hs: cerebral and sensory vesicle; nr: neural tube.

In such larvae, the central nervous system consists of a dorsal neural tube with an anterior brain-vesicle. This brain contains, on the right side, a rudimentary eye, with a pigment patch (Fig. 206). The brain opens, on the left side, with a ciliated, neuropore-like channel into the oral cavity. In addition, there is a small statocyst. The asymmetry of the two sense organs included in the brain (eye and statocyst) is an interesting feature. At least as far as the statocyst is concerned, it might perhaps be interpreted as 'displacement' of an 'unpaired' median structure.

During further development, the caudal part of the neural tube disappears and the brain vesicle is transformed into a ganglion, while eye and statocyst degenerate in the metamorphosis. The adult nervous system is then represented by an ovoid 'brain'-ganglion, from which some mixed nerves arise at both ends, supplying the buccal siphon, the gills, and the visceral organs, as well as the posterior part of the body. In some species, there are also lateral nerves. The nerves contain ganglion cells.

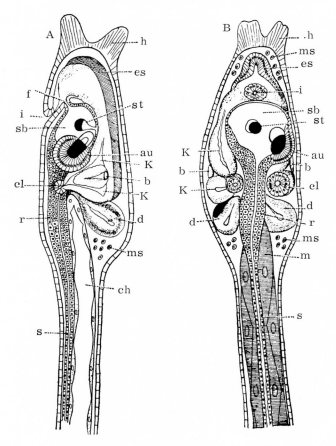

Figure 206. Anterior end of an Ascidian larva (Phallusia mammillata) after KOWA-
LEVSKY. (From PLATE, 1922.) A: lateral view; B: dorsal view; the cellulose mantle is
omitted; au: eye; b: blood sinus; ch: chorda; cl: cloacal pits; d: gut; es: endostyle;
f: ciliated pit; h: adhesive papilla; i: oral opening; k: branchial clefts; m: tail musculature; ms: mesenchyme; st: statolith; r: trunk ganglion; s: caudal neural tube; sb: brain
and sensory ventricle.

An extension of the ciliated channel becomes transformed into a
glandular body designated as neural or subneural gland (Fig. 207).
An outlet of this gland opens with a ciliated duct into the pharynx.
Although the gland is mostly ventral to the brain, it becomes dorsally
displaced in Cynthia (PLATE, 1922). There can be little doubt that,
from a topologic form-analytic viewpoint, the neural gland of tunicates
is homologous to the neurohypophysis of vertebrates.

Another interesting, but non-neural homology with corresponding structures in Cephalochorda (Amphioxus) and Vertebrata is evident as regards the endostyle, a longitudinal groove in the floor of the pharynx, which is kathomologous to the thyroid gland of vertebrates.

Seen from a functional viewpoint, the 'brain' of ascidians does not seem to be particularly important: if the cerebral ganglion of Ciona is extirpated, the animal is at first quite flaccid following decerebration, but after about 24 h, recovery takes place, and all body functions and 'vital reflexes' are carried out 'normally'. Body contractions, however, are said to be 'somewhat slower' (BARNES, 1963).

In adult Appendicularia, the lumen of the original neural tube obliterates, and the central nervous system becomes a solid strand.

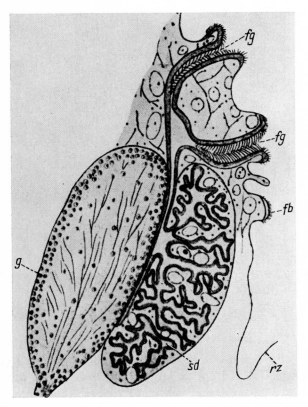

Figure 207. Longitudinal section through the ganglionic mass of a young Ascidia Ciona intestinalis, after SEELIGER. (From PLATE, 1922.) fb: ciliated arches of branchial gut; fg: ciliated pit; g: ganglion; rz: portion of branchial gut; sd: subneural gland.

Although the sessile living mode of adult Ascidiacea and Thaliacea represents, by itself, a very conspicuous difference between these tunicates and vertebrate animals in general, some additional relevant morphologic differences obtain. Thus, neither the adult nor the larval forms display a celomic cavity. Moreover, with the exception of the branchial slits, which can be regarded as manifesting a definite 'branchiomerism', no segmentation or metamerism is indicated.

Yet, if 'invertebrate' metazoa are arranged in a taxonomic array as, e. g., outlined in the present chapter, or in any other significantly similar manner, a tubular neuraxis, dorsal to the notochord, appears 'for the first time', at least during key-stages of ontogenetic development. Thus, regarding the Urochorda as invertebrates, we have here, since at said ontogenetic key-stages a one-one topologic mapping into a developmental stage of the vertebrate neuraxis, and a one-many mapping into the definitive vertebrate neuraxis can be conceptually performed, an instance of morphologic homology in the rigorous sense (Figs. 208, 209). This homology can be extended to the dorsal tubular nerve cord of Hemichorda.

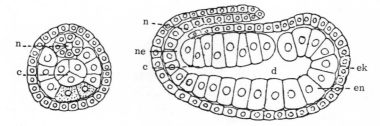

Figure 208. Configuration of primordial structures in larvae of the ascidian Phallusia mammillata. (After Kowalevsky from R. Hertwig, 1912.) At left cross section through the tail of a young larva. At right sagittal section through a larva at very early developmental stage, showing formation of notochord and neural tube. c: notochord; d: archenteron (gut); ek: ectoderm; en: entoderm; n: neural tube; ne: neurenteric canal.

As regards the hemichordate Enteropneusta, Kappers (1929) justly remarked that we find here both types of central nervous system, namely 'the invertebrate and vertebrate type, the former being represented by the oesophageal ring and ventro-median neuroepithelium, the latter by the medullary tube in the collar and by the frontal and caudal dorso-medial neuroepithelium'.

All other invertebrates manifest, as far as structural and morphological similarities of the nervous system are concerned, at best only analogies with respect to vertebrates. It is true that, if homologies would be based on ill-definable phylogenetic derivation from an identical anlage, some sort of homology, particularly based on the orthogon concept (cf. p. 337) could be established between the nervous system of invertebrates other than Hemichorda and Urochorda, and that of

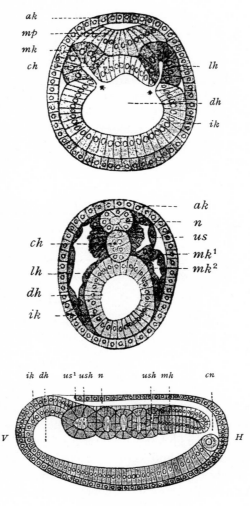

Fig. 209A

vertebrates. On the basis of the non-phylogenetic form-analytic postulates adopted in this presentation, however, such homologization is not permissible.

Nevertheless, the difficult question concerning the phylogenetic origin of vertebrates from invertebrates remains a legitimate and, moreover, most interesting problem, which shall be discussed in the following and concluding section of this chapter.

Fig. 209 B

Figure 209 A. Configuration of primordial structures in early ontogenetic stages of the cephalocordate ('vertebrate') Amphioxus. (After HATSCHEK, from O. HERTWIG's 'Lehrbuch der Entwicklungsgeschichte', Jena, 1915.) Top: cross section showing delamination of neural plate and chordamesoderm-formation. Center: cross section at a somewhat later stage, displaying typical vertebrate Bauplan. Bottom: sagittal section at stage intermediate between the two preceding ones, showing beginning segmentation of mesoderm. These semidiagrammatic figures should be compared with the somewhat different, yet in many respects strikingly similar configuration shown in Fig. 208. ak: ectoderm; ch: chorda dorsalis; cn: neurenteric canal; dh: enteric cavity; ik: entoderm; lh: celomic cavity; mk: mesoderm; mk¹, mk²: parietal and visceral layer of mesoderm (somatic and splanchnic mesoderm); mp: neural (medullary) plate; n: neural tube, neural canal; us: mesoderm segment (somite); ush: myocoele (cavity of somite); H: posterior end; V: anterior end.

Figure 209 B. Diagram of frontal section through a gastrula of the asteroid echinoderm Astropecten, showing formation of the two celomic pouches from the archenteron (adapted and simplified after HÖRSTADIUS, 1939). This configuration can be directly compared, by one-one mapping (except for the medullary plate involving a one to two transformation) into the configuration of Fig. 209 A, top. The resulting comparison is highly suggestive of a close relationship between echinoderms and chordates.

14. Theories on the Origin of Vertebrates

Since, among the invertebrates, and seen from the morphologic viewpoint, only larval Urochorda manifest a general Bauplan clearly comparable with that of vertebrates, while Hemichorda might perhaps be included among the animals of a morphologic configuration related to that of Urochorda, the phylogenetic derivation of vertebrates can be considered to comprise two different major problems.

The first one concerns the origin of chordate animals from simpler or perhaps, more cautiously, other forms of invertebrates, and the second problem concerns the derivation of vertebrates from 'primitive' chordates.

Now, if we attempt to derive one animal form from another by assuming actual morphologic changes in the course of biologic events, it becomes clear that a varying adult form is not derived from an original adult form in the manner of a wax model which could be modified by kneading, or by small additions to, and subtractions from, the several original parts. It is evident that the body of the varying form has never been, in a literal sense, the body of its parent form, and could not possibly originate by means of a plastic operation from it; 'in each case the body of the offspring is made again from the beginning, just as if the wax model had gone back into the melting-pot before the new model was begun' (BATESON, 1892)[61].

If, in accordance with the views of HAECKEL and others, phylogenetic conclusions can be based on the sequence of ontogenetic events, then it seems permissible to assume that a protozoan-like stage, a metazoan blastula stage perhaps akin to volvox, and a coelenterate-like stage 'are near the root' of the phylogenetic sequence obtaining for all 'higher' metazoa, and HAECKEL's fundamental gastraea-theory may be taken as a point of departure.

If, with respect to further phylogenetic evolution, the establishment of bilateral symmetry and the manifestation of cephalization is con-

---

[61] The relevant basic viewpoints and problems were discussed in the preceding chapter III under sections 6 (Evolution of Morphologic Pattern in Ontogeny) and 7 (Morphology and Phylogeny). Instead of BATESON's simile, a slightly different one was used in footnote 54, page 260. BATESON used his simile in a critique of the homology concept. This author erroneously believed that homology necessarily implies derivation of a varying form from another in the manner of a molded wax-model. It is, however, evident that BATESON did not understand the significance of homology, and that his critique was based on a complete misconception.

sidered as the next step, implying, in addition, increased centralization of the nervous system and the origin of a 'brain', then Platyhelminthes, particularly of a sort such as Turbellaria, represent a form that may reasonably be regarded as 'ancestral'.

Concerning the details of such possible or 'probable' evolutionary history, it is quite obvious that the available data do not provide any conclusive evidence. It is impossible to supply reasonably rigorous proof for either monophyletic or polyphyletic lines of evolution at these very 'early' stages[62]. Even HAECKEL's rather plausible gastraea-theory remains subject to argumentation. Thus, assuming that metazoa originated from 'colonial' protozoa, resulting in a blastaea or blastula, such hollow organism might have been transformed into, or passed through the stage of, a solid, round or elongated organism (planula), gradually assuming bilateral symmetry. Gastrulation would then represent a further secondary step, and primary gastrulation by invagination might be a cenogenetic feature[63].

Again, if one chooses to assume that bilateral symmetry is a fundamental primitive metazoan characteristic, then it becomes possible to regard the acoel Turbellaria as the most 'primitive' Metazoa. Thus, HADŽI (1963) believes that Cnidaria (coelenterates) evolved from turbellarian ancestors. According to this view, the Anthozoa are to be considered the most 'primitive' Cnidaria. It is presumed that a fundamentally symmetrical organization changed here to radial symmetry in correlation with a sessile mode of life. The other coelenterate classes are then supposed to have evolved from the Anthozoa. The

---

[62] Cf. chapter II, page 98, and chapter III, page 256. It should also be recalled that the significant differentiation into the main phyla presumably occurred approximately 400 million years ago. Also, whether continuous origin of new 'life' on the basis of colloidal chemical interaction, e.g. in oceanic waters, still goes on at the present time within the 'biosphere' of our planet, remains, on the basis of the available knowledge concerning this subject, a non-disprovable possibility. In the general biologic remarke to our study on vesicular stomatitis virus (H.K. and M.W. KIRBER, Confin. neurol. *22*: 1962), we have briefly commented on the difficulties to detect, with the methods of biologic investigation now in use, hypothetical 'living entities' of this type.

[63] The significance of a solid 'gastrula', that is, of a planula or planuloid stage, was particularly emphasized by E. METSCHNIKOFF, 1887. Again, reverting to the presumably preceding blastaea-stage, diverse early metazoan organisms of blastula-type could have manifested different promorphologic features, namely homaxonic, unpolarized organization, or monaxonic, polarized, isopleural organization (with anterior and posterior pole of the blastula). Either organization could easily change into the radial symmetric, or into the bilateral symmetric type.

'primitive' Turbellaria are imagined to have derived from very 'primitive' ciliates, which, in turn, are fancied as descendants of flagellate ancestors. These hypotheses, although not disprovable nor logically impossible, can be matched by quite different interpretations of the available data, leading to various alternative conclusions, and may be assessed as rather unconvincing.

The syncytial theories, as propounded by HADŽI (1953, 1963) and HANSON (1958), attempt to derive Metazoa from multinucleated ciliates. It is assumed that the ancestral metazoan form arising from this transformation was originally syncytial as well as bilaterally-symmetric, closely akin to present-day acoel turbellarians which 'still' display a tendency toward syncytial make-up. On the other hand, HAECKEL's colonial theory (including various subsequent minor modifications by various authors), derives the multicellular animals from colonial flagellates.

Stressing the promorphologic aspect of the argument, it should be repeated, once more, that radial symmetry might have been a primary metazoan pattern, becoming modified, by a secondary transformation, into the bilateral symmetry of Platyhelminthes. Yet, primary bilateral symmetry, or independent origin of both radial and bilateral symmetry from homaxonal isopleural forms represent equally possible alternatives. The diplodiametral ('biradial symmetric') and the (pseudo) bilateral symmetric patterns of Anthozoa can be very easily interpreted as secondary derivations from the radial symmetric type, granting, of course, that their derivation from a primary bilateral symmetry can hardly be rigorously disproved.

Although rather favorably impressed by HAECKEL's general concepts, I share the view of those biologists who consider the question concerning the origin of Metazoa from specific sorts of Protozoa, to be, at present, and perhaps permanently, undecidable. Because of their peculiar mode of development[64] and configuration, the Porifera

---

[64] Cf. section 1 and Figure 1. Interesting questions are here those concerning homology and terminology of germ layers. Assuming that a spherical structure called blastula should still be considered a blastula even if turned inside-out through a hole and becoming a spherical amphiblastula, and that the subsequently invaginated layer, lining the 'archenteron' of the resulting gastrula pattern should be named entoderm, then the same configurational terms apply to Porifera and to other Metazoa. Likewise, under these postulates, entoderm and ectoderm of Porifera are homologous to the identically designated configurations of other Metazoa. Now, since the sponge entoderm derives from micromeres, which provide the ectoderm in other Metazoa (and vice-versa with regard to macro-

seem to stand apart; this might (but not must) be interpreted as indicating an independent phylogenetic origin. Moreover, an independent origin could also be assumed for coelenterates, flatworms, and other forms. Polyphyletic theories, such, e.g., as recently proposed by GREENBERG (1959), are no less justifiable than monophyletic ones, and in some instances perhaps far more so.

Flatworms, mollusks, annelids, and arthropods display certain common similarities of early embryonic development particularly with regard to determinate cleavage as studied by experimental embryologists. The gastrulation process of flatworms is rather complicated and may represent a combination of 'planuloid' gastrulation (epiboly), leading to a solid gastrula ('stereogastrula'), and of invagination. It is not possible to draw convincing conclusions as regards phylogenetic ancestry from these different, and often blending ontogenetic events (Fig. 210). Some biologists believe that coelenterates and related forms represent a 'dead-end' phylum, and have not given rise to any higher group of animals. As far as the recent species of coelenterates are concerned, this is, of course, a truism.

Yet, the theory elaborated by LANG (1881b and elsewhere) is no less plausible and credible than any of the other ones. This author

---

meres), the sponge entoderm could be considered analogous to the ordinary metazoan ectoderm (and vice-versa as concerns sponge ectoderm). Playing on words (but without psychoanalytic intentions or implications), one might call the original blastula of (some calcareous) sponges an introvert blastula, and the metazoan blastula an extravert one. Temporarily, the sponge blastula then becomes (or 'reverts' to?) an extravert 'amphiblastula'. Subsequently, the relationship becomes again reversed in sponges, namely by introvert gastrulation (involving the micromeres), while the gastrula of other metazoan would be an extravert one. Moreover, one might ask whether the introvert blastula of sponges is a primary or a secondary feature. In this respect it is of interest to note that, although Volvox, in the fully grown stage, evidently represents an extravert blastula, developing volvocine daughter colonies form an introvert blastula, namely a so-called plakea, in which the flagella are on the inside (cf. e.g. BARNES, 1963). The plakea subsequently turns inside-out through an inversion process essentially identical with that occurring in some calcareous sponges. Again, volvocines, manifesting a synchronized flagellar beat, swim with one definite pole directed forward, and thus display a functionally monaxonic heteropolar, isopleural type. In some instances, even a structural polarization (anterior somatic and posterior reproductive cells) is clearly discernible.

Finally, if the phylogenetic definition of homology (which I do not accept) is adopted, and if the sponges and the other Metazoa had originated from a common form with extravert blastaea-gastraea sequence, then the entoderm of Porifera would indeed be homologous to the ectoderm of other Metazoa (and vice-versa as regards sponge ectoderm). Clearly, adoption or rejection of this interpretation and terminology depend upon arbitrary logical as well as semantic axiomatic postulates (cf. also Figs. 1B and 210).

assumes a derivation of Platyhelminthes, namely polyclad turbellarians, from ctenophore-like ancestors, that is, from coelenterate-like forms. LANG believes that some such ctenophore-like organisms, by sinking to the bottom, turned into bottom-dwellers and subsequently Polycla-

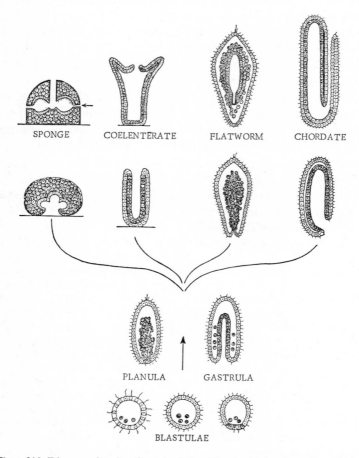

Figure 210. Diagram showing formal relationships in the configuration of blastula, gastrula, planula and related stages with respect to sponge, coelenterate, flatworm, and chordate pattern. (After H. E. ZIEGLER from NEAL and RAND, 1936.)

Although the diagram, as intended by its author, and as interpreted by NEAL and RAND (1936), was designed to show hypothetical ancestral stages, it is here depicted and evaluated as devoid of any specific phylogenetic implication. Because of the great variability and the diverse fluctuations displayed by biologic processes within a wide range allowed by fixed function rules with flexible application, a number of different phylogenetic interpretations could be elaborated.

dida. This can be supported by pointing out the peculiar group of platyctenid ctenophores, including Ctenoplana, Coeloplana, and Tjalfiella, which display a biradial (diplodiametral symmetric) body, two tentacles, and a ventral mouth opening. It has been objected that polyclads are not a 'primitive' flatworm order. This view, however, is quite debatable. As regards the nervous system, some polyclads possess an almost coelenterate-like nerve network, and a very small 'brain', located, moreover, in a rather aboral, almost central position, while other polyclads, however, do indeed display a very 'advanced' differentiation of the nervous system.

Reverting to other aspects of ontogenetic development, and assuming that some sort of gastrula, whether a secondarily transformed planula, or a primarily invaginated one, represents a relevant phylogenetic stage, the further fate of its opening, that is, of stomodeum or 'blastopore', becomes particularly significant[65].

K. GROBBEN (1905 and subsequently), amplifying previous studies by HATSCHEK, pointed out that all metazoa displaying a blastopore can be subdivided into two main groups, *Proterostomia* and *Deuterostomia*.

In Proterostomia the blastopore persists as the adult mouth. On the basis of this definition, Platyhelminthes, Nemathelminthes, Rotifera, Molluscoidea, Annelida, Arthropoda and Mollusca belong to the proterostome category.

In Deuterostomia, the blastopore becomes the anus, or has a location close to the definitive anus, and the adult mouth is formed in

---

[65] The question whether this single blastopore is primary, secondary, or otherwise complex, can here be evaluated as irrelevant in the aspect under consideration. Thus, even in the various classes of vertebrates, which can reasonably be regarded as presumably pertaining to one set of phylogenetically somehow 'related' sub-groups, a wide variety of different modes of blastopore behavior in ontogeny can be observed. Cf. also the remarks in chapter III, pages 244–245.

As regards the phylogenetic origin of Turbellaria or Platyhelminthes in general from a gastraea-form closely akin to coelenterates, I am somewhat less sceptical than HYMAN (1940) and her colleagues. There are the just mentioned aberrant, flattened ctenophores such as Coeloplana and others, some of which have taken to a mode of locomotion by creeping on the ground. Such ctenophores resemble polyclad flatworms. It is true that this resemblance is incomplete (or 'superficial') since Coeloplana and kindred Plactytena remain, by their essential Bauplan, typical ctenophores. Nevertheless, such recent 'worm-like' coelenterate forms remain highly suggestive for generalized phylogenetic implications. Although ctenophores can be classified as a separate phylum, I prefer to include that group among the coelenterates. Even zoologists stressing the 'phylum'-character of ctenophores (e.g. BARNES, 1963) are willing to admit the probability that said animals represent a 'specialized' 'offshoot from the ancestral medusoid coelenterate'.

an approximately opposite location, at the other end of a topologic longitudinal axis. Echinodermata, Hemichordata, Urochordata, Cephalochordata, and Vertebrata belong to the deuterostome category (cf. also below p. 310 concerning Chaetognatha).

This classification becomes more complicated, if it is attempted to conceptualize the ontogenetic derivation of mesoderm (mesoblast) and of celomic cavity. At least in some Proterostomia, part of the mesoblast can be regarded as of 'ectodermal' origin (Ecterocoelia), while in Deuterostomia, the mesoblast has closer relations to the 'entoderm' (Enterocoelia). Again, as regards triploblastic metazoa, Proterostomia display the so-called spiral pattern of cleavage, while Deuterostomia are said generally to manifest radial cleavage. R. HERTWIG (1931), a biologist of considerable experience, maintains a sceptical attitude with regard to the fundamental significance of proterostome, ecterocoele, and deuterostome, enterocoele ontogenetic modes of development[66].

Since I accept, as a reasonable postulate, the validity of HAECKEL's biogenetic rule, in a 'relaxed' or 'generalized' interpretation, I believe that the two different types of one-many transformations, with respect to the body axis, as manifested by the behavior of the enteric cavity, can be regarded as a highly suggestive clue. I am therefore inclined to attribute a substantial degree of importance to protostome and deuterostome ontogenetic development for phylogenetic theory. I would, however, classify coelenterates and turbellarian-like worms as *Archistomia*; the distinction between Proterostomia and Deuterostomia should be restricted to those forms displaying two openings (oral and anal) of the enteric cavity. The Coelenterata and Turbellaria would

---

[66] HERTWIG (1931, p. 246) states: 'Ich habe gegen eine derartige, rein entwicklungsgeschichtlich begründete Einteilung die grössten Bedenken, einmal weil die entwicklungsgeschichtlichen Verallgemeinerungen, auf welche sie sich stützt, namentlich soweit die Mesoblastbildung in Frage kommt, nicht einwandfrei sind, zweitens weil wir überhaupt noch zu wenig wissen, inwieweit man berechtigt ist, den ersten Vorgängen im Ei eine so bedeutsame Rolle für die Aufstellung des Systems einzuräumen.'

It certainly must be conceded that, not only in vertebrate Amniota as well as Anamnia, but quite generally among the different Metazoa, numerous variations in the details of the basic ontogenetic processes, such as gastrulation, coelom-formation, blastopore transformation, (chordate) neurulation and chordulation, etc., occur. Whether such differences should be evaluated as of 'primary' or 'secondary' significance remains often very dubious. Also, even the proper terminology and the most 'reasonable' interpretation, for purposes of comparison, in the case of 'similar' but 'modified' ontogenetic processes, poses at times undecidable questions.

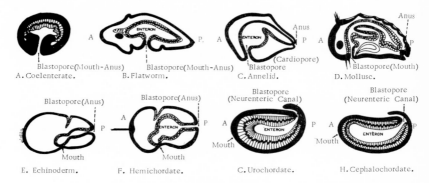

Blastopore(Mouth-Anus)
A. Coelenterate.

Blastopore(Mouth-Anus)
B. Flatworm.

Blastopore
(Cardiopore)
C. Annelid.

Blastopore(Mouth)
D. Mollusc.

Blastopore(Anus)
E. Echinoderm.

Blastopore(Anus)
F. Hemichordate.

Blastopore
(Neurenteric Canal)
Mouth
C. Urochordate.

Blastopore
(Neurenteric Canal)
Mouth
H. Cephalochordate.

Figure 211. Diagram of embryonic stages illustrating GROBBEN's concept of Protero-stomia (C, D) and Deuterostomia (E–H). From the viewpoint of the present treatise, Coelenterates and Flatworms (A, B) should not be evaluated as Proterostomia, but as Archistomia. (From NEAL and RAND, 1936.)

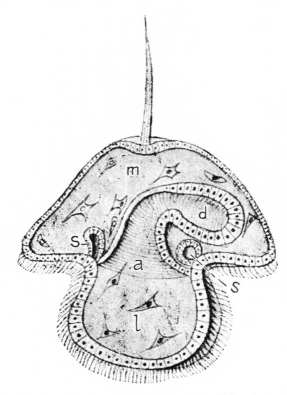

Figure 212. Pilidium larva of a Nemertean worm. (After METSCHNIKOFF from R. HERTWIG, 1912.) a: pharynx; d: stomach; s: diverticula; l: oral lobe.

thus represent Archistomia, while the Nemerteans might then be regarded as the most 'primitive' Proterostomia. The diagrams of Figure 211 illustrate the relevant concepts.

On the basis of such classification, and assuming that the generalized distinction between protostome and deuterostome metazoa is of phylogenetic significance, a dichotomy of metazoan evolution might be conceived as having occurred at a stage roughly corresponding to that of Turbellaria.

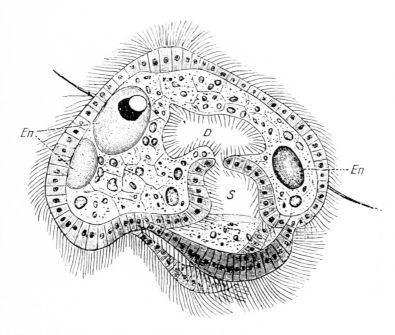

Figure 213. Larva of the turbellarian platyhelminth Stylochus pilidium. (After Goette in Korschelt-Heider from R. Hertwig, 1912.) D: gut; En: remnants of entodermal cells; S: pharynx.

The protostome line of evolution, again, presumably led in two main diverging directions to segmented forms such as articulates (annelids and arthropods), and to essentially non-segmented mollusks. A distant kinship of mollusks and annelids, perhaps traceable to common ancestral forms preceding the just mentioned dichotomy of the protostomian line, is strongly suggested by the trochophore type of larva occurring in both groups. The pilidium larva of nemerteans,

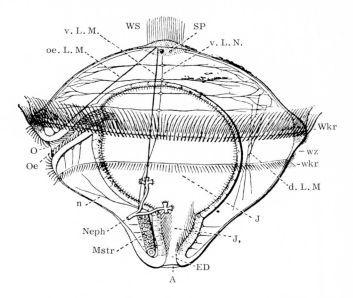

Figure 214. Trochophora larva of the polychaete annelid Polygordius. (After HAT-SCHECK, from R.HERTWIG, 1912.) A: anus; ED: end-gut (proctodeum); J, J_1: stomach, gut; Mstr: mesoderm strip; Neph: nephridium; O: mouth; Oe: esophagus; Sp: sensory plate; Wkz: ciliated crown (prototroch); Ws: apical tuft of cilia; d. L. M., oe. L. M., v. L. M.: muscles; n: nerve strand; Wkr: ciliated crown (metatroch); wz: ciliated zone.

and a rather similar sort of turbellarian larva likewise display some general, and sufficiently impressive resemblance to trochophore larvae (Figs. 212–215). Rotifers and Gastrotricha can be regarded as related to annelids. Said dichotomy of the protostomian line might have taken place before the pronounced metamerism characteristic for annelids became manifested.

A group of lophophorate Metazoa, namely Bryozoa, Phoronidea, and Brachiopoda, although definitely protostome, is of particular interest, because certain ontogenetic features displayed by some of these animals can be interpreted as similar to those in deuterostome Metazoa (e. g. radial cleavage, and type of mesoderm-formation). The lophophore, characterizing a variety of different essentially sessile invertebrates, is a fold of the body wall, bearing ciliated tentacles, and located around the mouth region. Some authors (e. g. HYMAN, 1959) believe that the three above-mentioned groups, classified as 'phyla' (Ectoprocta, Phoronidea, Brachiopoda) diverged from a coelomate line leading to the annelids[67]. Because of a few features shared with the Deuterostomia, HYMAN and some other authors suggest that the ancestors of the lophophorates in question have also given rise to the deuterostome line. While this is, of course, not impossible, I am less impressed by the phylogenetic evidence provided by the development of a celomic cavity (Fig. 216), and I believe that the complete conceptual separation of Ectoprocta and Entoprocta into two distinct, and un-related phyla, thus, as it were, 'eliminating' the Bryozoa as a phylum, appears, to say the least, somewhat debatable.

The deuterostome line of evolution, in turn, can be regarded as displaying one main dichotomy, leading to Echinodermata in one direction, and to Chordata in the other. A separate, but 'lesser' divergent deuterostome branch is represented by the Chaetognatha. These animals have some distant similarities to protostome Aschelminths (cf. p. 66) but display peculiarities distinct from those of all Protero-stomia as well as from those of Echinodermata, Hemichordata, and other Chordata. One may well agree with the interpretation of HYMAN (1959), who believes that the chaetognathe 'phylum' departed very early from the base of the deuterostome line and is only remotely related to the other deuterostome groups.

The Echinodermata might appear, with respect to their parameric 'radial symmetry', and because of their rather 'primitive' or 'low' type of central nervous system, to have very little in common with Chordata

---

[67] Since special emphasis is thus laid on the manifestation of a celomic cavity, the Entoprocta become then completely separated from the Ectoprocta, and the phylum Bryozoa is 'abolished' (cf. above, p. 66). It might be recalled that in the first volume of this series I have purposely presented, and dealt with, a *'first approximation'* to animal taxonomy. Such 'approximation', in the aspect under consideration, may be far more *accurate* than some of the more detailed and *precise* present-day taxonomic approaches. It is a common fallacy to confuse *accuracy* and *precision*. Thus, if we have two scales, of which one is divided no finer than millimeters, and the other divided to 0.01 mm, the second is evidently more *precise* than the first one. Yet, *precise* readings to 0.01 mm may be *inaccurate* because of shrunken or otherwise faulty scale, while *imprecise* readings (because the otherwise reliable scale is not finer than a millimeter) may be *accurate*. It is evidently absurd to have a scale divided to thousandths if its distortion may introduce errors in the tenths, or to insist upon an accuracy to a thousandths in a scale which is to be used only to tenths. Again, one cannot report 0.01 percent results based on 1 percent informa-tion. One should therefore be on guard against an *illusory accuracy* which appears to exist but actually does not. These remarks on *accuracy* and *precision*, paraphrased from comments by engineers (BERKELEY and WAINWRIGHT, 1962) apply, *mutatis mutandis*, to many aspects of biology, including taxonomic procedure.

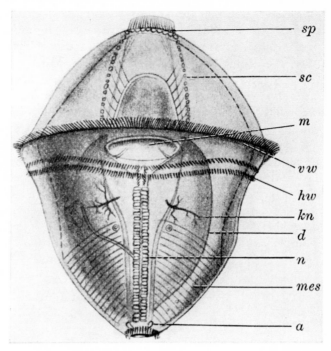

Figur 215. Trochophora larva of the gephyrean annelid Echiurus. (After HATSCHEK from R. HERTWIG, 1912.) a: anus; d: gut; hw: ciliated crown (mesotroch); kn: (proto) nephridium; m: mouth; mes: mesoderm strip (mesodermal bands); n: nerve cord; sc: pharyngeal ring of nerve cord; sp: sensory plate with apical tuft of cilia; vw: ciliated crown (prototroch). The actual occurrence of the mesodermal segmentation as indicated by HATSCHEK has been questioned by other authors.

and Vertebrata. Numerous other morphologic and behavioral features seem to indicate a substantial degree of separateness between, say, crinoids, sea-urchins, sea-cucumbers on one hand, and e. g. amphioxus or fishes on the other. Yet, strangely enough, the Echinodermata, on the basis of fairly convincing evidence[68], can reasonably be regarded, among all invertebrates, as the chordates' and vertebrates' closest 'relatives'.

It is not improbable that the 'radial symmetry' of echinoderms represents a secondary, 'acquired' feature, since their larvae display a conspicuous bilateral symmetry (Fig. 217). SEMON (1888) as well as numerous

[68] Cf. the biochemical 'evidence' briefly mentioned in chapter II, page 141. As regards the biochemistry of muscular contraction, there seems to obtain a similarity between echinoderms and vertebrates with respect to the role of creatine, in contradistinction to the relevant biochemical processes as displayed by a number of other invertebrates.

recent biologists assume that the ancestral echinoderm (pentactulate primordial form) was a ciliated bilaterally symmetric animal, perhaps possessing three coelomic compartments (protocoel, mesocoel, metacoel).

Moreover, the echinoderms and many hemichordates have very similar, almost identical types of larvae (Figs. 217–219). The echinoderm Pluteus larvae, and hemichordate Tornaria larvae display, furthermore, bands and tufts of cilia not unlike those of pilidium and trochophore larvae characteristic for plathelminths, annelids, mollusks, bryozoans, and phoronids. It is true, however, that the echinoderm and comparable hemichordate larvae display an arrangement of the ciliated bands and some other details of configuration which differ substantially from the corresponding features in similar larvae of protostomes. Nevertheless, the significant similarities remain highly suggestive and can (but not: must) be interpreted as indicating a common 'ancestry', such as a worm-like bilaterally-symmetric archistome form.

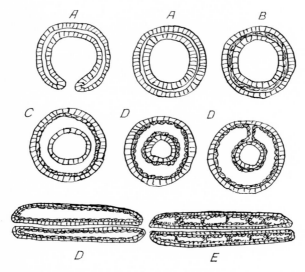

Figure 216. Diagrams illustrating the concepts of diploblastic, triploblastic, acoelomate, pseudocolomate, coelomate, non-metameric, and metameric organization. (Based on lecture sketches of L. PLATE and F. MAURER, 1919.) *A* True diploblastic configuration (ectoderm and entoderm) as manifested in various gastrula forms. *B* Diploblastic configuration with mesoglea (sponges, coelenterates); this could also be called pseudotriploblastic. *A* and *B* are acoelomate. *C* Triploblastic configuration with pseudocoelom. *D* Triploblastic configurations with true coelom. *E* Triploblastic configuration with segmentation, that is, metameric organization. *A* to *D* exemplify non-metameric organization; metamerism, however, may be manifested in forms without a true coelom.

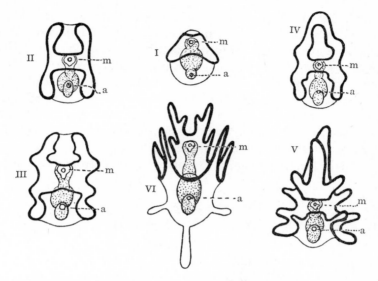

Figure 217. Diagrams of Echinoderm larvae. (After JOHANNES MÜLLER from R. HERTWIG, 1912.) I: early configuration of all larvae; II, III: developmental stages of the holothurian Auricularia; IV, V: developmental stages of the asteroid Bipinnaria; VI: Pluteus of echinoid Spatangus; a: anus; m: mouth; the heavy black line indiactes the ciliated crown.

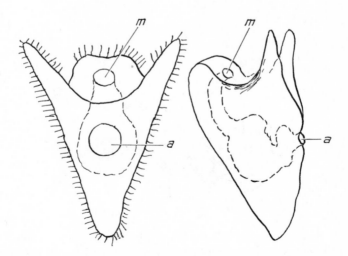

Figure 218 A. Pluteus larva of Echinus (sea-urchin). (Modified after SELENKA-GOLD-SCHMIDT, 1919.) a: anus; m: mouth; left, view from oral side; right, lateral view.

GROBBEN (1923–1924) has put forward a rather well founded argumentation demonstrating the possibility that echinoderms could have derived from ancestral forms identical with or closely similar to Cephalodiscus. Thus, stretching the point, it seems permissible to assume that both echinoderms and vertebrates are descendants of hemichordates, that is, of chordates in the wider sense. It might, of course, be objected that the hemichordate 'notochord' is 'neither homologous nor analogous' with the chordate one, and does therefore not represent a true notochord. Hence, 'modern' taxonomists have removed the Hemichordata, as a separate 'phylum', from the Chordata.

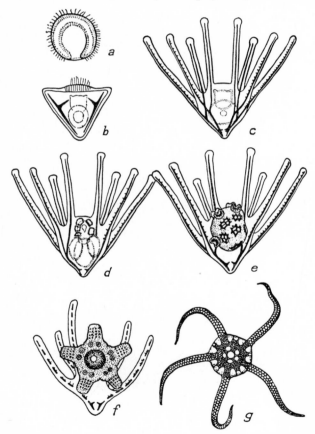

Figure 218 B. Ontogenetic evolution of an Echinoderm Ophiuroid starfish. The adult form originates from a circumscribed portion of the larva, whose remaining parts then disintegrate. (After R. GOLDSCHMIDT, 'Einführung in die Wissenschaft vom Leben.' Springer, Berlin 1927.) Compare c, d, e with Figs. 203 and 204!

Nevertheless, as stated further above, I interpret the notochord of balanoglossus as a true (kathomologous) notochord.

It is evidently also possible, as PLATE (1922) and other authors suggest, to assume a derivation of echinoderms from radial-symmetric sessile, anthozoan-like coelenterate ancestors. The bilateral symmetry of echinoderm larvae must then be considered a secondary feature (or 'adaptation') correlated with a motile, free swimming stage, or, in other words, a 'mask' or 'masquerade'[69].

For all that, the occurrence of tentaculated, sessile invertebrate metazoan forms at various levels of organization poses another inter-

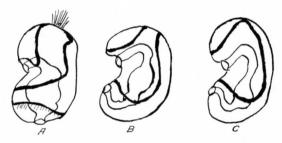

Figure 219. Comparison of Balanoglossus larva (A), Asteroid larva (B), and Holothuroid larva (C). (Modified after DELAGE and HÉROUARD.)

esting and undecidable problem. Did motile forms arise from sessile ones or vice-versa? Or, is it possible that, in the course of phylogeny, sessile and motile forms succeeded each other in various and perhaps even 'random' alternations? Certainly, within the observable onto-genetic sequences, alternating cycles of sessile and motile forms of 'one and the same' organism do occur.

Thus, one could assume that, from 'primitive' sessile arm-feeders such as coelenterates, two closely related, but diverging lines of evolution led to sessile, stalked, likewise 'primitive' crinoid-like echinoderms and, in the other direction, to pterobranch-like forms, of which the present-day representatives are Cephalodiscus[70] and Rhab-

[69] 'Bilaterale Symmetrie der Larven als Folge ihrer schwimmenden Bewegungsweise.' Thus, we have, as regards this bilateral symmetry, the alternative: 'bilaterale Maske der Larven' vs. 'radiäre Maske der ausgewachsenen Formen' (cf. PLATE, 1922).

[70] Although it is said that gill clefts are not developed in Pterobranchia (BARNES, 1963; cf. also above p. 291), it is possible to interpret a pair of pharyngeal pouches present in Cephalodiscus, but not in Rhabdopleura, as 'branchial' structures ('ein Paar allenfalls als Kiemen zu deutende Darmspalten', R. HERTWIG, 1912).

dopleura. From pterobranch-like animals, hemichordates such as Balanoglossus, and various types or urochordates might then have arisen, changing from tentacle-feeding to gill-feeding. Again, the sequence of evolutionary events leading from pterobranch-like forms to hemichordates and urochordates could have given origin to additional dichotomies conducing, in a variety of possible ways, to Cephalochorda and Craniota. According to such interpretations, the bilateral symmetry of chordates and their ancestors would have arisen secondarily by early transformation from radial symmetry, and the motile vertebrates would have originated, as it were, comparatively 'late' from stalked, sessile ancestors.

Yet, tentacle bearing, or lophophorate forms, displaying considerable external resemblance, analogies, or parallelism, are found in various presumably quite unrelated groups pertaining to preponderantly motile Archistomia, Proterostomia, and Deuterostomia[71].

GARSTANG (1894, 1929) suggested that a tunicate larva, e.g. of ascidian type, might have derived from an echinoderm larva such as the Auricularia (holothuroid) by means of comparatively minor changes. With increasing size of larva, the ciliated bands or surfaces, becoming inadequate for locomotion because of the increasing discrepancy between motile surface and total volume of the animal, are believed to have been replaced by the development of musculature. Thus chordates might have evolved by 'paedomorphosis' of echinoderm larvae. Still, there is no cogent or even convincing evidence for such changes, since echinoderms and chordates might just as well have both evolved from divergent transformations of platyhelminth-larvae or similar ones (cf. footnote 12 p. 72, and p. 312).

It seems rather obvious that, despite considerable evidence for a close relationship of chordates and echinoderms, various perhaps permanently undecidable questions remain. Did chordates and echinoderms diverge from a common, coelenterate-like form, or from a plathelminth-like form, or in still another manner? Did chordates derive from echino-

---

[71] Thus, various hydroid polyps, Campanularia, Bougainvillea, Anthozoa, then Endoprocta, Ectoprocta, Phoronidea, Brachiopoda, Crinoids, Holothuroids (Cucumaria), Pterobranchs, even Annelida such as Serpulids, Terebella and others, display diverse sorts of 'analogous' tentacular patterns in sessile as well as motile organisms. In a wider sense, we have the likewise sessile Crustaceans such as the Cirriped Lepas and others, whose extremities, as it were, imitate the function of lophophore tentacles. Again, there are the 'similar' tentacles of highly motile cephalopods. Finally, even ciliate Protozoa 'imitate' sessile arm-feeders, e.g. Carchesium, Stentor, and related forms.

derms, or echinoderms from chordates (hemichordates)? Also, alternatively or additionally, in which way could a particular form, reasonably similar to some of the known ones, be regarded as the common ancestor of Echinodermata, Chordata, and Chaetognatha? What was the role of sessile or of motile forms in the postulated sequence of ancestral events? Should paedomorphic changes or changes involving non-paedomorphic types of transformations be assumed? And, if both sorts of events occurred, what was their sequential order? What are ancestral status and phylogentic significance (*qua* primary, secondary, independent) of radial symmetry and of bilateral symmetry? One is justified to assert that not a single one of these different questions could be answered with any claim to reasonable certainty.

Again, regardless whether the origin of chordates and of vertebrates is assumed through transformations of paedomorphic larvae, or through transformations involving the reproductive activities of non-paedo-morphic forms, it would remain most likely that the significant changes occurred as events modifying the course of larval development before the attainment of a reproductive stage. But one is here faced with still another at present undecidable question, namely, whether such changes were of a very gradual character (e. g. 'micromutations') or whether the relevant events took place in the manner of considerable 'sudden jumps', essentially in accordance with GOLDSCHMIDT's hypothesis of 'macro-mutations' (cf. chapter II, section 7). In other words, were the trans-formations, loosely speaking, of approximately 'continuous' character, or were they substantially 'discrete'?

Finally, it should be kept in mind that the entire sequence of events here under consideration, namely the presumed evolution from proto-zoan stage to early metazoan representatives, and of these latter into the various main invertebrate phyla, including 'lower' chordates, as well as the presumed evolution of some chordates into vertebrates, was already completed, as regards the overall formal or 'taxonomic' aspect, during the Ordovician period of the Palaeozoic era, that is, about 360 to 400 million or more years ago according to some credible estimates of geologic time.

The foregoing evaluation, although rather inconclusive and unsatisfactory, has, nevertheless, the advantage of almost altogether avoiding unduly questionable *ad hoc* conjectures, which, in speculations of this type, are easily piled one upon another. However, the distinction between Proterostomia and Deuterostomia is presupposed to be of significance and to indicate two phylogenetically divergent metazoan groups. Before concluding this discussion of cautious evolutionary inferences with an appraisal of the relevant evidence provided by the morphology of the nervous system, an abbreviated survey, followed by a critique, of the multitudinous, widely divergent, and less restrained theories on the origin of vertebrates seems appropriate.

The '*Nemertean Hypothesis*' might here be considered first. HUB-RECHT (1883, 1887) assumed that the paired dorsal nerve cord of Nemerteans united in the midline, while the proboscis sheath then formed the notochord (Fig. 220). The remnant of the proboscis is presumed to become part of the hypophysis. HUBRECHT's hypothesis is not without merits. The objection that the proboscis sheath originates from mesoderm, while the vertebrate notochord is entodermal, cannot be upheld, since vertebrate chordulation and mesoderm formation are, in a complex manner, closely interrelated (chorda-mesoderm). Yet, it is true that in Amphioxus, Urochorda, and Hemichorda, the notochord derives from the roof of the entodermal gut. The homologization of proboscis and hypophysis remains most

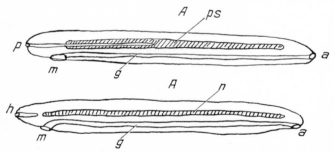

Figure 220. Diagrams illustrating HUBRECHT's Nemertean Hypothesis. (Modified and adapted from NEAL and RAND, 1936.) *A* Diagram of Nemertean. *B* Diagram of Chordate. a: anus; g: gut; h: hypophysis; m: mouth; n: notochord; p: proboscis; ps: proboscis sheath.

unconvincing, but the strongest objection to HUBRECHT's view can be based upon the protostome character of Nemerteans. Nevertheless, these worms, closely related to Turbellaria, display a much more highly organized structure, and can be regarded as exhibiting features anticipating conditions in taxonomically higher protostome invertebrate groups. It is therefore not unlikely that similar forms, although not exactly of the Nemertean type, might have evolved into primitive chordates related to Hemichorda, Urochorda, or Cephalochorda. Modified, and interpreted in this manner, HUBRECHT's hypothesis becomes acceptable with due reservations, and agrees, in its essential feature, with the orthogon-concept to be taken up further below.

The various '*Annelid and Arthropod Hypotheses*' are based on the fact, already stressed about 1822 by GEOFFROY DE ST. HILAIRE, that arthropods, or 'articulates' in general, and chordates can be transformed into each other, conceptually, and without much difficulty, by reversing the respective dorsal and ventral sides (cf. above, p. 283). DOHRN (1875) and SEMPER (1874) independently elaborated, on this basis, a derivation of *Chordates from Annelids*. It is stressed that annelids and chordates are metameric and coelomate. Some similarities obtain with regard to circulatory and urogenital system. Various *ad hoc* hypotheses can be contrived in order to account for the differences manifested by the nervous system, and other difficulties, e. g. the origin of a notochord, can be similarly resolved. It is, however, very difficult to account for the origin of gill clefts. Yet, these structures might have just arisen in chordates (even Rhabdopleura, it will be remembered, is without gills). Upside-down position during swimming locomotion is not an unusual occurrence among invertebrate animals. Figure 221 illustrates the 'transformation' by reversal.

A more recent, and modified annelid hypothesis was propounded by DELSMAN (1922, 1924 and other publications). This author assumed that the ectodermal stomodeum of annelids becomes transformed into the neural tube of vertebrates[72]. It is true that conditions in tunicates seem to indicate connections between stomodeum and neural tube, but DELSMAN's interpretation remains most unconvincing. Moreover, since the neural tube of chordates would then be formed by the annelid stomodeum, the fate of the original ventral annelid nerve cord, now

---

[72] A number of previous authors (KOWALEWSKY, SEDGWICK, VAN WIJHE, and others) have likewise, in various manners, suggested that the chordate neural tube might have functioned as part of the digestive system. The hypothesis of GASKELL, to be discussed further below, is based on perhaps the most extreme version of such concepts. A readable critical review of these theories on the Origin of Vertebrates, referring to many of the multitudinous different views and arguments, is included in an elementary treatise on (Vertebrate) Comparative Anatomy by NEAL and RAND (1936). Some detailed elaborations, including references to literature, are found in the treatises by DELSMAN (1922, 1924), GASKELL (1908), PATTEN (1912), and SPITZER (1910). A recent monograph by BERRILL (Clarendon Press, Oxford 1955), as well as the numerous pontifications by the present-day, highly vocal 'neo-evolutionists', do not, in my opinion, bring significant new data or argumentations. References to the writings of these gentlemen can be easily located by scanning the three volumes 'Evolution after DARWIN' (SOL TAX, ed., University of Chicago Press, 1960).

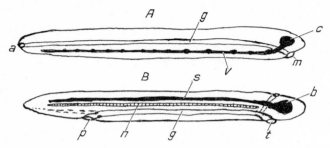

Figure 221. Diagrams illustrating conceptual transformation of Annelid into Chordate. *A* Annelid. *B* Chordate. a: anus; b: brain; c: cerebral ganglion: g: gut; m: mouth; n: notochord; p: chordate (vertebrate) anus or proctodeum; s: spinal cord; t: chordate (vertebrate) stomodeum; v: ventral nerve cord.

dorsal by reversal, and running parallel to the newly created tubular neuraxis, has to be explained by means of a very far-fetched hypothesis (transformation into spinal ganglia). Numerous other objections based on the fate of the blastopore could be elaborated.

In an earlier communication, DELSMAN (1913) had suggested that the different configurations characterizing the 'separate' 'phyla', such as chordates, annelids and arthropods, and mollusks, could be traced to changes of growth processes in those regions which determine the transformation of a larva such as the trochophore into the adult organism (Fig. 222). While DELSMAN's construction, as indicated in the figure, does not appear convincing, his suggestion, in a generalized interpretation, represents an expedient and appropiate formulation of the commonly recognized significance of ontogenetic transformations, and is in full agreement with well-established concepts of phylogeny. It seems indeed plausible to assume that the divergence of the protostome and deuterostome lines of evolution occurred by different transformations, say, of pilidium or trochophora-like archistome larvae, long before either annelid, mollusk, or chordate phyla 'made their appearance'[73]. Yet, in his later elaborations, DELSMAN appears indeed 'to have abandoned his attempt to derive chordates and other phyla from a trochophore larva and to favor the opinion that the adult annelid is in the direct line of chordate ancestry' (NEAL and RAND, 1936).

[73] This, of course, means: long before a succession of changes resulted in the establishment of different populations that, on the basis of their configurational and other characteristics, could reasonably be classified as pertaining to abstract sets such as annelid, mollusk, or chordate phyla.

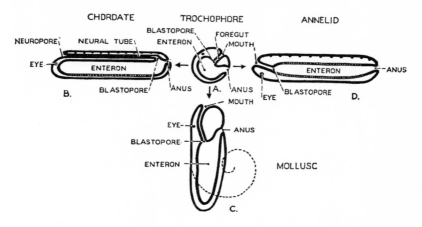

Figure 222. Diagram illustrating DELSMAN's theory. (From NEAL and RAND, 1936.)

The so-called '*Arthropod Hypothesis*' has been ably presented, with a considerable amount of detail, and in two different versions, by GASKELL (1908) and PATTEN (1912). In GASKELL's opinion, the neural tube of chordates (an ectodermal configuration) is derived directly from the digestive tube (an entodermal structure with, however, ectodermal stomodeum) of arthropod ancestors. The vertebrate brain ventricles correspond here to the rostral part of the arthropod stomach, and the ventricular ependymal lining is the transformed mucosa of the arthropod digestive tract (Figs. 223–236). GASKELL's hypothesis, in contradistinction to the original concept of GEOFFROY (DE) ST. HILAIRE, and to PATTEN's hypothesis, which will be discussed further below, does not require a reversal of the arthropod body. In fact, GASKELL believes that 'the difficulties in the way of accepting such reversal of surfaces are insuperable'.

The arthropod which, in that authors opinion, represents the progenitor of vertebrates, is assumed to be a trilobite-like organism 'with markedly polychaetan affinities', and pertaining to the group Protostraca. As can be seen from Figure 223, these animals possessed a deep ventral groove, assumed to extend, in a rostro-caudal direction, 'from one end of the body to the other, and also pleural fringes, as in many trilobites. This might be called the Trilobite stage'.

'This groove became converted into a tube and so gave rise to the notochord, while the appendages were still free and the pleura had not met to form a new ventral surface. This might be called the Chordate

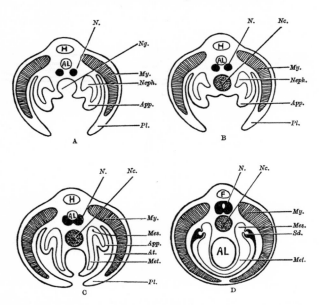

Figure 223. Diagrams illustrating GASKELL's hypothesis, and showing the conceptual transformation of a trilobite-like animal (*A*) into a vertebrate (*D*). *B* and *C* are hypothetical transitional stages. All stages are shown in cross sections. (From GASKELL, 1908.) App: appendage; Al: alimentary canal; At: atrial chamber; F: fat body; H: heart; Mes: mesonephros; Met: metacoele; Nc: notochord; Neph: nephrocoele; Ng: notochordal groove.

Trilobite stage.' (It will be noted that this chorda is of ventral ectodermal origin.)[74]

'Then, passing from the protostracan to the palaeostracan stage, the oral and respiratory chambers were formed, not communicating with each other,' ... 'a ventral groove in the metasomatic region being the only connection between respiratory chamber and cloaca. This might be called the Chordate Palaeostracan stage.'

---

[74] From the viewpoint of a rigorous form-analytic approach, the notochord, together with neuraxis and digestive tract including stomodeum and proctodeum, represents one of the basic configurational components characterizing the specific chordate and vertebrate morphologic pattern. GASKELL comments in this respect: 'I have endeavoured in this chapter to make some suggestions upon the origin of the notochord and of the vertebrate gut in accordance with my theory of the origin of vertebrates. I feel, however, strongly that these suggestions are much more speculative than those put forward in the previous chapters, and of necessity cannot give the same feeling of soundness as those based directly upon comparative anatomy and histology. Still, the fact remains that the origin of the notochord is at present absolutely unknown, and that my speculation that it may have originated as an accessory digestive tube is at all events in accordance with the most

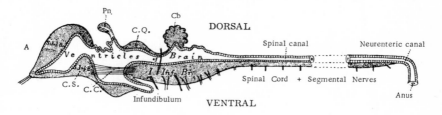

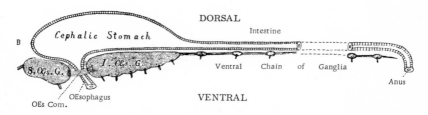

Figure 224. Diagram illustrating transformation of arthropod alimentary canal (*B*) into ventricular system of vertebrate neuraxis (*A*), according to GASKELL's hypothesis. (From GASKELL, 1908.) Diagram *B* of this figure should be compared with my sketch of Fig. 77, and with Fig. 73 and 78. Cb: cerebellum; CC: crura cerebri; CQ: corpora quadrigemina; CS: corpus striatum; I. Inf. Br: infra-infundibular brain and cranial segmental nerves; I. Oes. G.: infra-oesophageal ganglia; Pn: pineal gland; S. Inf. Br.: supra-infundibular brain; S. Oes. G.: supra-oesophageal ganglia; Oes. Com.: oesophageal commissures.

'Finally, with the conversion of this groove into a tube, the opening of the oral into the respiratory chamber, and the formation of an atrium by the ventralwards growth of the pleural folds, the formation of a Vertebrate was completed' (GASKELL, 1908, p. 452–454). It will be seen that the newly formed digestive tube, resulting from an invagination of the ventral body surface, has, as far as its lining is concerned, an ectodermal origin.

---

widely spread opinion that it arises in close connection with an alimentary canal.' Now, if, by 'origin of the notochord', GASKELL means here the phylogenetic origin, he is obviously right. Yet, the formal 'origin' of the notochord in ontogenetic evolution can be regarded as fairly well known from many actual observations. Although, in various vertebrate groups, a number of differences as regards some of the details of formal origin obtain, GASKELL's remark, that the notochord arises in close connection with an alimentary canal, is likewise fully justified. Yet, GASKELL's concept regarding the origin of that alimentary canal can hardly be regarded as convincing and is not substantiated by a reasonable interpretation of ontogenetic events. In order to adjust GASKELL's hypothesis to the actual sequence of these observed events, a whole chain of additional *ad hoc* hypotheses would have to be elaborated.

The transformations involving the central nervous system according to GASKELL's hypothesis are shown in Figures 224 to 226. The author assumes that the enlargement of the brain, through which the esophagus passed, meant the strangulation of the esophagus, while the atrophy of the brain meant 'degeneration'. Only a new intestinal tract (as shown and discussed above) could solve this 'problem' or 'dilemma'.

The discrepancy between a dorsal heart of the presumed ancestral arthropod and the ventral heart of vertebrates raises another difficult problem, which GASKELL solves by additional *ad hoc* hypotheses, implying the formation of a new heart and of a new circulatory system.

With regard to objections based on the germ-layer theory, GASKELL claims that this theory has become discredited and therefore can be ignored. Now, while some of the extreme formulations of the 'germ-layer theory' with regard to specificity and primordial organogenesis must indeed be considered erroneous, the germ-layer concept still retains many very significantly valid aspects, upon which the morphologic evaluation of organ systems and organs can be based. These relevant parameters cannot, in my opinion, be lightly disregarded.

PATTEN's '*Arachnid Hypothesis*' requires, in the 'orthodox' fashion of GEOFFROY ST. HILAIRE (cf. above p. 319), a reversal of dorsal and

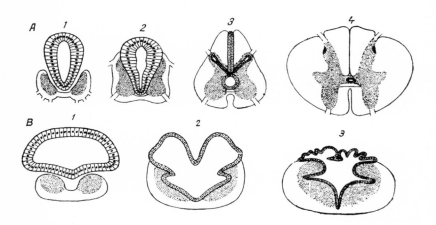

Figure 225. Additional diagrams showing 'method of formation of the vertebrate spinal cord from the ventral chain of ganglia and the intestine of an arthropod', represented in 1 (A). The lower row (B) shows 'method of formation of the vertebrate medulla oblongata from the infra-oesophageal ganglia and the cephalic stomach of an arthropod'. (From GASKELL, 1908.)

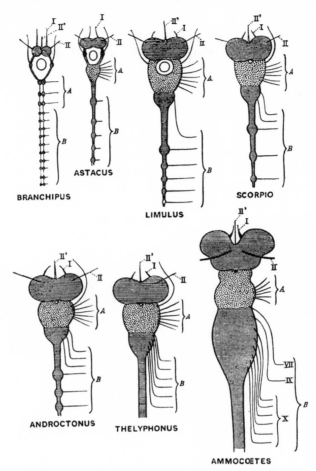

Figure 226. Comparison of invertebrate brains with the brain of the larval cyclostome Ammocoetes. (From GASKELL, 1908.) Branchipus ('fairy shrimp') is a phyllopod crustacean, Astacus is the crayfish, Androctonus is a scorpion, and Thelyphonus a 'whip scorpion'. I: olfactory nerve; II: optic nerve; supraoesophageal ganglia and their derivatives on top (cross-hatched); prosomatic ganglia stippled; mesosomatic ganglia bottom (cross-hatched); A: prosomatic nerves; B: mesosomatic nerves.

ventral side (Figs. 227–229)[75]. PATTEN (1912) assumes that an arachnid (in the wider sense), namely an aquatic form akin to limulus, perhaps

[75] The interesting series of transformations indicated by these diagrams of PATTEN (as well as by those of GASKELL, Figs. 223, 224) are reminiscent of the conceptual transformations performed by PETRUS CAMPER (cf. chapt. III, p. 260, footnote 54) by which, e.g. a cow was changed into a bird.

an extinct 'water scorpion' of the subclass Eurypterida[76] represented the vertebrate ancestor. Because of the reversal, most of the original intestinal tract persisted as such, although, in agreement with GASKELL, a new mouth had to be formed.

The arachnid nerve cord is converted into the tubular neuraxis of vertebrates, and PATTEN attempts to demonstrate a numerical correspondence between the subdivisions of the limulus central nervous system and the transitory neuromeres of the vertebrate brain. Complicated *ad hoc* theories account for the transformation of other arachnid organ systems into those of vertebrates. The vertebrate notochord is here derived from the lemmatochord related to the nerve cord of arachnids.

In elaborating his theory, PATTEN has emphasized a large amount of similarities in structural details of arachnids and vertebrates. Such actual resemblances, which that author, however, often greatly exaggerates, are, from a rigorous morphologic viewpoint, analogies and not homologies[77]. PATTEN overestimates minor points, and conveniently ignores all the fundamental differences. In this respect, it is most amusing to note that on the basis of identical material, 'two able biologists such as GASKELL and PATTEN', reach, except for very few, and rather minor points, 'diametrically opposite conclusions' (NEAL and RAND, 1936).

It is hardly necessary to add that I do not share the views, on vertebrate evolution, of DELSMAN, GASKELL, and PATTEN. Some features of

---

[76] The Eurypterida or Gigantostraca lived from the Cambrian to the Permian period and attained the perhaps largest size of any known arthropods. One species of the genus Pterygotus was almost three meters long (BARNES, 1963). Eurypterids were quite similar to limulus as regards the ascertainable general body Bauplan, displaying the same prosomal (cephalothoracic) appendages and a telson (last body segment lacking appendages), as well as lateral and median eyes. Yet, the opisthosoma (abdomen) of Eurypterids was composed of separate segments. It was again subdivided into pre-abdomen (mesosoma) with seven segments bearing appendages, and post-abdomen (metasoma) of five narrower segments lacking appendages. The elongated and still narrower telson was attached to the fifth metasomatic segment.

[77] As regards a few details and analogies, DELSMAN (1922) expresses the opinion that 'hardly two of the great subdivisions or phyla of the animal kingdom show such a close agreement, even in the details of their structure, as annelids and vertebrates, and in no other case can the structure of one be derived so completely from that of the other'. Discounting the exaggerations, this statement applies likewise to the comparison of certain vertebrate and arthropod features, as elaborated by PATTEN. In a far more sober, and I believe, reasonable evaluation, we have the parallelism as well as the analogies justly stressed by ZAWARZIN (1924, 1925) and NOVIKOFF (1930).

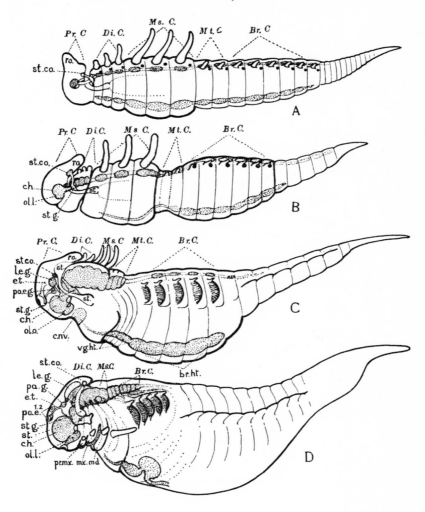

Figure 227. Diagrams illustrating PATTEN's hypothesis, and 'showing the five characteristic body regions of arthropods, and their progressive concentration to form the head
of a vertebrate. The principal points illustrated are: a: the early location of the principal
functions; b: the concentration of the cardiomers in the branchial region; c: the enlargement and concentration of the anterior cephalic neuromeres; d: the change in position
of the optic ganglia and oral arches; e: the closure of the old mouth and the formation of
a new one; f: the transfer of locomotor organs from the mesocephalon to the postbranchial
metameres'. (From PATTEN, 1912.)

A and *B*: insect; *C*: arachnid; *D*: vertebrate. Readers interested in further details
should consult PATTEN's treatise.

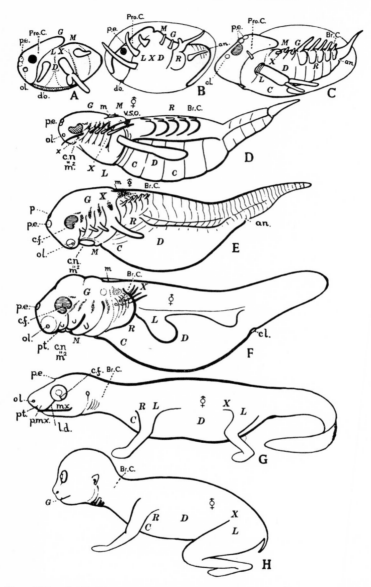

Figure 228 and *229*. Diagrams illustrating the principal stages in the evolution of segmented animals (syncephalata) according to PATTEN's hypothesis. (From PATTEN, 1912).

In Fig. 228 external view, in Fig. 229 midsagittal section. In Fig. 228 the capitals included in the drawings signify the location of principal functions: C: cardiac and circulatory; D: digestive; G: gustatory; L: locomotor; M: masticatory; R: respiratory; X: excretory; conventional notation for sexual function; large capitals signify:

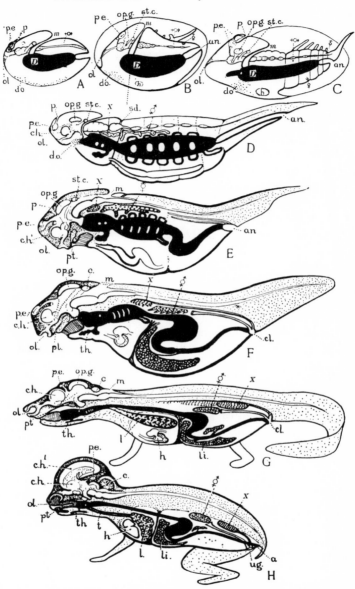

A: nauplius stage; B: ostracode; C: cladoceran; D: merostome; E: transitional; F: larval fish; G: amphibian; H: mammalian. The most striking features are: (1) closing of old mouth and stomodeum and the formation of a new opening into the mesenteron in the region of a 'dorsal organ'; (2) the substitution of lungs for gills; (3) the perforation of the walls separating gill sacs and enteric diverticula; (4) the rise and decline of metamerism. Readers interested in further details should consult PATTEN's treatise.

these hypotheses are so extreme that they seem to border on what one could reasonably call the 'lunatic fringe'. The critical reader might wonder, why, then, a discussion of these hypotheses, and a display of these authors' diagrams was here included. The reason is very simple. The cited authors were very capable biologists with considerable morphologic acumen, and a wide experience. A few, relatively unimportant modifications would convert their extravagant hypotheses into sober and fairly rigorous exercises in theoretical form-analysis. The elaborations of said authors, although otherwise intended, should be evaluated as permissible solutions of a purely conceptual morphologic problem, namely: by what sort, and by what series of transformations, could an annelid or an arthropod be changed into a vertebrate, and what particular role, in these various theoretically possible transformations, would the different organ systems have to play? In other words, these different hypotheses become fully justified if regarded as studies in pure morphology, not in any way directly related to presumably actual events; as studies of this type, they remain indeed of considerable interest and value[78]. It will be noted that, in analogy with *Diophantine* (indeterminate) equations, an undefined number of different solutions is conceptually possible. Clearly, we have the undisputable fact that inverted arthropods (or annelids), or, for that matter, non-inverted arthropods, can easily be conceptually transformed into vertebrates. This, however, does not mean that such actual transformation took place. A divergent evolution, in accordance with several different sets of 'possibilities', or, as determined by different sets of parameters, might well have taken place.

Thus, e. g., reverting to the more familiar vertebrates, and considering the telencephalon of birds, the basal ganglia (B and D_1 components) became preponderating, while in mammals the pallial cerebral cortex

---

[78] Except, of course, since their 'heuristic' value might justly be questioned, from the now widely prevalent viewpoint of the βαναυσία. Gentlemen of the predominating and influential βάναυσοι-group will, undoubtedly with most valid reasons, regard such exercises as 'meaningless games'. I shall not argue about such evaluations, amounting to 'undecidable questions', and merely refer to a relevant quip, by the mathematician HILBERT, concerning the value of pure and applied mathematics. This eminent scholar is reported to have said: 'We are often told that pure and applied mathematics are hostile to each other. This is not true. Pure and applied mathematics are not hostile to each other. Pure and applied mathematics have never been hostile to each other. Pure and applied mathematics will never be hostile to each other. Pure and applied mathematics cannot be hostile to each other because, in fact, there is absolutely nothing in common between them.'

(D_2 and D_3 components) became morphologically predominant. Evidently, lacking early embryonic stages as a point of departure, and without any additional relevant information, it would still be relatively easy to perform a reasonably valid topological transformation of a bird telencephalon into a mammalian one. Yet, few biologists would reach the conclusion that the complex avian telencephalon evolved into the mammalian telencephalon, although the topologic mappings representing such transformations might be considered, at least by some morphologists, to be of considerable theoretical or 'scientific' (whatever that may mean) interest.

Again, to point out some of the overall uncertainties obtaining in problems of evolution, it might be recalled that the phylogenetic transformation of the vertebrate primordial mandibular articulation into the mammalian incudo-malleolar articulation of the middle ear is rather convincingly suggested by the data of comparative anatomy. Yet, no convincing reconstruction of the actual different steps in this rather drastic transformation, involving the 'simultaneous' production of a new mandibular articulation, can be elaborated on the basis of the available data. In particular, did the required changes occur in gradual small steps or in 'sudden' larger jumps, or in a combination of both? Similar questions arise with respect to the transformations concerning branchial arches, urogenital system, etc.

After this discussion of the first major problem concerning the origin of vertebrates, namely the derivation of chordates in general (including vertebrates) from other invertebrates, we may now consider the second problem, that is, the derivation of vertebrates from 'primitive' chordates.

The '*Balanoglossus Hypothesis*', propounded by BATESON (1886) and others, stresses those features of hemichordates that can be justly regarded as transitional between chordate and non-chordate Metazoa. In Balanoglossus there is a rudimentary notochord, which is still more prominent and quite unmistakable in the closely related hemichordate Harrimania (Figs. 197, 230). In addition, gill slits similar to those of amphioxus, and a partly tubular dorsal nerve cord are displayed. The gonads, and the early embryonic stages are likewise definitely corresponding to those observed in amphioxus. If these homologies are considered significant, balanoglossus is clearly closely related to amphioxus, and thereby to vertebrates.

The '*Appendicularia Hypothesis*' is based upon KOWALEWSKY's studies (1877) on urochordates and amphioxus. If dorsal tubular

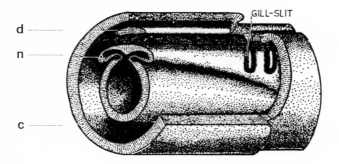

Figure 230. Stereogram of collar and anterior pharyngeal region in the hemichordate Harrimania. (Modified after RITTER, from NEAL and RAND, 1936.) c: collar; d: dorsal nerve cord; n: esophageal notochord plate; the topologic identity of the sectioned configurations with the pattern obtaining in larval amphioxus (Fig. 209) is evident.

neuraxis with anterior 'cerebral' vesicle, gill-slits, endostyle (thyroid anlage), and ventral heart are regarded as the relevant configurational elements, the identical chordate Bauplan of urochordates, amphioxus and vertebrate is so evident, upon inspection (Figs. 231, 232), in appendicularia larvae, as to make further argumentation unnecessary.

Both Appendicularia (Urochorda) and Balanoglossus (Hemichorda) can, furthermore, be easily compared with the hemichordate 'lophophorate' pterobranch Cephalodiscus, although this latter form displays a far less obvious chordate morphologic pattern (Fig. 204). We have here, albeit in a most rudimentary form, a notochord anlage, and a dorsal nerve strand, as well as a barely indicated 'gill-like' structure.

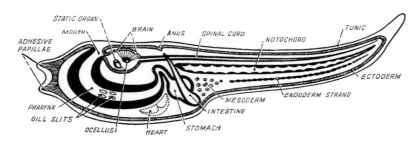

Figure 231. Diagram of larval urochordate including a few details omitted in the following figure. (Modified after VAN BENEDEN and JULIN from NEAL and RAND, 1936.)

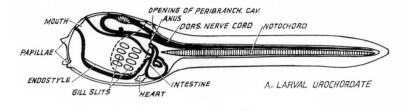

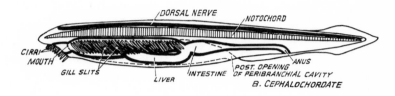

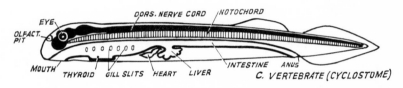

Figure 232. Diagrams of larval urochordate, cephalochordate (Amphioxus), and vertebrate (Cyclostome), indicating the basic configurational characteristics. (After HESSE-DOFLEIN from NEAL and RAND, 1936.)

Nevertheless, the actual phylogenetic relationships between cephalodiscus, balanoglossus, urochordates, amphioxus, and vertebrates remain, at least presently, perhaps definitively, an undecidable problem. It is idle to speculate which forms, or which traits, should be considered 'degenerate'. Because well preservable features are absent, it is not very probable that strongly convincing paleontological evidence can be discovered. Again, few recent metazoan forms are significantly identical with the paleontological forms pertaining to their own taxonomic category[79]. Thus, it seems reasonable to assume that neither recent hemichorda nor urochorda, nor amphioxus provide

[79] Among the few recent animals that may be considered significantly similar to extinct, paleontologic forms, one could mention, e. g., the brachiopod Lingula, the horse-shoe crab Limulus, and the crustacean Hutchinsoniella; as regards vertebrates, and with considerable reservations, the coelacanth Latimeria, and, with still more reservations as well as very loosely speaking, the rhynchocephalian Sphenodon might perhaps be cited as examples.

a 'true' picture of the postulated 'primitive' chordates from which craniote vertebrates originated, although the close relationship of said non-craniote chordates to vertebrates can be reasonably taken for granted. Moreover, neither the 'Balanoglossus Hypothesis' nor the 'Appendicularia Hypothesis', which are both rather plausible, appear very satisfactory, since, in the wider sense, the scope of both hypotheses remains within the limit of the phylum, but without providing specific clues as to the details of the presumptive configurational transformations from a 'primitive chordate', say even amphioxus, to an ancestral craniote vertebrate.

This second major problem, concerning the derivation of vertebrates from a generalized 'primitive' chordate configuration subsuming forms such as balanoglossus, tunicates and amphioxus, includes, again, two separate questions. The first one (a) as just briefly discussed, refers to the most probable type of organization displayed by such hypothetical 'ancestor', and the second one (b) concerns the diverging, or 'radiating' sequences of transformations leading from that hypothetical ancestral form to the various recent vertebrate 'classes', 'orders', and specific organic forms. No attempt will be made to supply a detailed answer, which (certainly on the basis of the available information) simply cannot be given with any reasonable degree of reliability. Some generalized phylogenetic trees were suggested in chapter II (Vol. 1, Fig. 6 and Fig. 7. It is intended to discuss a few additional conclusions in the last part of this entire work, after sufficient data on the comparative anatomy of the vertebrate neuraxis have been presented and evaluated.

A number of other difficult problems pertaining to origin and evolution of vertebrates arise with regard to the evolutionary history of different organ systems besides tubular neuraxis, notochord, gill clefts, and intestinal tract in general. Reverting to some of the questions considered in chapter III, section 7, page 277, it becomes obvious, in comparing the vast array of recent invertebrate metazoan organic forms, that various systems, such as muscular, urinary, and reproductive, represent, as it were, independent variables with regard to a presupposed phylogenetic evolution. This has been repeatedly pointed out by numerous authors, and is often used as an indeed potent argument against any particular phylogenetic hypothesis[80]. Thus, the

---

[80] Cf. e.g. the discussion of these problems in NEAL's and RAND's 'Comparative Anatomy' (1936).

excretory system of annelids displays certain similarities with that of vertebrates; the gonadic sacs of nemerteans can be regarded as related to the celomic segments of vertebrates, but the nemertean musculature cannot be compared, in a relevant manner, with that of chordates.

If one assumes, with SMITH (1953, 1961, ref. to chapt. II), a 'renocentric' viewpoint, the observed fact that 'nothing like the vertebrate glomerulus is found in the excretory organ of any invertebrate, the nearest approach being the nephridium of the earthworm, Lumbricus', seems to take considerable significance. In Hemichordata, no specialized excretory organ is found; in Urochordata, excretion may be carried out by cellular elements associated with the intestinal tract but presumably derived from the celom; in Amphioxus, there are numerous segmented nephridia, perhaps more of 'ectodermal' than of 'mesodermal' origin; these nephridia differ considerably from the glomerular-tubular nephron of craniote vertebrates. SMITH (1953, 1961) believes that these discrepancies in the excretory system, 'despite all other purported homologies with respect to "branchial baskets", "notochords", and the like', are enough 'to reduce the Amphioxus theory' (whatever this is supposed to be) 'to a jelly in all discussions of the origin of vertebrates, and to leave that question as open as it was a century ago'.

Now, if we consider the substantial changes that may occur during various stages of ontogenetic evolution, such e.g. as between insect larvae and imagines, whereby the individual certainly loses numerous very characteristic features it once possessed, and reduces itself, by 'histolysis' (cf. p.132), at least, figuratively speaking, and in some respect, to an 'amorphous jelly', it seems not altogether unreasonable to allow for considerable changes affecting phylogenetically and morphogenetically 'secondary systems'. Moreover, the well-known instances of sexual dimorphism[81] manifested by some Metazoa can be so extreme that, if merely the morphology of isolated female and male individuals

---

[81] Thus, in the Gephyrean annelid Bonellia, the ciliated dwarf male, between one and three millimeters long, is structurally markedly different from the female, which may attain the length of one meter. The male lives as an 'endoparasite' in the female's uterus or celomic cavity. In the arthropod crustacean cirripedians, the dwarf males, of quite different structural organization than the females, live in the latters' mantle cavity near the genital opening. The male represents, loosely speaking, not more than an organism consisting merely of penis and testis. Among the multitudinous other instances of considerable sexual dimorphism are those displayed by the plathyhelminth Bilharzia (schistosomum) haematobia, and by various crustacean copepods.

were known, such individuals would most likely not be suspected of belonging to the same species. Again, taxonomically and presumably phylogenetically closely related forms may display very significant differences in the structure and configuration of organ systems[82].

Thus, the undeniable differences in the excretory system of hemichordates, urochordates, cephalochordates and various vertebrates do not, in any way, preclude close phylogenetic relationships between these forms, if neuraxis, notochord, branchial system, and digestive tract do indeed represent the systems of primary phylogenetic importance.

Since this treatise concerns the morphology of the nervous system, we may ask whether it is justified to postulate, for this particular system, such 'primary phylogenetic importance'. As pointed out in chapter III, volume 1, WIEDERSHEIM (1893, cf. references to chapt. III) had stressed the conservative character of the nervous system in the presumptive phylogeny of vertebrates, and PLATE (1922) reached an identical conclusion with regard to the invertebrate nervous system[83]. The relative independence of the nervous system in development was likewise pointed out by CHILD (1921), who collected and analyzed a number of relevant data from normal ontogeny and from experimental work, including his own pertinent studies. This author, in connection with his theory of 'gradients', reached the conclusion that the nervous system, more than any other organ, is 'the expression of the primary physiological factors of the organismic pattern and integration'.

---

[82] Such structural differences are particularly noticeable in species 'adapted' to a parasitic life. As regards extreme configurational differences obtaining between species of one and the same order (or 'subclass'), there is the parasitic barnacle Sacculina, which, in the adult state, has completely lost true appendages and segmentation. The peduncle becomes modified into a plexus of root-like absorptive processes which invade the tissues of the host (mostly decapod crustaceans) and feed the saccular body of the parasite. This latter displays, in the adult stage, hardly any resemblance to related forms such as, e. g. lepadids (Lepadomorpha).

Again, with respect to the considerable structural and configurational differences obtaining in what, on the basis of an overall estimate, could be justly regarded as a single taxonomic set (e. g. phylum or class, etc.) of presumably common phylogenetic origin, it can be, and has been stated that such conceptually 'graded' or 'scaled' differences in the 'development' of a system are not distributed in a single series, but may occur repetitiously within apparently disconnected and heterogeneous sets.

[83] PLATE (1922) remarks: 'Da das Nervensystem verhältnismässig langsam und schwer durch die Umwelt beeinflusst wird, so eignet es sich ganz besonders zu deszendenztheoretischen Betrachtungen.'

HANSTRÖM (1928) summarizes those data concerning the comparative anatomy of the invertebrate nervous system, which, in his opinion, can be regarded as significant for phylogenetic theory.

The phylogenetic origin (Ausgangspunkt) of the metazoan nervous system is assumed to be represented by the diffuse ectodermal and entodermal plexus of bipolar and multipolar nerve cells of coelenterates. HANSTRÖM believes that such plexus was originally even more diffuse than in the recent forms. Within this plexus, concentration of fibers and nerve cells led to the formation of cords.

In *Turbellaria*, these cords display a very distinctive geometric or perhaps better topologic pattern designated as *orthogon* by E. REISINGER (1925), consisting of eight longitudinal cords with numerous connectives, and thus representing a net-like, rectangular plexus (netzförmiger, rechtwinkeliger Plexus). The brain or 'endon' is believed to be formed by condensation and displacement of orthogon components near the rostral end of the body[84]. Although REISINGER (1925) explicitly denies any phylogenetic significance of his platyhelmintic orthogon[85], HANSTRÖM (1928), on the basis of his considerable ex-

---

[84] REISINGER (1925) states: 'Zusammenfassend sehen wir also, dass sich das Nervensystem der Turbellarien und mithin das aller Plathelminthen auf ein einfaches, geometrisches Grundschema zurückführen lässt, auf das eines netzförmigen, rechtwinkeligen Plexus, das Orthogon. Dieses Nervennetz liegt innen dem Hautmuskelschlauch an und steht mit einem zarten, wohl allen Platoden eigenen, unter der Basalmembrane gelegenen, unregelmässig gestalteten Hautnervenplexus in Verbindung. (GRAFF bezeichnet leider das Orthogon der Landplanarien als 'Hautnervenplexus', obwohl dasselbe der Haut gar nicht angehört und überdies ein echter Hautnervenplexus auch bei diesen Formen vorhanden ist. Das sei, um Irrtümern vorzubeugen, besonders erwähnt.) Verlagerung von Nervengewebe des Orthogons ins Innere des Körpers, wohl im Anschluss an die Ausbildung des statischen Sinnesorgans, mögen zur Ausbildung des Endons geführt haben, das seine höchste Spezialisierung einerseits im Kapselhirn der Polycladen, andererseits in der Nervenplatte der Landplanarien findet. Ein Endon der erstgenannten Ausbildungsweise spricht von hoher Centralisierung, es stellt ein Gehirn im wahrsten Sinne des Wortes dar, eines vom Typus der Landplanariennervenplatte hingegen weist auf ausgesprochene Decentralisierung, ein für ein nervöses Centrum höherer Ordnung ganz einzig dastehendes und wohl sehr abgeleitetes Verhalten.'

[85] REISINGER (1925) remarks in this respect: 'Ich habe es versucht, in dieser Abhandlung zu zeigen, wie wir auf Grund morphologischer Befunde und durch gedankliche Abstraktion zu einem gewissen Grundschema eines Organes innerhalb einer Tiergruppe kommen können, und verfehle nicht, nochmals eindringlichst darauf hinzuweisen, dass ich dieses Schema auf keinen Fall historisch im Sinne einer "hypothetischen Urform" aufgefasst wissen will. Ebenso mache ich darauf aufmerksam, dass alle aus den Worten "ursprünglich primitiv usw." herauslesbaren stammesgeschichtlichen Erwägungen unter der stillschweigenden Voraussetzung gezogen wurden, dass das Einfachere auch das

perience with conditions found in other invertebrate groups, has adopted the concept of orthogon as a generalized pattern, from which the nervous system of nematodes, annelids, arthropods and vertebrates can easily be derived (Fig. 233). HANSTRÖM points out that, in the ctenophore Beroë (Fig. 7), the eight ciliated bands or comb rows subdivide the diffuse nervous net into longitudinal strips from which, in turn, the turbellarian orthogon (Fig. 20) could be derived without difficulty. HANSTRÖM justly adds that this coincidence does by no means prove a genetic relationship between ctenophores and turbellarians[86], but may, nevertheless, indicate the way by which the turbellarian orthogon originated. The development of a brain, presumably in connection with sensory organs such as eyes and statocysts, and the establishment of bilateral symmetry are considered significant factors in the formation of the type of orthogon characteristic for Platyhelminths. Again, the pattern of the annelid nervous system, easily derived from that of the Platyhelminths, displays, in some polychaete larvae, a most typical rectangular network of only slightly modified orthogon type (Fig. 235).

Although the nervous systems of most mollusk forms appears, *prima facie*, to differ significantly from the orthogon pattern, the nervous system of the Amphineura, considered to represent the most 'primitive' mollusks, can easily be derived from a modified orthogon.

---

phyletisch Frühere war, dass also das Vervollkommnungsprinzip Geltung habe und dass der gleiche Gedanke zu verschiedenen Zeiten immer wieder neu von der Natur aufgegriffen werden kann. Ob dem tatsächlich so ist, das kann niemand wissen und wird niemand wissen. Bei der Unzulänglichkeit, in unserem Falle dem völligen Mangel paläontologischen Materiales, tappen wir hinsichtlich der wirklichen Vergangenheit vollständig im Dunkel und dürfen uns nicht schämen zu sagen, dass wir über die Turbellarienstammesgeschichte sowie die der meisten übrigen Tiergruppen nichts wissen können. Man breche endlich mit der Unlogik, Gedachtes für Wirkliches zu nehmen; im Interesse reinlicher Arbeit!'

REISINGER's rigorous formulation and cautious restraint are, of course, fully justified, and my own form-analytic concepts are in complete agreement with these views. Nevertheless, since I consider the evidence for phylogenetic evolution quite convincing, although not providing a 'rigorous' proof, I believe that 'reasonable' phylogenetic hypotheses, formulated with the necessary reservations and stressing the sceptical outlook, are not only justified but necessary. Thus, paradoxically (actually: depending on a fluctuating viewpoint), I agree both with REISINGER's restriction and with HANSTRÖM's expansion of the orthogon concept.

[86] Other configurational similarities between ctenophores and turbellarians are discussed in footnote 65, page 305.

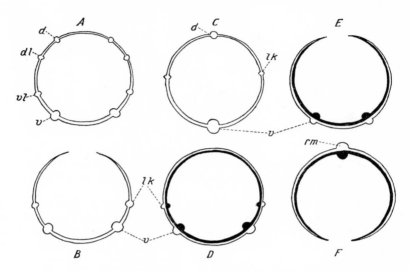

Figure 233. Diagram showing the *orthogon pattern* of the invertebrate nervous system and its variations, including the vertebrate configuration, as seen in a transverse (cross sectional) plane. (From HANSTRÖM, 1928.) A: Turbellarian (Platyhelminth); B: Amphineura (Molluscs); C: Nematoda; D: Annelida; E: Arthropoda; F: Vertebrate. d: dorsal connective; dl: dorso-lateral connective; lk: lateral connective; rm: vertebrate spinal cord; v: ventral connective (or ventral nerve cord); vl: ventrolateral connective. Closed ring formations can be found in turbellarians, nematodes, and annelids; in molluscs (with few exceptions) and arthropods, the ring is interrupted on the dorsal side; in vertebrates the disruption occurs on the ventral side; the mainly motor regions of ventral medulla and of spinal cord are indicated by the solid black marking in annelids, arthropods, and vertebrates.

Since the typical platyhelminth orthogon is definitely related to a bilateral symmetric promorphologic pattern, which may, or again may not, have arisen from a radial symmetric coelenterate precursor, considerable difficulties are encountered, if one attempts to derive, in a convincing, and fairly distinctive way, the peculiarly patterned nervous system of the radial parameric symmetric echinoderms from that of other forms, either platyhelminths or coelenterates[87].

Yet, it does seem apparent that the circumoral ring of e. g. asteroid echinoderms represents a topologic transform of a closed ring en-

---

[87] HANSTRÖM (1928) remarks that he has omitted the echinoderms from his elaboration of the phylogeny of the invertebrate nervous system based on the orthogon concept. He adds: 'Ich sehe auch noch keine Möglichkeiten, ihr Nervensystem mit dem der Cölenteraten oder der bilateralen Tiere mit einiger Sicherheit zu verknüpfen.'

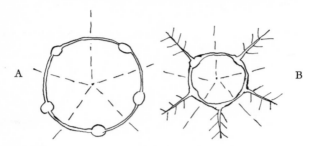

Figure 234. Tentative extension of HANSTRÖM's orthogon concept to include the ectoneural nervous system of echinoderms, in accordance with the views of the present treatise.

A Holothuroid echinoderm; *B* Asteroid echinoderm. The ring represents here the circumoral nerve ring. Very tentatively, the trivium of holothuroids is regarded as consisting of fused ventral connectives and of the two lateral connectives; the bivium is drawn as consisting of the two dorsal connectives (cf. Vol. 1, chapter III, Fig. 13 C); the interpretation in asteroids is purely arbitrary; both diagrams merely intend to suggest that some such sort of transformation could be inferred.

circling the rostral gut in various vermian phyla. Again, this ring has topologic relationships with longitudinal connectives. Some tentative conclusions might then be drawn, which I have indicated, with respect to the echinoderm ectoneural system, in Figure 234. A more detailed analysis, in diverse 'lower' invertebrate phyla, of larval nerve-grids such as shown in Figure 235 might perhaps yield some significant indications or suggestions.

Thus, with respect to the homologies of the invertebrate central nervous system, the orthogon concept seems to provide a most satisfactory clue for the tracing of the relevant formanalytic homologies, with which I have merely dealt in a generalized and cursory manner, because my inquiry concerns the vertebrate central nervous system. The invertebrates are here considered mainly as far as a summary acquaintance with the great variety of their forms becomes an indispensable prerequisite to an understanding of vertebrate configurational relationships.

As regards the vertebrates, no serious difficulties are encountered, if their neuraxis is regarded as formed by the midline fusion of the dorsal longitudinal cords (Fig. 233 F). This derivation applies likewise to hemichordate forms such as balanoglossus. It is true that in turbellarians the brain is more massively connected with the ventral cords, although likewise in direct continuity with the dorsal cords. Nematodes

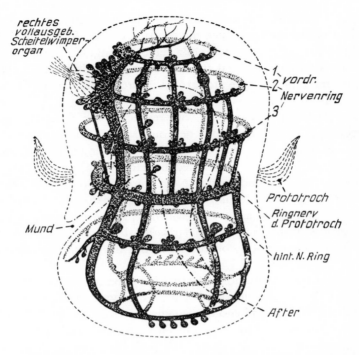

Figure 235. Nervous system in the larva of the polychaete annelid Lopadorhynchus, displaying a turbellarian orthogon pattern. (After MEYER in BÜTSCHLI, 1921, from HANSTRÖM, 1928). The peculiar orientation of the gut with respect to the grid of nerve cords should be noted.

and enteropneusts display a fused, unpaired dorsal cord most intimately merging into the cerebral ganglion. As far as topologic relations are concerned, there is no significant discrepancy between the relationships of cerebral ganglion (REISINGER's 'endon'), and dorsal cord in turbellarians, nematods, enteropneusts, and vertebrates. Moreover, the derivation of the vertebrate nervous system from the orthogon explains, in a most satisfactory way, as regards the relationship of central nervous system and intestinal tract, the fundamental difference between vertebrates on one hand, and annelids as well as arthropods on the other hand. The reversal of motor and sensory regions becomes self-evident (cf. Fig. 233 E, F), without requiring the assumption that vertebrates represent upside-down annelids or arthropods.

There remains, nevertheless, a certain difficulty with respect to proterostome and deuterostome dichotomy. However, in view of the varieties of archistome localization in platyhelminths, it may seem plausible to assume that, once the cephalic end of *Bilateralia* became established by the development of a cerebral ganglion, the subsequent formation of a gut with oral and anal opening could have involved a forward 'migration' of the archistoma in proterostomia, and a caudal one in deuterostomia.

Considering morphogenesis with respect to the close relationship between the neuroectodermal nervous system and the overlying epithelium of the ectodermal epidermis, the striking similarities in the configurational features manifested by Hemichordata such as Bala-noglossus, by Echinodermata, Nematomorpha (e.g. Nectonema), some Annelida (e.g. Sigalion), and, for that matter, by Coelenterata such as Hydra, might again be recalled. A sober phylogenetic evalu-ation of this unspecific proximity relationship does not allow for de-finitive and unequivocal conclusions about the precise ancestral line-age.

As regards segmentation, a feature common to, and conspicuously displayed by, widely differing forms, I believe that we have here a generalized biologic phenomenon characterized by a 'rhythmical', repetitive formative process along an axial gradient, representing a translatory symmetry (cf. chapt. III, p. 211). Thus, I do not think that the manifestation of metamerism in different organic forms implies a close phylogenetic relationship, or for that matter, any such relation-ship. If we consider, for instance, animal tissues, we have, in general, delimited cellular units; occasionally, however, there are seemingly syncytial and plasmodial structures. Yet, it cannot be claimed that organisms displaying cellular structures are thereby directly phylo-genetically related, nor that such is necessarily the case for organisms displaying in part, or entirely, syncytial structure. On the other hand, and in order to formulate some sort of 'reasonable' theory, I assume (in the manner of a 'fictional postulate') that the configurational behavior of intestinal tract (Archistomia, Proterostomia, Deuter-ostomia) and of the nervous system (REISINGER's and HANSTRÖM's orthogon) is of phylogenetic significance. While this 'postulate' is evidently unprovable, it seems to me 'reasonable' because of its thought-economical nature[88] (in MACH's sense). Although, unavoi-dably, going beyond evidence, this generalized interpretation does not seem to be contrary to evidence.

---

[88] That is: requiring a minimum of *ad hoc* hypotheses and unprovable postulates.

To summarize, it could then be stated that, from the rigorous form-analytic viewpoint, the neuraxis of vertebrates, consisting of brain and spinal cord, is, at some early ontogenetic stages, orthohomologous to that of adult cephalochordates (amphioxus), and of urochordate (ascidian) larvae. It is kathomologous to that of hemichordates. In the adult condition, the vertebrate neuraxis with its subdivisions is kathomologous to the cephalochordate and larval ascidian central nervous system.

If the form-analytic postulates are relaxed or modified, one could perhaps claim that the dorsal nerve cords and the 'endon' of platyhelminths are kathomologous to the chordate neuraxis. Such interpretation, however, remains questionable[89].

Diverse biologists, haply unduly impressed by the at present possibly somewhat overrated glamour status of macromolecular biochemistry, biophysics, and related fields of scientific inquiry, might opine that the unsatisfactory and uncertain results of phylogenetic speculations based on morphology are due to the nature of this outmoded and useless science. Thus, it could be remarked: 'Seht, das kommt davon, wenn man von derartig veralteten und fragwürdigen Grundlagen ausgeht!'.

Now, while some of the results of molecular biochemistry and allied branches, such as, e.g., genetics, are indeed quite impressive, their value (at least up to now) for phylogenetic hypotheses is most questionable. The scattered significant and interesting data contained in the 3rd volume of the Proceedings of the Fifth International Congress of Biochemistry (Moscow 1961), diluted by a good deal of loose speculation purporting to elucidate various 'breakthroughs' in 'Evolutionary Biochemistry', fall very short of providing any solid support for unambiguous phylogenetic interpretations, old or new. It can still be maintained that, on the whole, morphologic, i.e. configurational data, presumably represent the best clues for phylogenetic inferences or conjectures.

From a phylogenetic viewpoint, and combining here configurational as well as functional factors in agreement with some views of HERRICK (1924) and CHILD (1921, 1924), the following 'tendencies' character-

---

[89] Since platyhelminths, lacking a notochord, have no Bauplan in common with chordates (except at the 'gastraea'-stage), it becomes necessary, for the purpose of such homologization, to postulate a simplified adult common Bauplan. This latter would have to consist of an elongated bilateral symmetric body with cranio-caudal and dorso-ventral polarized axes, and comprising only three Grundbestandteile: (1) ectodermal covering, (2) orthogon, (3) entodermal gut.

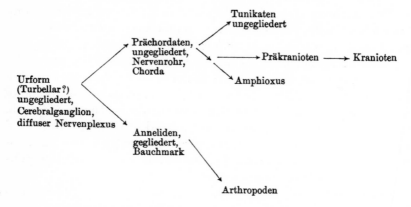

Allgemeine Ableitung der Wirbeltiere von den Wirbellosen.
(Nach einem Schema von PLATE.)

Figure 236. Phylogenetic derivation of Vertebrates from Invertebrates according to the concept adopted in the 'Vorlesungen' of 1927. (From K., 1927.)

izing the evolution of the invertebrate nervous system could be enumerated:

1. Condensation of the diffuse nerve net *(centralization)*, whereby a central nervous system becomes distinguishable from a peripheral nervous system.
2. Development and prevalence of *bilateral symmetry*, allowing, however, for some exceptions (e. g. echinoderms).
3. Tendency toward a definite rostral dominance with differentiation of a brain *(cephalization)*, in correlation with an axial physiologic gradient[90].

With regard to a tentative generalized diagram indicating the derivation of Vertebrates from Invertebrates, as well as the evolution of some major Invertebrate groups, it is perhaps of some interest to compare my interpretation of 1927 (Fig. 236) with my present one

---

[90] From the viewpoint of the vertebrate 'paleoneurologist', T. EDINGER (1960, references to chapt. III) distinguishes cerebralization in contrast to cephalization. Cerebralization is said to be 'a quantitative process correlated with progressive complication, often specialization, in brain structure'. In the general phylogenetic aspect here under consideration, it appears unnecessary to make a distinction between cephalization and cerebralization.

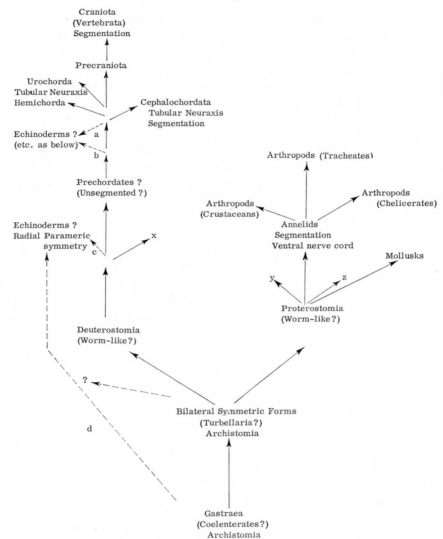

Figure 237. Hypothetic main evolutionary relationships of Metazoa, illustrating a possible general derivation of Vertebrates from Invertebrates, according to the tentative concepts adopted in the present treatise. a, b, c, d: 'logically' permissible different phylogenetic derivations of Echinoderms; x: Chaetognatha (and possibly additional 'minor' groups as might be demonstrated to be Deuterostomia); y: protostome lophophorate Metazoa; z: other 'minor groups'. Evidently, a variety of different schemes of derivation could be elaborated. A very thorough morphologic analysis of the peculiar deep sea organic forms, about which only fragmentary data are available, might provide significant clues leading to some modifications of phylogenetic speculations.

(Fig. 237). The diagram of 1927 was strongly influenced by, and was based on, the views of PLATE, who, here in agreement with R. HERTWIG, did not particularly stress the importance of protostome and deutero-stome ontogenetic development.

On the basis of my subsequent studies concerning these questions, however, I am inclined to attribute a rather probable and substantial phylogenetic significance to this ontogenetic characteristic[91]. Yet, as can be seen, my present phylogenetic interpretation does not thereby significantly differ from that of more than 36 years ago. Despite the large amount of additional data and speculations that have accumulated since that time, I can here repeat, without any modifications, my statement of 1927 (p. 20): 'Wenn auch zum mindesten die Möglichkeit, um nicht zu sagen die Wahrscheinlichkeit einer solchen allgemeinen Ableitung der Wirbeltiere von Wirbellosen zugegeben werden muss' (cf. the two diagrams of Figs. 236 and 237), 'so bleibt doch zunächst jeder speziellere Ableitungsversuch eine auf sehr unsicheren Grund-lagen ruhende theoretische Konstruktion.'

---

[91] On the other hand, it will be seen that, rightly or wrongly, I do not regard segment-ation and celom-formation as sufficiently significant features with respect to phylogenetic relationship. I 'believe' thus that segmentation and celomic cavity are configurational manifestations which have 'independently' arisen in different groups such as e. g. verte-brates and articulates (annelids and arthropods).

15. References to Chapter IV

ADELMAN, W. J. and DALTON, J. C.: Interaction of calcium with sodium and potassium in membrane potentials of the lobster giant axon. J. gen. Physiol. *43*: 609–619 (1960/61).

ALEXANDROWICZ, J. S.: Zur Kenntnis des sympathischen Nervensystems der Krustazeen. Jena. Z. Naturw. *45*: 395–444 (1909).

ALEXANDROVICZ, J. S.: The innervation of the heart of the cockroach. J. comp. Neurol. *41*: 291–309 (1913).

ALTEN, H. VON: Zur Phylogenie des Hymenopterengehirns. Jen. Z. Naturw. *46*: 511–590 (1910).

APATHY, S.: Das leitende Element des Nervensystems und seine topographischen Beziehungen zu den Zellen. Mitt. zool. Stn. Neapel *12*: 495–748 (1897).

ASCOLI, G.: Zur Neurologie der Hirudineen. Zool. Jb. Abt. Anat. Ontog. *31*: 473–494 (1911).

ASCOLI, G.: Zur Kenntnis der neurofibrillären Apparate der Hirudineen. Arch. mikr. Anat. *82*: 414–425 (1913).

ASHWORTH, J. H.: The giant nerve cells and fibers of Halla parthenopeia. Phil. Trans. R. Soc. B *200*: 489–521 (1909).

AUTRUM, H.: Die Belichtungspotentiale und das Sehen der Insekten (Untersuchungen an Calliphora und Dixippus). Z. vergl. Physiol. *32*: 176–227 (1950).

AUTRUM, H. und STUMPF, H.: Das Bienenauge als Analysator für polarisiertes Licht. Z. Naturf. *5b*: 116–122 (1950).

BALFOUR, F. M.: The anatomy and development of Peripatus capensis. Quart. J. micr. Sci. *23*: 213–259 (1883).

BARNES, R. D.: Invertebrate zoology (Saunders, Philadelphia 1963).

BATESON, W.: The ancestry of the Chordata. Quart. J. micr. Sci. *26*: 535–571 (1886).

BATESON, W.: On numerical variation in teeth, with a discussion of the conception of homology. Proc. zool. Soc. London *1892*: 102–115.

BATHAM, E. S.; PANTIN, C. F. A. and ROBSON, E. A.: The nerve net of the sea anemone Metridium senile: The mesenteries and the column. Quart. J. micr. Sci. *101*: 487–510 (1960).

BAUER, V.: Zur inneren Metamorphose des Centralnervensystems der Insekten. Zool. Anz. *26*: 655–656 (1903).

BECCARI, N.: Il problema del neurone. 2 vols. (Nuova Italia, Firenze 1945, 1947).

BELLONCI, G.: Intorno alla struttura e alle connessioni dei lobi olfattori negli Arthropodi superiori e nei Vertebrati. Atti. R. Accad. Lincei, ser. 3, *13*: 555–564 (1882).

BENNETT, E. L. and CALVIN, M.: Failure to train planarians reliably. Neuroscience Res. Progr. Bull. *2*: 3–24 (1964).

BERKELEY, E. C.: Giant brains or machines that think (Wiley, New York 1949).

BERKELEY, E. C. and WAINWRIGHT, L.: Computers. Their operations and applications (Reinhold, New York 1962).

BETHE, A.: Das Nervensystem von Carcinus maenas. Arch. mikr. Anat. *50*: 460–546 (1897).

BETHE, A.: Vergleichende Untersuchungen über die Funktionen des Zentralnervensystems der Arthropoden. Pflügers Arch. ges. Physiol. *68*: 449–545 (1897).

BETHE, A.: Allgemeine Anatomie und Physiologie des Nervensystems (Thieme, Leipzig 1903).

BIEDERMANN, W.: Über den Ursprung und die Endigungsweise der Nerven in den Ganglien wirbelloser Thiere. Jena. Z. Naturw. *25*: 429–466 (1891).

BLANCHARD, E.: Recherches anatomiques et zoologiques sur le système nerveux des animaux sans vertèbres. Du système nerveux des insectes. Ann. Sci. Nat. 3. sér. *5*: 273–379 (1846).

BÖHMIG, L.: Tricladenstudien. I. Tricladina maricola. Z. wiss. Zool. *81*: 344–504 (1906).

BOYCOTT, B.B.: The functional organization of the brain of the cuttlefish Sepia officinalis. Proc. roy. Soc. B *153*: 503–534 (1961).

BOYCOTT, B.B. and YOUNG, J.Z.: The subpedunculate body and nerve and other organs associated with the optic tract of cephalopods. In: BERTIL HANSTRÖM, Zoological papers in honour of his sixty-fifth birthday. Zool. Inst. Lund. p. 76–105 (1956).

BOYCOTT, B.B. and YOUNG, J.Z.: Reaction to shape in Octopus vulgaris. Proc. zool. Soc. London *126*: 491–547 (1956a).

BOYCOTT, B.B. and YOUNG, J.Z.: A memory system in Octopus vulgaris. Proc. roy. Soc. B. *143*: 449–480 (1956b).

BOYCOTT, B.B. and YOUNG, J.Z.: Effects of interference with the vertical lobe on visual discrimination in Octopus vulgaris *Lamarck*. Proc. roy. Soc. B. *146*: 439–459 (1957).

BOZLER, E.: Untersuchungen über das Nervensystem der Coelenteraten. I. Teil: Kontinuität oder Kontakt zwischen den Nervenzellen. Z. Zellforsch. *5*: 244–262 (1927).

BRAGG, W.: The Universe of Light (Dover, New York 1959).

BRANDES, G.: Das Nervensystem der als Nemathelminthen zusammengefassten Wurmtypen. Abhandl. naturforsch. Ges. Halle *21*: 273–299 (1899).

BRETSCHNEIDER, F.: Der Zentralkörper und die pilzförmigen Körper im Gehirn der Insekten. Zool. Anz. *41*: 560–569 (1910).

BRETSCHNEIDER, F.: Über die Gehirne der Küchenschabe und des Mehlkäfers. Jena. Z. Naturw. *52*: 269–362 (1914).

BRETSCHNEIDER, F.: Über das Gehirn des Wolfmilchschwärmers. Jena. Z. Naturw. *57*: 423–462 (1921).

BROWN, F.A. Jr.: Responses of the planarian, Dugesia, and the protozoan, Paramecium, to very weak horizontal magnetic fields. Biol. Bull. *123*: 264–281 (1962a).

BROWN, F.A. Jr.: Responses of the planarian, Dugesia, to very weak horizontal electrostatic fields. Biol. Bull. *123*: 282–294 (1962b).

BUCHSBAUM, R.: Animals without backbones. An introduction to the invertebrates (University of Chicago Press, 1950).

BUDDENBROCK, W. VON: The senses (University of Michigan Press, Ann Arbor 1958).

BULLOCK, T.H.: The giant fiber system in Balanoglossus. J. comp. Neurol. *80*: 355–367 (1944).

BULLOCK, T.H.: Functional organization of the giant fiber systems of lumbricus. J. Neurophysiol. *8*: 55–71 (1945).

BULLOCK, T.H.: Properties of some natural and quasi-artificial synapses in polychaetes. J. comp. Neurol. *98*: 37–68 (1953).

BULLOCK, T.H. and HORRIDGE, G.A.: Structure and function in the nervous system of invertebrates. 2 vols. (Freeman and Co., San Franscisco and London 1965).

BÜRGER, O.: Zur Kenntnis von Nectonema agile Verr. Zool. Jb. Abt. Anat. Ontog. *4*: 631–652 (1891).

BUTENANDT, A.: Biochemistry and the insect world. Triangle *5*: 24–27 (1961).

BÜTSCHLI, O.: Vorlesungen über vergleichende Anatomie (Springer, Berlin und Leipzig 1921).

CAJAL, S. R. Y: Neuroglia y neurofibrillas del Lumbricus. Trab. Lab. Invest. biol. Madrid *3*: 277–285 (1904).

CAJAL, S. R. Y: Nota sobre la estructura de la retina de la mosca (Musca vomitoria). Trab. Lab. Invest. biol. Madrid *7*: 217–257 (1909).

CAJAL, S. R. Y: Contribución al conocimiento de la retina y centros opticos de los Cefalopodos. Trab. Lab. Invest. biol. Madrid *15*: 1–82 (1917).

CAJAL, S. R. Y: Observaciones sobre la estructura de los ocelos y vias nerviosas ocelares de algunos insectos. Trab. Lab. Invest. biol. Madrid *16*: 109–139 (1918).

CAJAL, S. R. Y: Signification probable de la morphologie des neurones des invertébrés. Trab. Lab. Invest. biol. Madrid *26*: 131–153 (1929).

CAJAL, S. R. Y y SANCHEZ, D.: Contribución al conocimiento de los centros nerviosos de los insectos. Trab. Lab. Invest. biol. Madrid *13*: 1–167 (1915).

CARTHY, J. D.: Animal navigation (Allen and Unwin, London 1956).

CAZAL, P. et BOGORAZE, D.: Recherches sur les corps blancs du Poulpe (Octopus vulgaris Lam.). Leur fonction globuligène et néphrocytaire. Bull. Inst. océanogr. *842*: 1–12 (1943a).

CAZAL, P. et BOGORAZE, D.: Un organe neuricrine du Poulpe: La glande pédonculaire. Bull. Inst. océanogr. *847*: 1–10 (1943b).

CHEN, Y. T.: Studies on the neuromotor system of Stylonychia pustulata and Stylonychia mytilus. J. Morph. *75*: 335–345 (1944).

CHILD, C. M.: The origin and development of the nervous system (University of Chicago Press, 1921).

CHILD, C. M.: Physiological foundations of behavior (Holt, New York 1924).

CLARK, R. B.: The posterior lobes of the brain of Nephtys and the mucus glands of the prostomium. Quart. J. micr. Sci. *96*: 545–565 (1955).

COGGESHALL, R. E. and FAWCETT, D. W.: The fine structure of the central nervous system of the leech, Hirudo medicinalis. J. Neurophysiol. *27*: 229–289 (1964).

COOK, P. M.: Observations on giant fibers of the nervous system of Locusta migratoria. Quart. J. Micr. Sci. *92*: 297–305 (1951).

COONFIELD, B. R.: The peripheral nervous system of earthworms. J. comp. Neurol. *55*: 7–17 (1932).

CORNING, W. C. and JOHN, E. R.: Effect on retention of conditioned response in regenerated planarians. Science *134*: 1363–1365 (1961).

CROZIER, W. J. and AREY, L. B.: Sensory reactions of Chromodoris zebra. J. exp. Zool. *29*: 261–310 (1919).

CUÉNOT, L.: Études morphologiques sur les Echinodermes. Arch. Biol. *11*: 313–678 (1891).

DADE, H. A.: Anatomy and dissection of the honeybee (Bee Research Ass., London 1962).

DANTZIG, T.: Number. The language of science. 4th ed. (Macmillan, New York 1954).

DAWSON, A. B.: The intermuscular cells in the earthworm. J. comp. Neurol. *32*: 155–171 (1920).

DECHANT, E.: Beitrag zur Kenntnis des peripheren Nervensystems des Regenwurmes. Arb. zool. Inst. Wien *16*: 361–382 (1906).

DEINEKA, D.: Das Nervensystem von Ascaris. Z. wiss. Zool. *89*: 242–307 (1908).

DELAGE, Y. et HÉROUARD, E.: Traité de zoologie concrète. II, III, V, VII (Paris 1897 to 1903).

DELSMAN, H. C.: Der Ursprung der Vertebraten. Eine neue Theorie. Mitt. zool. Stn. Neapel, *20*: 647–710 (1910–1913).

DELSMAN, H. C.: The ancestry of vertebrates (Visser, Weltevreden, Java 1922).

DELSMAN, H. C.: The origin of vertebrates. Amer. J. Sci. *8*: 151–158 (1924).

DERENYI, G. S.: Observations on neurofibrils in the living nervous tissue of the lobster (Homarus americanus). J. comp. Neurol. *48*: 441–457 (1929).

DIETL, J.: Untersuchungen über die Organisation des Gehirns wirbelloser Thiere (Cephalopoden, Tethys). S.-B. Akad. Wiss. Wien, Abt. 1, *77*: 481–533 (1878).

DIJKGRAAF, S.: Die Sinneswelt der Fledermäuse. Experientia *2*: 438–448 (1946).

DOHRN, A.: Der Ursprung der Wirbelthiere und das Prinzip des Funktionswechsels. (Engelmann, Leipzig 1875).

DOHRN, A.: Studien zur Urgeschichte des Wirbelthierkörpers. Mitt. zool. Stn. Neapel *3*: 252–279 (1882); *4*: 172–189 (1883); *6*: 1–92 (1886).

DUJARDIN, F.: Mémoires sur le système nerveux des insectes. Ann. Sci. nat. *14* (ser. 3): 195–205 (1850).

EDINGER, L.: Einführung in die Lehre vom Bau und den Verrichtungen des Nervensystems (Vogel, Leipzig 1912).

EGGERS, F.: Die mutmassliche Funktion des *Johnstonschen* Sinnesorgans bei Gyrinus. Zool. Anz. *68*: 184–192 (1926).

EMERSON, A. E.: Populations of social insects. Ecological Monogr. *9*: 287–300 (1930).

ESCH, H.; ESCH, I. and KERR, W. E.: Sound: An element common to communication of stingless bees and to dances of the honey bee. Science *149*: 320–321 (1965).

EXNER, S.: Die Physiologie der facettierten Augen von Krebsen und Insekten (Deuticke, Leipzig und Wien 1891).

FAIVRE, E.: Recherches sur les propriétés et les fonctions des nerfs chez un insecte, le Dytiscus marginalis. Ann. Sci. nat. zool. 4. sér. *17*: 329–361 (1862).

FARRELL, S. and KUHLENBECK, H.: Preliminary computation of the number of cellular elements in some insect brains. Anat. Rec. *148*: 369–370 (1964).

FEDOROW, B.: Zur Anatomie des Nervensystems von Peripatus. II. Das Nervensystem des vorderen Körperendes und seine Metamerie. Zool. Jahrb. Abt. Anat. Ontog. *50*: 279–322 (1929).

FERNÁNDEZ-MORÁN, H.: Fine structure of the light receptors in the compound eyes of insects. Exp. Cell Res. Suppl. *5*: 586–644 (1958).

FERRIS, G. F.: The contradictions of the insect head. Microentomol. Stanford *12*: 59–64 (1947).

FEYEL, TH.: Recherches histologiques sur Nectonema agile verr. Arch. Anat. micr. *32*: 197–234 (1936).

FLÖGEL, J. H. L.: Über den einheitlichen Bau des Gehirns in den verschiedenen Insektenordnungen. Z. wiss. Zool. *30* (Suppl.): 550–592 (1878).

FONTAINE, A. R.: Neurosecretion in the Ophiurid Ophiopolis aculeata. Science *138*: 908–909 (1962).

FOREL, A.: Das Sinnesleben der Insekten (Reinhardt, München 1910).

FOREL, A.: Les fourmis de la Suisse. 2. éd. (Imprimerie Coopérat., La Chaux-de-Fonds 1920).

FOREL, A.: Le monde social des fourmis du globe, comparé à celui de l'homme. 5 vols. (Kundig, Genève 1921–1923).

FORTUYN, DROOGLEVER, A. B.: Die Leitungsbahnen im Nervensystem der Wirbellosen (Bohn, Haarlem 1920).

FRISCH, K. VON: Bees, their vision, chemical senses, and language (Cornell University Press, Ithaca, N.Y. 1950).

FRISCH, K. VON: The dancing bees (Harcourt, Brace Co., New York n.d., after 1953).

FROST, S.W.: Insect life and insect natural history. 2nd ed. (Dover, New York 1959).

GABE, M.: Particularités histologiques des cellules neuro-sécrétrices chez quelques Lamellibranches. C.R. Acad. Sci. (Paris) 240: 1810–1812 (1955).

GALAMBOS, R. and GRIFFIN, D.R.: The supersonic cries of bats. Anat. Rec. Suppl. 78: 95–96 (1940).

GARSTANG, W.: Preliminary note on a new theory of the phylogeny of the Chordata. Zool. Anz. 17: 122–125 (1894).

GARSTANG, W.: The morphology of the tunicata, and its bearings on the phylogeny of the Chordata. Quart. J. micr. Sci. 72: 51–187 (1929).

GASKELL, W.H.: Über den Ursprung der Wirbelthiere. Anat. Anz. 13: 503–512 (1897).

GASKELL, W.H.: On the origin of vertebrates (Longmans, Green & Co., London and New York 1908).

GEGENBAUR, C.: Vergleichende Anatomie der Wirbeltiere mit Berücksichtigung der Wirbellosen. 2 vols. (Engelmann, Leipzig 1898, 1901).

GEWERZHAGEN, A.: Beiträge zur Kenntnis der Bryozoen. I. Das Nervensystem von Cristatella mucedo Cuv. Z. wiss. Zool. 107: 309–345 (1913).

GOETSCH, W.: Vergleichende Biologie der Insektenstaaten (Becker und Erler, Leipzig 1940).

GOLDSCHMIDT, R.: Das Nervensystem von Ascaris lumbricoides und megalocephala. Ein Versuch, in den Aufbau eines einfachen Nervensystems einzudringen. Z. wiss. Zool. 90: 73–136 (1908). II. Ibid. 92: 306–357 (1909).

GOLDSCHMIDT, R.: Das Nervensystem von Ascaris lumbricoides und megalocephala. Ein Versuch, in den Aufbau eines einfachen Nervensystems einzudringen. III. Teil. Festschr. z. 60. Geburtstag R. Hertwigs. 2: 253–354 (Fischer, Jena 1910).

GOOSSEN, H.: Untersuchungen an Gehirnen verschieden grosser, jeweils verwandter Coleopteren- und Hymenopteren-Arten. Zool. Jb. Abt. Allg. Zool. Physiol. Tiere. 62: 1–64 (1951).

GOTTLIEB, K.: Über das Gehirn des Skorpions. Z. wiss. Zool. 127: 185–243 (1926).

GREENBERG, M.J.: Ancestors, embryos, and symmetry. System. Zool. 8: 212–221 (1959).

GREGORY, R.L.: The brain as an engineering problem. p. 303–330. in: Current problems in animal behavior; THORPE, W.H., and ZANGWILL, O.L. eds. (Cambridge University Press, 1961).

GRIFFIN, D.R.: Echolocation by blind men, bats, and radar. Science 100: 589–590 (1944).

GRIFFIN, D.R.: Sensory physiology and the orientation of animals. Am. Scientist 41: 209–244, and 281 (1953).

GRIFFIN, D.R.: Listening in the dark. The acoustic orientation of bats and men (Yale U. Press, New Haven 1958).

GRIFFIN, D.R.: Echoes of bats and men. Seeing with sound waves (Anchor Books, Doubleday, New York 1959).

GROBBEN, K.: CLAUS, Lehrbuch der Zoologie (Elwert, Marburg 1905).

GROBBEN, K.: Theoretische Erörterungen betreffend die phylogenetische Ableitung der Echinodermen. S.-B. Akad. Wiss. math.-nat. Kl. *132*: 263–290 (1923–1924).

GROŠELJ, P.: Untersuchungen über das Nervensystem der Aktinien. Arb. zool. Inst. Wien: *17*: 269–308 (1909).

HADENFELDT, D.: Das Nervensystem von Stylochoplana maculata und Notoplana atomata. Z. wiss. Zool. *133*: 586–638 (1929).

HADŽI, J.: Über das Nervensystem von Hydra. Arb. zool. Inst. Wien-Triest *17*: 225–268 (1909).

HADŽI, J.: The evolution of the Metazoa (Macmillan, New York 1963).

HAGIWARA, S.: Nervous activities of the heart in Crustacea. Ergebn. Biol. *24*: 287–311 (1961).

HALLER, B.: Lehrbuch der vergleichenden Anatomie (Fischer, Jena 1904).

HALLER, B.: Über das Zentralnervensystem des Skorpions und der Spinnen. Arch. mikr. Anat. *79*: 504–524 (1913).

HAMA, K.: Some observations on the fine structure of the giant nerve fibers of the earthworm, Eisenia foetida. J. biophys. biochem. Cytol. *6*: 61–66 (1959).

HANSON, E. D.: On the origin of the Eumetazoa. System. Zool. *7*: 16–47 (1958).

HANSTRÖM, B.: Comparison between the brains of the newly hatched larva and the imago in Pieris brassicae. Ent. Tidskr. *46*: 43–52 (1925).

HANSTRÖM, B.: The olfactory centers in Crustaceans. J. comp. Neurol. *38*: 221–250 (1925).

HANSTRÖM, B.: Untersuchungen über die relative Grösse der Gehirnzentren verschiedener Arthropoden unter Berücksichtigung der Lebensweise. Z. mikr.-anat. Forsch. *7*: 135–190 (1926a).

HANSTRÖM, B.: Über den feineren Bau des Nervensystems der tricladen Turbellarien. Acta zool. *7*: 101–121 (1926b).

HANSTRÖM, B.: Vergleichende Anatomie des Nervensystems der wirbellosen Tiere unter Berücksichtigung seiner Funktion (Springer, Berlin 1928).

HANSTRÖM, B.: Neue Untersuchungen über Sinnesorgane und Nervensytem der Crustaceen. Z. Morphol. Ökol. Tiere *23*: 80–236 (1931).

HANSTRÖM, B.: Über das Organ X, eine inkretorische Gehirndrüse der Crustaceen. Psychiat. en Neurol. Bladen *38*: 405–418 (1934); also: Feestbundel C. U. ARIËNS KAPPERS, p. 141–154 (1934).

HANSTRÖM, B.: Bemerkungen über das Gehirn und die Sinnesorgane der Onychophoren. Lunds Universitetets Årskr. N. F., A. 2, *31*: 3–38 (1935).

HANSTRÖM, B.: Die Sinusdrüse und der hormonal bedingte Farbwechsel der Crustaceen. Kungl. Svenska Vetens. Akad. Handl. Ser. 3, Bd. 16, No. *3*: 3–99 (1937a).

HANSTRÖM, B.: Untersuchungen aus dem Öresund XXIII. Vermischte Beobachtungen über die chromatophoraktivierenden Substanzen der Augenstiele der Krustazeen und des Kopfes der Insekten. Lunds Universitetets Årskr. N. F. A. 2 *32*: 3–11 (1937b).

HANSTRÖM, B.: Untersuchungen aus dem Öresund XXVI. Zwei Probleme betreffs der hormonalen Lokalisation im Insektenkopf. Lunds Univ. Årskr. N. F. A. 2, *34*: 3–17 (1938).

HANSTRÖM, B.: Inkretorische Organe, Sinnesorgane und Nervensystem des Kopfes einiger niederer Insektenordnungen. Kungl. Svenska Vetens. Akad. Handl. Ser. 3, Bd. 18, *3*: 3–266 (1940).

HANSTRÖM, B.: Einige Parallelen im Bau und in der Herkunft der inkretorischen Organe der Arthropoden und der Vertebraten. Acta Univ. Lund N.F. *37*: 1–19 (1941).

HANSTRÖM, B.: On the transformation of ordinary nerve cells into neurosecretory cells. K. fysiogr. Sällsk. Lund. Förh. *24,8:* 1–8 (1954).

HANSTRÖM, B.: Neurosecretory pathways in the head of crustaceans, insects and vertebrates. Nature *171*: 72–73 (1963).

HARADA, I.: Das Nervensystem von Bolbosoma turbinella (Dies). Jap. J. Zool. *3*: 161–199 (1931).

HARMS, J.W.: Über ein inkretorisches Cerebralorgan bei Lumbriciden sowie Beschreibung eines verwandten Organs bei drei neuen Lycastis-Arten. Wilhelm Roux' Arch. Entwickl.-Mech. Org. *143*: 332–346 (1947/49).

HARVEY, E.N.: Some recent experiments on the nature of the nerve impulse. J. nerv. ment. Dis. *55*: 503–505 (1922).

HASSENSTEIN, B.: Ommatidienraster und afferente Bewegungsintegration. Z. vergl. Physiol. *33*: 301–326 (1951).

HAVET, J.: Contribution à l'étude de la névroglie des invertébrés. Trab. Lab. Invest. biol. Madrid *14*: 35–85 (1916).

HAVET, J.: Relations de la névroglie avec l'appareil vasculaire chez les invertébrés. C.R. Acad. Sci. (Paris) *162*: 568–570 (1916).

HEIDER, K.: Vom Nervensystem der Ctenophoren. Z. Morphol. Ökol. Tiere *9*: 638–678 (1927).

HENRY, L.M.: The nervous system and the segmentation of the head in the annulata. V. Onychophora. VI. Chilopoda. VII. Insecta. Microentomol. Stanford *13*: 27–48 (1948).

HERRICK, C.J.: Neurological foundations of animal behavior (Holt, New York 1924).

HERRICK, C.J.: An introduction to neurology, 5th ed. (Saunders, Philadelphia 1931).

HERTWECK, H.: Anatomie und Variabilität des Nervensystems und der Sinnesorgane von Drosophila melanogaster (Meigen). Z. wiss. Zool. *139*: 559–663 (1931).

HERTWIG, O.: Das Nervensystem und die Sinnesorgane der Medusen (Vogel, Leipzig 1878).

HERTWIG, O. und HERTWIG, R.: Über das Nervensystem und die Sinnesorgane der Medusen. Jena. Z. Naturw. *11*: 355–374 (1877).

HERTWIG, O. und HERTWIG, R.: Die Aktinien anatomisch und histologisch mit besonderer Berücksichtigung des Nervensystems untersucht. Jena. Z. Naturw. *13*: 457–640 (1879); *14*: 39–82 (1880).

HERTWIG, R.: Lehrbuch der Zoologie. 10. Aufl.; 15. Aufl. (Fischer, Jena 1912, 1931).

HERTZ, M.: Über figurale Intensitäten und Qualitäten in der optischen Wahrnehmung der Biene. Biol. Zbl. *53*: 10–40 (1933).

HERTZ, M.: Zur Physiologie des Formen- und Bewegungssehens. Z. vergl. Physiol. *20*: 430–449; *21*: 579–603; 604–615 (1934).

HESS, A.: The fine structure of nerve cells and fibers, neuroglia, and sheaths of the ganglion chain in the cockroach (Periplaneta americana). J. biophys. biochem. Cytol. *4*: 731–742 (1958).

HESSE, R.: Das Sehen der niederen Tiere (Fischer, Jena 1908).

HICKSON, S.J.: The eye and optic tracts in insects. Quart. J. micr. Sci. *25*: 215–251 (1885).

HILLIG, R.: Das Nervensystem von Sepia officinalis L. Z. wiss. Zool. *101*: 736–800 (1912).

HILTON, WM. A.: The structure of the nerve cells of an insect. J. comp. Neurol. *21*: 373–381 (1911a).

HILTON, WM. A.: Some remarks on the motor and sensory tracts of insects. J. comp. Neurol. *21*: 383–395 (1911b).

HILTON, WM. A.: The nervous system of Pycnogonids. J. comp. Neurol. *26*: 463–473 (1916).

HILTON, WM. A.: The central nervous system of simple Crustacea. J. comp. Neurol. *28*: 429–440 (1917).

HILTON, WM. A.: The nervous system of Phoronida. J. comp. Neurol. *34*: 381–389 (1922).

HILTON, WM. A.: Afferent and efferent pathways in an abdominal segment of an insect. J. comp. Neurol. *36*: 299–308 (1923/24).

HÖRSTADIUS, S.: Über die Entwicklung von Astropecten aranciacus L. Publ. Staz. zool. Napoli *17*: 221–312 (1939).

HOLMGREN, N.: Zur vergleichenden Anatomie des Gehirns von Polychaeten, Onychophoren, Xiphosuren, Arachniden, Crustaceen, Myriapoden und Insekten. K. Svenska Vetenskapsakad. Handl. *56*: 3–303 (1916).

HOLST, E. v.: Untersuchungen über die Funktionen des Zentralnervensystems beim Regenwurm (Lumbricus terrestris L. = L. herculeus Sav.) Zool. Jb. allg. Zool. Physiol. *51*: 547–588 (1932).

HOLST, E. v.: Weitere Versuche zum nervösen Mechanismus der Bewegung beim Regenwurm (Lumbricus terr. L.). Zool. Jb. allg. Zool. Physiol. *53*: 67–100 (1933).

HOLSTE, G.: Das Nervensystem von Dytiscus marginalis. Z. wiss. Zool. *96*: 419–476 (1910).

HOLSTE, G.: Das Gehirn von Dytiscus marginalis. Z. wiss. Zool. *120*: 251–290 (1923).

HORRIDGE, G. A.: The nervous system of the ephyra larva of Aurelia aurita. Quart. J. micr. Sci. *97*: 59–74 (1956).

HUBER, F.: Sitz und Bedeutung nervöser Zentren für Instinkthandlungen bei Männchen des Gryllus campestris. Z. Tierpsychol. *12*: 12–48 (1955).

HUBER, F.: Über die Funktion der Pilzkörper beim Gesang der Keulenheuschrecke Gomphocerus rufus. Naturwissenschaften *43*: 566–567 (1955).

HUBER, F.: Auslösung von Bewegungsmustern durch elektrische Reizung des Oberschlundganglions bei Orthopteren. Verh. dtsch. zool. Ges., Zool. Anz. Suppl. *23*: 248–269 (1959).

HUBER, F.: Untersuchungen über die Funktion des Zentralnervensystems und insbesondere des Gehirnes bei der Fortbewegung und der Lauterzeugung der Grillen. Z. vergl. Physiol. *44*: 60–132 (1960).

HUBER, F.: Vergleichende Physiologie der Nervensysteme von Evertebraten. Fortschr. Zool. *15*: 164–213 (1963).

HUBRECHT, A. A.W.: Zur Anatomie und Physiologie des Nervensystems der Nemertinen. Verh. K. Akad. Wet. Amsterdam *20*: 1–47 (1880).

HUBRECHT, A. A.W.: On the ancestral form of the Chordata. Quart. J. micr. Sci. *23*: 349–368 (1883).

HUBRECHT, A. A.W.: The relation of the Nemertea to the Vertebrata. Quart. J. micr. Sci. *27*: 605–644 (1887).

HUGHES, G. M.: Giant fibers in dragonfly nymphs. Nature, Lond. *171*: 87–88 (1953).

HUGHES, G. M. and WIERSMA, C. A. G.: Neuronal pathways and synaptic connexions in the abdominal cord of the crayfish. J. exp. Biol. *37*: 291–307 (1960).

HYMAN, L. H.: The invertebrates. Vol. I: Protozoa through Ctenophora (McGraw-Hill, New York 1940).

HYMAN, L. H.: The invertebrates. Vol. II: Platyhelminthes and Rhynchocoela (McGraw-Hill, New York 1951).

HYMAN, L. H.: The invertebrates. Vol. III: Acanthocephala, Aschelminthes, and Entoprocta (McGraw-Hill, New York 1951).

HYMAN, L. H.: The invertebrates. Vol. IV: Echinodermata (McGraw-Hill, New York 1955).

HYMAN, L. H.: The invertebrates. Vol. V: smaller Coelomate groups. McGraw-Hill, New York 1959).

IVANOV, A. V.: The nervous system of Pogonophora (Russian, with English summary). Zool. Zhur. 37: 1682–1693 (1958).

JACOBS, W.: Verhaltensbiologische Studien an Feldheuschrecken (Parey, Berlin und Hamburg 1953).

JACOBSOHN-LASK, L.: Die Kreuzung der Nervenbahnen und die bilaterale Symmetrie des tierischen Körpers. Abh. Neurol. Psychiat. Psychol. H. 26 (Karger, Berlin 1924).

JACOBSOHN-LASK, L.: Warum kreuzen sich die Leitungsbahnen im Zentralnervensystem? (eine Ergänzung). Z. ges. Neurol. Psychiat. 112: 317–330 (1928).

JANDER, R.: Die optische Richtungsorientierung der roten Waldameise (Formica rufa L.). Z. vergl. Physiol. 40: 162–238 (1957).

JANDER, R.: Menotaxis und Winkeltransponieren bei Köcherfliegen Trichoptera. Z. vergl. Physiol. 48: 680–686 (1960).

JENNINGS, H. S.: The behavior of the lower organisms (Columbia University Press, New York 1906).

JOHNSON, B. and BOWERS, B.: Transport of neurohormones from the corpora cardiaca of insects. Science 141: 264–266 (1963).

JOHNSON, G. E.: Giant nerve fibers in crustaceans with special reference to cambarus and palaemonetes. J. comp. Neurol. 36: 323–372 (1924).

JONES, W. C.: Is there a nervous system in sponges? Biol. Rev. 37: 1–50 (1962).

JONESCU, C. N.: Vergleichende Untersuchungen über das Gehirn der Honigbiene. Jena. Z. Naturw. 45: 111–180 (1909).

KALMUS, H.: Animals as mathematicians. Nature 202: 1156–1160 (1964).

KAPPERS, C. U. A.: The evolution of the nervous system in invertebrates, vertebrates and man (Bohn, Haarlem 1929).

KEIM, W.: Das Nervensystem von Astacus fluviatilis (Potamobius astacus L.). Ein Beitrag zur Morphologie der Dekapoden. Z. wiss. Zool. 113: 485–545 (1915).

KELLOGG, W. N.: Auditory perception of submerged objects by porpoises. J. acoust. Soc. of Amer. 31: 1–6 (1959).

KENYON, F. C.: The brain of the bee. J. comp. Neurol. 6: 133–210 (1896).

KEPNER, W. A.: Animals looking into the future (Macmillan, New York 1925).

KILIAN, R.: Zur Morphologie und Systematik der Gigantorhynchidae (Acantocephala). Z. wiss. Zool. 141: 246–345 (1932).

KLEINENBERG, N.: Hydra. Eine anatomisch-entwicklungsgeschichtliche Untersuchung (Engelmann, Leipzig 1872).

KORSCHELT, E. und HEIDER, K.: Lehrbuch der vergleichenden Entwicklungsgeschichte der wirbellosen Tiere. 7 vols. (Fischer, Jena 1890–1910).

KOWALEWSKY, A.: Weitere Studien über die Entwicklung der einfachen Ascidien. Arch. micr. Anat. 7: 101–130 (1871).

KOWALEWSKY, A.: Weitere Studien über die Entwicklungsgeschichte des Amphioxus lanc. nebst einem Beitrag zur Homologie des Nervensystems der Würmer und Wirbelthiere. Arch. micr. Anat. *13*: 181–204 (1877).

KUFFLER, S.W. and POTTER, D.D.: Glia in the leech central nervous system: Physiological properties and neuron-glia relationships. J. Neurophysiol. *27*: 290–320 (1964).

KUHLENBECK, H.: Vorlesungen über das Zentralnervensystem der Wirbeltiere (Fischer, Jena 1927).

KUHLENBECK, H.: Brain and consciousness. Some prolegomena to an approach of the Problem (Karger, Basel/New York 1957).

KUHLENBECK, H.: Schopenhauers Bedeutung für die Neurologie (Zum 100. Todestag des Philosophen). Nervenarzt *32*: 177–182 (1961).

KUHLENBECK, H.: Mind and matter. An appraisal of their significance for neurological theory (Karger, Basel/New York 1961).

KUHLENBECK, H.: Gehirn und Intelligenz. Confinia neurol. *25*: 35–62 (1965).

KUHLENBECK, H. and M.WIENER KIRBER: Neuroectodermal and other cells in mouse-brain tissue cultures. Confin. neurol. *19*: 59–104 (1959.

KUHLENBECK, H. and M.WIENER KIRBER: Some observations on neurotropic effects ˜of vesicular stomatitis virus in the mouse brain. Their relationship to some general problems of biology and virologic neurology. Confin. neurol. *22*: 65–120 (1962).

KÜHNE, H.: Die neurosekretorischen Zellen und der retrocerebrale neuro-endokrine Komplex von Spinnen (Araneae, Labidognatha) unter Berücksichtigung einiger histologisch erkennbarer Veränderungen während des postembryonalen Lebenslaufes. Zool. Jb. Abt. Anat. *77*: 527–600 (1959).

LANDOIS, H. und LANDOIS, L.: Über die numerische Entwicklung der histologischen Elemente des Insectenkörpers. Z. wiss. Zool. *15*: 307–327 (1865).

LANG, A.: Untersuchungen zur vergleichenden Anatomie und Histologie des Nervensystems der Platyhelminthen. I. Das Nervensystem der marinen Dendrocoelen. Mitt. zool. Stn. Neapel *1*: 459–488 (1879).

LANG, A.: Untersuchungen zur vergleichenden Anatomie und Histologie des Nervensystems der Platyhelminthen. Mitt. zool. Stn. Neapel *3*: 76–95 (1881a).

LANG, A.: Der Bau von Gunda segmentata und die Verwandtschaft der Platyhelminthen mit Coelenteraten und Hirudineen. Mitt. zool. Stn. Neapel *3*: 187–250 (1881b).

LANG, A.: Lehrbuch (Handbuch, in 2nd ed.) der vergleichenden Anatomie der wirbellosen Tiere. 1st and 2nd ed. (G.Fischer, Jena 1888–1901).

LASHLEY, K.S.: Experimental analysis of behavior. Psychol. Rev. *45*: 445–471 (1938).

LENDER, T. and KLEIN, N.: Mise en évidence de cellules sécrétrices dans le cerveau de la Planaire Polycelis nigra. Variation de leur nombre au cours de la régénération postérieure. C. R. Acad. Sci. (Paris) *253*: 331–333 (1961).

LENHOFF, H. M.: Hydra. Science *134*: 1989–1990 (1961).

LENHOSSEK, M. VON: Ursprung, Verlauf und Endigung der sensiblen Nervenfasern bei Lumbricus. Arch. mikr. Anat. *39*: 102–136 (1892).

LEYDIG, F.: Lehrbuch der Histologie des Menschen und der Thiere (Meidinger, Frankfurt a. M. 1857).

LIBBY, J.L.: The nervous system of certain abdominal segments of the Cecropia larva. Ann. Entomol. Soc. Amer. *52*: 469–480 (1959).

LINDAUER, M.: Communication among social bees (Harvard University Press, Cambridge 1961).

LORENZO, A. I. DE: Electron microscopy of electrical synapses in the crayfish (Abstract). Biol. Bull. *119*: 325 (1960).

LORLEBERG, O.: Untersuchungen über den feineren Bau des Nervensystems der Ascidien. Z. wiss. Zool. *88*: 212–248 (1907).

LUND, E. E.: The neuromotor system of Oxytricha. J. Morph. *58*: 257–277 (1935).

MACKIE, G. O.: The structure of the nervous system in Velella. Quart. J. micr. Sci. *101*: 119–131 (1960).

MAGNAN, A.: Le vol des insectes. La locomotion chez les animaux. Vol. 1 (Hermann, Paris 1934).

MANTON, S. M.: Studies on the Onychophora VII. The early embryonic stages of Peripatopsis and some general considerations concerning the morphology and phylogeny of the arthropoda. Philos. Trans. (B) *233*: 483–580 (1949).

MARCUS, E.: Beobachtungen und Versuche an lebenden Meeresbryozoen. Zool. Jahrb. (Syst.) *52*: 1–102 (1926).

MARCUS, E.: Beobachtungen und Versuche an lebenden Süsswasserbryozoen. Zool. Jahrb. (Syst.) *52*: 279–350 (1926).

MARCUS, E.: Zur vergleichenden Anatomie und Histologie der Tardigraden. Zool. Jb. Abt. allg. Zool. *45*: 99–158 (1928).

MARTINI, E.: Studien über die Konstanz histologischer Elemente. I. Oikopleura longicauda. Z. wiss. Zool. *92*: 563–626 (1909).

MARTINI, E.: Studien über die Konstanz histologischer Elemente. III. Hydatina senta. Z. wiss. Zool. *102*: 425–645 (1912).

MAYER, A. G.: Rhythmical pulsations in Scyphomedusae (Carnegie Inst. of Washington Publ. No. 47, Washington, D. C. 1906; Papers from the Tortugas Laboratory, Carnegie Inst. Publ. No. 102: 115–131, Washington, D. C. 1908).

MAYNARD, D. M.: Circulation and heart function. In: Physiol. of crustacea, T. H. WATERMAN, ed., p. 161–226 (Academic Press, New York 1960).

McALEAR, J. H.; MILBURN, N. S. and CHAPMAN, G. B.: The fine structure of Schwann cells, nodes of Ranvier and Schmitt-Lanterman incisures in the central nervous system of the crab, Cancer inoratus. J. ultrastruct. Res. *2*: 171–176 (1958).

McCRACKEN, I.: The egg-laying apparatus in the silkworm (Bombyx mori) as a reflex apparatus. J. comp. Neurol. *17*: 262–285 (1907).

McCONNELL, C. H.: Development of the ectodermal nerve net in the buds of Hydra. Quant. J. micr. Sci. *75*: 495–509 (1932).

McCONNELL, J. V.: Memory transfer through cannibalism in planarians. J. Neuropsychiat. *3* (Suppl. 1): (S) 42 – (S) 48 (1962).

METSCHNIKOFF, E.: Embryologische Studien an Medusen (Holder, Wien 1887).

MEYER, R.: Untersuchungen über den feineren Bau des Nervensystems der Asteriden (Asterias rubens). Z. wiss. Zool. *81*: 96–144 (1906).

MILL, P. J.: The structure of the abdominal nervous system in Aeschnid nymphs. J. comp. Neurol. *122*: 157–171 (1964).

MISKOLCZY, D.: Warum kreuzen sich die zentralen Bahnen des Nervensystems? Z. Anat. Entwickl.-Gesch. *81*: 641–647 (1926).

MITTELSTAEDT, H.: Prey capture in mantids. In: Recent Adv. in Invert. Physiol., B. T. SCHEER ed., p. 51–71 (University of Oregon Publ., Eugene 1957).

MITTELSTAEDT, H.: Control systems of orientation in insects. Ann. Rev. entomol. *7*: 177–198 (1962).

MONTI, R.: Sur les relations mutuelles entre les éléments dans le système nerveux central des insectes. Arch. Anat. micr. *15*: 349–433 (1913).

MOODY, M.F.: Evidence for the intraocular discrimination of vertically and horizontally polarized light by Octopus. J. exp. Biol. *39*: 21–30 (1962).

MOORE, A.R.: Chemical differentiation of the central nervous system in invertebrates. Proc. nat. Acad. Sci. (Wash.) *3*: 598–602 (1917).

MÜLLER, JOHANNES: Zur vergleichenden Physiologie des Gesichtssinnes desMenschen und der Thiere, nebst einem Versuch über die Bewegungen der Augen und über den menschlichen Blick (Cnobloch, Leipzig 1826).

NABERT, A.: Die Corpora allata der Insekten. Z. wiss. Zool. *104*: 181–358 (1913).

NACHTWEY, R.: Untersuchungen über Keimbahn, Organogenese und Anatomie von Asplanchna. Z. wiss. Zool. *126*: 239–492 (1925).

NEAL, H.V. and RAND, H.W.: Comparative anatomy (Blakiston, Philadelphia 1936).

NESBITT, H.H.J.: The comparative morphological study of the nervous system of the Orthoptera and related orders. Ann. entomol. Soc. Amer. *34*: 51–81 (1941).

NICOL, J.A.C.: The giant axons of annelids. Quart. Rev. Biol. *23*: 291–323 (1948).

NICOLS, D.: The histology and activities of the tube feet of Antedon bifida. Quart. J. micr. Sci. *101*: 105–117 (1960).

NOLTE, A.: Ultrastruktur des 'Neurosekretmantels' des Nervus labialis medius von Planorbarius corneus L. (Basommatophora). Naturwissenschaften *51*: 148 (1964).

NOLTE, A. und KUHLMANN, D.: Histologie und Sekretion der Cerebraldrüse adulter Stylommatophoren (Gastropoda). Z. f. Zellforsch. *63*: 550–567 (1964).

NOVIKOFF, M.: Das Prinzip der Analogie und die vergleichende Anatomie. Eine Studie über die Gesetzmässigkeit in der Biologie (Fischer, Jena 1930).

OGAWA, F.: Nerve cells in earthworm (Abstract). Nature *134*: 666 (1934).

OGAWA, F.: The nervous system of earthworm (Pheretima communissima) in different ages. Science Rep. Tôhoku Univ. (4) *13*: 395–488 (1939).

ORLOV, J.: Die Innervation des Darmes der Insekten. Z. wiss. Zool. *122*: 425–502 (1924).

ORLOW, J.: Über den histologischen Bau des Mundmagennervensystems der Insekten. Z. mikr. Anat. Forsch. (Jb. Morph. mikr. Anat., 2. Abt.) *2*: 39–110 (1925).

ORTMANN, R.: Neurosecretion. Handb. of Physiol., J. FIELD *et al.* eds.; Neurophysiology II, chapter 40, p.1039–1065 (American Physiological Society, Washington 1960).

PANDAZIS, G.: Über die relative verschiedenartige Ausbildung der Gehirnzentren bei biologisch verschiedenen Ameisenarten. Z. Morphol. Ökol. Tiere *18*: 114–169 (1930).

PANTIN, C.F.A.: The elementary nervous system. Proc. roy. Soc. B *140*: 147–168 (1952).

PARKER, G.H.: The elementary nervous system (Lippincott, Philadelphia 1919).

PATTEN, WM.: The evolution of the vertebrates and their kin (Blakiston, Philadelphia 1912).

PÉREZ, C.: Contributions à l'étude des métamorphoses. Thèse Fac. Sci. (Paris) Sér. A. *417*: 195–427 (1902).

PÉREZ, C.: Recherches histologiques sur la métamorphose des Muscides (Calliphora erythrocephala Mg.). Arch. Zool. exp. gén. *4*: 1–274 (1910).

PFEFFERKORN, A.: Das Nervensystem der Octopoden. Z. wiss. Zool. *114*: 425–531 (1915).

PIERCE, G.W.: The songs of insects (Harvard University Press, Cambridge 1949).

PIÉRON, H.: Contribution à la psychologie du poulpe. L'acquisition d'habitudes. Bull. Inst. gén. psychol. *11*: 111–119 (1911).

PIETSCHKER, H.: Das Gehirn der Ameise. Jena. Z. Naturw. *47*: 43–114 (1911).

PIPA, R.L.; COOK, E.F. and RICHARDS, A.G.: Studies on the hexapod nervous system. I. The peripheral distribution of the thoracic nerves of the adult cockroach, Periplaneta americana. Ann. ent. Soc. Amer. *52*: 695–710 (1959a).

PIPA, R.L; COOK, E.F. and RICHARDS, A.G.: Studies on the hexapod nervous system. II. The histology of the thoracic ganglia of the adult cockroach, Periplaneta americana. J. comp. Neurol. *113*: 401–434 (1959b).

PLATE, L.: Allgemeine Zoologie und Abstammungslehre. Bd. I (Fischer, Jena 1922).

POLYAK, S.: The vertebrate visual system (KLÜVER, H., ed.; Un. of Chicago Press 1957).

PORTMANN, A.: Die Kriechbewegungen von Aiptasia carnea. Ein Beitrag zur Kenntnis der neuromuskularen Organisation der Aktinien. Z. vergl. Physiol. *4*: 659–667 (1926).

PORTMANN, A.: New paths in biology. World Perspectives, vol. 30 (Harper and Row, New York 1964).

POWER, M.E.: The brain of Drosophila melanogaster. J. Morph. *72*: 517–559 (1943).

POWER, M.E.: The antennal centers and their connections within the brain of Drosophila melanogaster. J. comp. Neurol. *85*: 485–517 (1946).

POWER, M.E.: The thoracico-abdominal nervous system of an adult insect, Drosophila melanogaster. J. comp. Neurol. *88*: 347–409 (1948).

PRINGLE, J.W.S.: Insect flight (Cambridge University Press, 1957).

PROSSER, C.L.: The physiology of nervous systems of invertebrate animals. Physiol. Rev. *26*: 337–382 (1946).

PUMPHREY, R.J. and RAWDON-SMITH, A.F.: Synaptic transmission of nervous impulses through the last abdominal ganglion of the cockroach (Periplaneta americana). J. exp. Zool. *108*: 243–262 (1937).

PUMPHREY, R.J. and YOUNG, J.Z.: The rates of conduction of nerve fibres of various diameters in cephalopods. J. exp. Biol. *15*: 452–466 (1938).

RABL-RÜCKHARD, H.: Studien über Insektengehirne. Arch. Anat. Physiol. *42*: 480–499 (1875).

RÁDL, E.: Neue Lehre vom zentralen Nervensystem (Engelmann, Leipzig 1912).

RATZERDORFER, C.: Volumetric indices for the parts of the insect brain. A comparative study in cerebralization of insects. J. New York entomol. Soc. *40*: 129–152 (1952).

REICHARDT, W.: Nervöse Verarbeitung optischer Nachrichten im Facettenauge. Jb. Max-Planck-Ges.: 97–126 (1962).

REISINGER, E.: Untersuchungen am Nervensystem der Bothrioplana semperi Braun. (Zugleich ein Beitrag zur Technik der vitalen Färbung und zur vergleichenden Anatomie des Plathelminthennervensystems.) Z. Morphol. Ökol. Tiere *5*: 119–149 (1925).

REMANE, A.: Morphologie und Verwandtschaftsbeziehungen der aberranten Gastrotrichen. I. Z. Morphol. Ökol. Tiere *5*: 625–754 (1927).

RETZIUS, G.: Zur Kenntnis des Nervensystems der Krustazeen. Biol. Unters. N. F. 1 (Stockholm 1890).

RETZIUS, G.: Zur Kenntnis des zentralen Nervensystems der Würmer. Biol. Unters. N. F. 2 (Stockholm 1891).

RETZIUS, G.: Das Nervensystem der Lumbricinen. Biol. Unters. N. F. 3 (Stockholm 1892).

ROBERTS, M.B.V.: The giant fiber reflex of the earthworm, Lumbricus terrestris L. I. The rapid response. II. Fatigue. J. Exp. Biol. *39*: 219–237 (1962).

ROBERTSON, J.D.: Ultrastructure of excitable membranes and the crayfish median giant synapse. Ann. N.Y. Acad. Sci. *94*: 339–389 (1961).

ROEDER, K. D.: Organization of the ascending giant fiber system in the cockroach (Periplaneta americana). J. exp. Zool. *108*: 243–262 (1948).

ROEDER, K. D.: The nervous system. Ann. Rev. ent. *3*: 1–18 (1958).

ROEDER, K. D.: Nerve cells and insect behavior (Harvard University Press, Cambridge, Mass. 1963).

RÖHNISCH, S.: Das neuroendokrine System der Cerebralganglien von Planorbarius corneus L. (Basommatophora). Naturwissenschaften *51*: 147–148 (1964).

RÖHNISCH, S.: Untersuchungen zur Neurosekretion bei Planorbarius corneus L. (Basommatophora). Z. f. Zellforsch. *63*: 767–798 (1964a).

ROSS, L. S.: Cytology of the large nerve cells of the crayfish (Cambarus). J. comp. Neurol. *34*: 37–71 (1922).

ROTH, L. M. and EISNER, T.: Chemical defenses of arthropods. Ann. Rev. ent. 7: 107–134 (1962).

RUCK, P.: The electrical responses of the dorsal ocelli in cockroaches and grasshoppers. J. Insect Physiol. *1*: 109–123 (1957).

SANCHEZ (SANCHEZ Y SANCHEZ), D.: El sistema nervioso de los hirudineos. Trab. Lab. Invest. biol. Madrid *7*: 31–187 (1909); *10*: 1–143 (1912).

SANCHEZ, D.: Datos para el conocimiento histogénico de los centros ópticos de los insectos. Evolución de algunos elementos retinianos del 'Pieris brassicae L.' Trab. Lab. Invest. biol. Madrid *14*: 189–231 (1916).

SANCHEZ, D.: Sobre la existencia de un aparato tactil en los ojos compuestos de las abejas. Trab. Lab. Invest, biol. Madrid *18*: 207–244 (1920–1921).

SANCHEZ, D.: L'histolyse dans les centres nerveux des insectes. Trav. Lab. Invest. biol. Madrid *21*: 385–422 (1923).

SANCHEZ, D.: Les agents histolysants du système nerveux des insectes. Trav. Lab. Rech. biol. Madrid *25*: 1–39 (1927).

SANCHEZ, D.: Contribution à l'étude de l'origine et de l'évolution de certains types de neuroglie chez les insectes. Trav. Lab. Rech. biol. Madrid *30*: 299–353 (1935).

SANCHEZ, D.: Contribution à la connaissance des centres nerveux des insectes. Nouveaux apports sur la structure du cerveau des abeilles (Apis mellifica). Trab. Inst. Cajal, Madrid *33*: 165–236 (1941).

SCHARRER, B.: Über 'Drüsen-Nervenzellen' im Gehirn von Nereis virens Sars. Zool. Anz. *113*: 297–302 (1936).

SCHARRER, B. (C. J.): The differentiation between neuroglia and connective tissue sheath in the cockroach (Periplaneta americana). J. comp. Neurol. *70*: 77–88 (1939).

SCHARRER, B.: Neurosecretion. II. Neurosecretory cells in the central nervous system of cockroaches. J. comp. Neurol. *74*: 93–108 (1941).

SCHARRER, B.: Neurosecretion. III. The cerebral organ of the nemerteans. J. comp. Neurol. *74*: 109–130 (1941).

SCHARRER, B.: Über neuroendokrine Vorgänge bei Insekten. Pflügers Arch. ges. Physiol. *255*: 154–163 (1952).

SCHARRER, B.: Neurosecretion. XI. The effects of nerve section on the intercerebralis-cardiacum-allatum system of the insect Leucophaea maderae. Biol. Bull. *102*: 261–272 (1952).

SCHARRER, B.: Comparative physiology of invertebrate endocrines. Ann. Rev. Physiol. *15*: 457–472 (1953).

SCHARRER, E.: The capillary bed of the central nervous system of certain invertebrates. Biol. Bull. *87*: 52–58 (1944).

SCHARRER, E. and SCHARRER, B.: Über Drüsen-Nervenzellen und neurosekretorische Organe bei Wirbellosen und Wirbeltieren. Biol. Rev. *12*: 185–216 (1937).

SCHARRER, E. and SCHARRER, B.: Neuroendocrinology (Columbia University Press, New York 1963).

SCHMIDT, H.: Über den Alterstod der Biene. Jena. Z. Naturw. *59*: 343–362 (1923).

SCHMITT, J. B.: The cervicothoracic nervous system of a grasshopper. Smithsonian Inst. Publ. Misc. Coll. *137*: 307–329 (1959).

SCHMITT, J. B.: The comparative anatomy of insect nervous systems. Ann. Rev. entomol. *7*: 137–156 (1962).

SCHNEIDER, K. C.: Histologie von Hydra fusca mit besonderer Berücksichtigung des Nervensystems der Hydropolypen. Arch. mikr. Anat. *35*: 321–379 (1890).

SCHNEIDER, K. C.: Lehrbuch der vergleichenden Histologie (Fischer, Jena 1902).

SCHRADER, K.: Untersuchungen über Normalentwicklung des Gehirns und Gehirn-transplantationen bei der Mehlmotte Ephestia kühniella Zeller nebst einigen Bemerkungen über das Corpus allatum. Biol. Zbl. *58*: 52–90 (1938).

SCHULTZE-RÖBBECKE, G.: Untersuchungen über Lebensdauer, Altern und Tod bei Arthropoden. Zool. Jb. allg. Zool. Physiol. Tiere: 366–394 (1951).

SCHWARZ, H. G.: Studies in the regeneration of central nervous tissues. I. Origin of nerve cells in regenerated cerebral ganglia in the earthworm. J. comp. Neurol. *55*: 545–571 (1932).

SELENKA, E. und GOLDSCHMIDT, R.: Zoologisches Taschenbuch für Studierende zum Gebrauch bei Vorlesungen und praktischen Übungen. 1. Wirbellose (Thieme, Leipzig 1919).

SEMON, R.: Die Entwicklung der Synapta digitata und ihre Bedeutung für die Phylogenie der Echinodermen. Jena. Z. Naturw. *22*: 175–309 (1888).

SEMPER, C.: Die Stammesverwandtschaft der Wirbelthiere und Wirbellosen. Arb. zool.-zootom. Inst. Würzburg *2*: 25–76 (1874).

SILÉN, L.: On the nervous system of Phoronis. Ark. Zool. (2) *6*: 1–40 (1954).

SMITH, J. E.: The motor nervous system of the starfish, Astropecten irregularis (Pennant), with special reference to the innervation of the tube feet and ampullae. Philos. Trans. (B) *234*: 521–558 (1950).

SNODGRASS, R. E.: Principles of insect morphology (McGraw-Hill, New York 1935).

SPANGENBERG, D. B and HAM, R. G.: The epidermal nerve net of Hydra. J. exp. Zool. *143*: 195–200 (1960).

SPITZER, A.: Über die Kreuzung der centralen Nervenbahnen und ihre Beziehungen zur Phylogenese des Wirbeltierkörpers (Deuticke, Leipzig und Wien 1910).

STEINER, J.: Die Functionen des Centralnervensystems und ihre Phylogenese. 3. Abt. Die wirbellosen Thiere (Vieweg, Braunschweig 1898).

STIBITZ, G. R. and LARRIVEE, J. A.: Mathematics and computers (McGraw-Hill, New York 1957).

STOUGH, H. B: Giant fibers of the earthworm. J. comp. Neurol. *40*: 409–463 (1926).

SUGA, N. and KATSUKI, Y.: Central mechanisms of hearing in insects. J. exp. Biol. *38*: 545–558 (1961).

SWAINE, J. M.: The nervous system of the larva of Stenopsis thule Strecker. Can. Ent. *52*: 275–283 (1920).

SZÜTZ, A. VON: Studien über die feinere Beschaffenheit des Nervensystems des Regenwurms. Arch. Zellforsch. *13*: 270–317 (1915).

THOMPSON, C. B.: A comparative study of the brains of three genera of ants, with special reference to the mushroom bodies. J. comp. Neurol. *23*: 515–571 (1913).

THOMPSON, C. B.: The posterior root of the mushroom bodies in the worker of Bombus spec. J. comp. Neurol. *24*: 283–289 (1914).

THOMPSON, C. B.: The brain and the frontal gland of the castes of the 'white ant' Leucotermes flavipes, Kollar. J. comp. Neurol. *26*: 553–603 (1916).

THORE, S.: Beiträge zur Kenntnis der vergleichenden Anatomie des zentralen Nervensystems der dibranchiaten Cephalopoden. Pubbl. Staz. zool. Napoli *17*: 313–506 (1939).

TINBERGEN, N.: The study of instincts (Oxford U. Press 1951).

TONNER, F.: Ein Beitrag zur Anatomie und Physiologie des peripheren Nervensystems von Astacus fluviatilis. Zool. Jb. allg. Zool. Physiol. *53*: 101–152 (1933).

TURNER, C. H.: The homing of ants, an experimental study of ant behavior. J. comp. Neurol. *17*: 367–437 (1907).

TURNER, R. S.: Observations on the central nervous system of Leptoplana acticola. J. comp. Neurol. *85*: 53–65 (1946).

UNGER, H.: Neurohormone bei Seesternen (Marthasterias glacialis). Sympos. biol. hungar. *1*: 203–207 (1960).

VANDEL, A.: Généralités sur les arthropodes. In: Traité de Zoologie, P. GRASSÉ, ed., *6*: 79–158 (Masson, Paris 1949).

VERWORN, M.: Allgemeine Physiologie. Ein Grundriss der Lehre vom Leben. 7. Aufl. (Fischer, Jena 1922).

VIALLANES, H.: Études histologiques et organologiques sur les centres nerveus et les organes des sens des animaux articulés. 2. Le ganglion optique de la libellule (Aeschna maculatissima). Ann. Sci. nat. Sér. 6, *17*: 1–34 (1884).

VIALLANES, M. H.: Le cerveau de la guèpe (Vespa crabro, vespa vulgaris). Ann. Sci. nat. Sér. 7, *2*: 5–100 (1886).

VIALLANES, H.: Le cerveau du criquet (Oedipoda caerulescens et Caloptenus italicus). Ann. Sci. nat. Sér. 7, *4*: 1–120 (1887).

VOLTZENLOGEL, E.: Untersuchungen über den anatomischen und histologischen Bau des Hinterendes von Ascaris megalocephala und Ascaris lumbricoides. Zool. Jb. Abt. Anat. *16*: 491–510 (1902).

VOWLES, D. M.: The structure and connexions of the Corpora pedunculata in bees and ants. Quart. J. micr. Sci. *96*: 239–255 (1955).

VOWLES, D. M.: Neural Mechanisms in insect behavior. p. 5–29. in: Current Problems in Animal Behavior. THORPE, W. H. and ZANGWILL, O. L., eds. (Cambridge University Press, 1961).

WATANABE, A. and GRUNDFEST, H.: Impulse propagation at the septal and commissural junctions of crayfish lateral giant axons. J. gen. Physiol. *45*: 267–308 (1961).

WATERMAN, T. H.: Flight instruments in insects. Am. Scientist *38*: 222–238 (1950).

WELLS, M. J.: The function of the brain of Octopus in tactile discrimination. J. exp. Biol. *34*: 131–142 (1957).

WELLS, M. J.: Centres for tactile and visual learning in the brain of Octopus. J. exp. Biol.: *38*: 811–862 (1961).

WELLS, M. J. and WELLS, J.: Hormonal control of sexual maturity in Octopus. J. exp. Biol. *36*: 1–33 (1959).

WELSH, J. H. and SCHALLEK, W.: Arthropod nervous systems: A review of their structure and function. Physiol. Rev. *26*: 447–478 (1946).

WEYER, F.: Cytologische Untersuchungen am Gehirn alternder Bienen und die Frage nach dem Alterstod. Z. Zellforsch. mikr. Anat. *14*: 1–54 (1931).

WEYER, F.: Über drüsenartige Nervenzellen im Gehirn der Honigbiene, Apis mellifica L. Zool. Anz. *112*: 137–141 (1935).

WHEELER, W. M.: Ants, their structure, development, and behavior (Columbia University Press, New York 1913).

WHEELER, W. M.: Social life among the insects (Columbia University Press, New York 1923).

WHEELER, W. M.: The social insects (Harcourt, Brace, New York 1928).

WIERSMA, C. A. G.: On the number of nerve cells in a crustacean central nervous system. Acta physiol. Pharmacol. neerl. *6*: 135–142 (1957).

WIERSMA, C. A. G.: On the functional connections of single units in the central nervous system of the crayfish, Procambarus clarkii Girard. J. comp. Neurol. *110*: 421–471 (1958).

WIERSMA, C. A. G.: The organization of the arthropod central nervous system. Amer. Zool. *2*: 67–78 (1962).

WIERSMA, C. A. G. and HUGHES, G. M.: On the functional anatomy of neuronal units in the abdominal cord of the crayfish, Procambarus clarkii (Girard). J. comp. Neurol. *116*: 209–228 (1961).

WIGGLESWORTH, V. B.: Principles of insect physiology (Methuen, London 1939).

WIGGLESWORTH, V. B.: The physiology of insect metamorphosis (Cambridge University Press, 1954).

WIGGLESWORTH, V. B.: The histology of the nervous system of an insect. Quart. J. micr. Sci. *100*: 299–315 (1959).

WIGGLESWORTH, V. B.: The nutrition of the central nervous system in the cockroach Periplaneta americana L. J. exper. Biol. *37*: 500–512 (1960).

WILSON, D. M.: The central nervous control of flight in a locust. J. exp. Biol. *36*: 471–490 (1961).

WIRZ, K.: Étude biométrique du système nerveux des céphalopodes. Bull. biol. France et Belgique *93*: 78–117 (1959).

WOLFF, M.: Das Nervensystem der polypoiden Hydrozoa und Scyphozoa. Z. allg. Physiol. *3*: 191–281 (1904).

YOUNG, J. Z.: The giant nerve fibres and epistellar body of cephalopods. Quart. J. micr. Sci. *78*: 367–386 (1936).

YOUNG, J. Z.: The structure of nerve fibres in cephalopods and crustacea. Proc. R. Soc. B *121*: 319–337 (1936/37).

YOUNG, J. Z.: The functioning of the giant nerve fibres in the squid. J. exp. Biol. *15*: 170–185 (1938).

YOUNG, J. Z.: Fused neurons and synaptic contacts in the giant nerve fibres of cephalopods. Phil. Trans. R. Soc. B *229*: 465–503 (1939).

YOUNG, J. Z.: The visual system of octopus. (1) Regularities in the retina and optic lobes of octopus in relation to form discrimination. Nature *186*: 636–839 (1960).

YOUNG, J. Z.: Unit processes in the formation of representations in the memory of octopus. Proc. R. Soc. B *153*: 1–17 (1960/61).

YOUNG, J. Z.: Rates of establishment of representations in the memory of octopuses with and without vertical lobes. J. exp. Biol. *38*: 43–60 (1961).

YOUNG, J. Z.: A model of the brain (Clarendon Press, Oxford 1964).

ZAWARZIN, A.: Histologische Studien über Insekten. IV. Die optischen Ganglien der Aeschna-Larven. Z. wiss. Zool. *108*: 175–257 (1914).

ZAWARZIN, A.: Histologische Studien über Insekten. VI. Zur Morphologie der Nervenzentren. Das Bauchmark der Insekten. Z. wiss. Zool. *122*: 323–424 (1924).

ZAWARZIN, A.: Der Parallelismus der Strukturen als ein Grundprinzip der Morphologie. Z. wiss. Zool. *124*: 118–212 (1925).

ZIEGLER, H. E.: Lehrbuch der vergleichenden Entwicklungsgeschichte der niederen Wirbeltiere (Fischer, Jena 1902).

ZIEGLER, H. E.: Der Begriff des Instinktes einst und jetzt. Mit einem Anhang: Die Gehirne der Bienen und Ameisen. 3. Aufl. (Fischer, Jena 1920).

Addenda

The following references, quoted in the text, were accidentally omitted from the preceding list:

KARLSON, P., and BUTENANDT, A.: Pheromones in insects. Ann. Rev. Ent. 4: 39–59 (1959). Quoted on p. 202.

KUHLENBECK, H.: The human diencephalon (Karger, Basel / New York 1954). Quoted on p. 247.

MAKI, T.: Studies of the skeletal structures, musculature, and nervous system of the alder fly Chauliodes formosanus Peterson. Mem. Fac. Sci. Taihoku Univ. 16: 117–243 (1936). Quoted on p. 135.

MAYNARD, D. M.: Invertebrate neuropile. Amer. Zool. 2: 79–96 (1962). Quoted on p. 251.

WALD, G.: (1963) cf. references to vol. 1, chapter II. Quoted on p. 264.